The Original

Pets Welcome!

Summer 2012

FHG

Quality properties
where pets are warmly welcomed

**Including
Pet-Friendly Pubs
Dog-Friendly Walks**

59th edition

YETI

www.pets-welcome.co.uk   www.holidayguides.com

Foreword

We are delighted to introduce this 59th edition of **Pets Welcome!** with its varied selection of holidays for pets and their owners. The choice of accommodation includes not only self-catering properties and caravans as one might expect, but also many hotels, guest houses and B&B establishments.

As in previous issues, we urge owners to behave responsibly and to ensure their pet does not jump on furniture or beds, and they should not be left unattended for long periods. In this climate of environmental awareness and concern about pollution on our beaches and elsewhere, pet owners should abide by the relevant local authority rules regarding 'doggy' access to beaches and other areas. But for many of us enjoying a country holiday means taking the dog on scenic walks and you'll find a useful selection of especially recommended walks on **pages 24-33.**

Most of our entries are of long standing and are tried and tested favourites with animal lovers. However as publishers we do not inspect the accommodation advertised in Pets Welcome! and an entry does not imply our recommendation. Some proprietors offer fuller facilities for pets than others, and in the classified entry which we give each advertiser we try to indicate by symbols whether or not there are any special facilities and if additional charges are involved. However, we suggest that you raise any queries or particular requirements when you make enquiries and bookings.

If you have any problems or complaints, please raise them on the spot with the owner or his representative in the first place. We will follow up complaints if necessary, but we regret that we cannot act as intermediaries nor can we accept responsibility for details of accommodation and/or services described here. Happily, serious complaints are few. Finally, if you have to cancel or postpone a holiday booking, please give as much notice as possible. This courtesy will be appreciated and it could save later difficulties.

Preparing your Dogs and Cats for Travel Abroad (Page 8), **Holidays with Horses** (Page 405), and **Pet Friendly Pubs** (Page 403) are now regular features. Our popular feature, **Readers' Pets Pictures**, starts on page 16. A selection of **Readers' Offer Vouchers,** allowing free or reduced rate entry to attractions which allow pets, appears on pages 409-414.

We would be happy to receive readers' suggestions on any other useful features. Please also let us know if you have had any unusual or humorous experiences with your pet on holiday. This always makes interesting reading! And we hope that you will mention **Pets Welcome!** when you make your holiday inquiries or bookings.

Contents

Accommodation Standards: Star Grading Scheme

The AA, VisitBritain, VisitScotland, and the VisitWales now use a single method of assessing and rating serviced accommodation. Irrespective of which organisation inspects an establishment the rating awarded will be the same, using a common set of standards, giving a clear guide of what to expect.   They have full details of the grading system on their websites.

www.enjoyEngland.com   www.visitScotland.com

 www.visitWales.com   www.theaa.com

Using a scale of 1-5 stars the objective quality ratings give a clear indication of accommodation standard, cleanliness, ambience, hospitality, service and food.

This shows the full range of standards suitable for every budget and preference, and allows visitors to distinguish between the quality of accommodation and facilities on offer in different establishments.
All types of board and self-catering accommodation are covered, including hotels, B&Bs, holiday parks, campus accommodation, hostels, caravans and camping, and boats.

Gold and Silver awards are given to Hotels and Guest Accommodation that provide exceptional quality, especially in service and hospitality.

The more stars, the higher level of quality

★
acceptable quality; simple, practical, no frills

★★
good quality, well presented and well run

★★★
very good level of quality and comfort

★★★★
excellent standard throughout

★★★★★
exceptional quality, with a degree of luxury

National Accessible Scheme Logos for mobility impaired and older people

If you have particular mobility impairment. look out for the National Accessible Scheme. You can be confident of finding accommodation or attractions that meet your needs by looking for the following symbols.

 Older and less mobile guests
If you have sufficient mobility to climb a flight of steps but would benefit from fixtures and fittings to aid balance.

 Part-time wheelchair users
You have restricted walking ability or may need to use a wheelchair some of the time and can negotiate a maximum of 3 steps.

 Independent wheelchair users
You are a wheelchair user and travel independently. Similar to the international logo for independent wheelchair users.

 Assisted wheelchair users
You're a wheelchair user and travel with a friend or family member who helps you with everyday tasks.

Preparing your Pet for travel abroad

Pet travel rules from 1 January 2012

It is now easier to travel abroad with pets since new rules have been introduced at the start of 2012. The UK has harmonised its pet movement rules with the rest of the European Union, bringing the UK's Pet Travel Scheme into line with the most recent science. The UK will maintain its high level of protection against animal diseases; forcing pets to spend six months in quarantine is no longer necessary because of vastly improved rabies vaccines and treatments.

All pets still need to be vaccinated against rabies. Pets from the EU and listed non-EU countries such as the USA and Australia no longer need a blood test and only have to wait 21 days before they travel. Pets from unlisted non-EU countries such as India, Brazil and South Africa will be able to enter the UK if they meet certain strict criteria to ensure they are protected against rabies, including a blood test and a 3-month wait before they enter the UK. Animals which do not meet all the rules must be licensed into quarantine. They might then be able to obtain early release if they can be shown to comply with the necessary pet travel requirements.

REMEMBER - you are responsible for making sure that your pet meets all the rules for entering/re-entering the UK. Make sure you have the procedures carried out in the correct order and that documentation is correctly completed. If you do not, your pet may not be able to enter the country, or may have to go into quarantine on arrival - expensive and upsetting.

What you need to do if you are entering the UK from the EU and listed non-EU countries

•*Step 1* – Have your pet microchipped – before any of the other procedures for pet travel are carried out, your pet must be fitted with a microchip so it can be properly identified.

•*Step 2* – Have your pet vaccinated – after the microchip has been fitted your pet must be vaccinated against rabies. There is no exemption to this requirement, even if your pet has a current rabies vaccination. Rabies boosters must be kept up to date. The length of the waiting period before entry to the UK is 21 days after the first vaccination date. A waiting period is not required for subsequent entries into the UK, provided rabies boosters are kept up to date. If the vaccination is in two parts the 21 day wait will be from the date of the second vaccination.

•*Step 3* – Get pet travel documentation – for animals being prepared in an EU country, you should get an EU Pet Passport. If you are preparing your animal in a non-EU listed country or territory you will need to obtain an official third country veterinary certificate although note that Croatia, Gibraltar, Norway, San Marino and Switzerland are also issuing passports.

• *Step 4* – Tapeworm treatment – it is expected that the European Commission will come forward with proposals to allow the UK to still require pets to be treated against tapeworms. There will be no mandatory requirement for tick treatment.

• *Step 5* – Arrange for your animal to travel with an approved transport company on an authorised route – your pet must enter the UK from a listed country or territory travelling with an approved transport company on an authorised route.

What you need to do if you are entering the UK from unlisted non-EU countries

• *Step 1* – Have your pet microchipped – before any of the other procedures for pet travel are carried out, your pet must be fitted with a microchip so it can be properly identified.

• *Step 2* – Have your pet vaccinated – after the microchip has been fitted your pet must be vaccinated against rabies. There is no exemption to this requirement, even if your pet has a current rabies vaccination. Rabies boosters must be kept up to date.

• *Step 3* – Arrange a blood test – after your pet has been vaccinated, it must be blood tested to make sure the vaccine has given it a satisfactory level of protection against rabies. The blood sample must be taken at least 30 days after vaccination. The length of the waiting period before entry to the UK is three calendar months from the date your vet took the blood sample which led to a satisfactory test result. The three month waiting period will not apply if your pet was vaccinated and blood tested in the EU and issued with an EU pet passport before it went to an unlisted country

• *Step 4* – Get pet travel documentation –you will need to obtain an official third country veterinary certificate.

• *Step 5* – Tapeworm treatment – it is expected that the European Commission will come forward with proposals to allow the UK to still require pets to be treated against tapeworms. There will be no mandatory requirement for tick treatment.

• Step 6 – Arrange for your animal to travel with an approved transport company on an authorised route – your pet must enter the UK with an approved transport company on an authorised route.

More information can be obtained from:

Department of Environment, Food and Rural Affairs
website: www.defra.gov.uk/pets
e-mail: pettravel@ahvla.gsi.gov.uk

defra Department for Environment
Food and Rural Affairs

Pet Travel Scheme Helpline: Tel: 0870 241 1710
Monday to Friday - 8am to 6pm UK time (closed Bank Holidays).

Pet Travel Scheme

Holidays in France
For you and your pets

Taking a holiday abroad with a pet use to be inconvenient and hard to arrange, but the increase in pet-friendly accommodation and a change in regulations for travelling with animals means that a holiday with your 'best friend' is a much more realistic prospect.

France is a popular choice, not only because of the relatively short travel time, but also because ease of access through the Channel Tunnel or on a ferry means that there is no need for the extra expense and stress (for you and your pet!) involved in air travel.

See below, or check out our website **www.holidayguides.com** for other options.

Maison Renard

South-facing Charentaise house, set in a quiet hamlet near to the market town of La Rochefoucauld, with its chateau, restaurants, shops etc only a few minutes' drive away. This area of South West France is famous for its rolling countryside, lakes, and rivers, and for the production of wine, cognac and pineau, all to be tasted!! and explored.
The house sleeps up to 6 people, with two bathrooms, fully equipped kitchen, lounge and dining room.

British satellite TV, Wi-Fi internet connection, and phone are provided. The indoor pool is seasonally heated and leads on to the patio and BBQ areas.
WELL BEHAVED PETS ARE WELCOME.
July & August £650 per week • All other times £450 per week

Contact: *John & Sally Fox,*
Tel: *01724 720384 or 00 33 54 521 73 87*
e-mail: foxjns@aol.com
or enquiries@maisonrenard.co.uk

Visit our website: www.maisonrenard.co.uk

La Rochefoucauld (Charente Lakes)

Quiet hamlet, surrounded by lakes and beautiful countryside, in the heart of the Charente. Restaurant bars and shops a few minutes away. Ideal for walking, cycling, birdwatching, golf, fishing and water sports in the Charente Lakes.

MAISON RENARD. Tastefully restored Charentaise house in quiet hamlet. Sleeps 6. Fully equipped kitchen, BBQ, indoor pool. South-facing garden. Contact: JOHN & SALLY FOX (01724 720384 or 00 33 54 521 73 87). [🐾]
e-mail: foxjns@aol.com or enquiries@maisonrenard.co.uk   website: www.maisonrenard.co.uk

SINCE 1927

Winalot

iron for vitality & protein for muscles

WINALOT® WALKS IS BACK!

Winalot® Walks is back and it is bigger and better than ever!

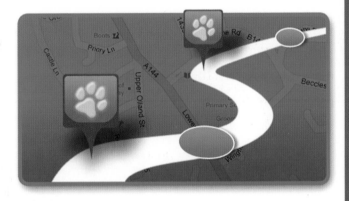

On our simple new Walks page you can quickly and easily find walks to suit you or help other **Winalot®** families enjoy a great day out by marking your own favourite walking routes.

Visit the website today!

www.winalot-dog.co.uk

® Reg. Trademark of Sociétié des Produits Nestlé S.A.

PURINA .

Your Pet, Our Passion.®

WINALOT® Shapes

6 Wholesome biscuits for your dog to enjoy every day!

Winalot Shapes® are wholesome biscuits for you to feed your dog as a snack, treat or tasty addition to the main meal.

Winalot Shapes® are full of calcium, vitamin D, fibre and all manner of nutritious ingredients to help you give him the extra bounce he needs to be a part of the family.

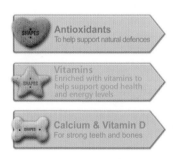

Antioxidants
To help support natural defences

Vitamins
Enriched with vitamins to help support good health and energy levels

Calcium & Vitamin D
For strong teeth and bones

Fibre
To help support a healthy digestion

NEW
Iron
To help support vitality

NEW
Omega 3 & 6
For a shiny coat

For more information about how to feed your dog, go to

www.winalot-dog.co.uk

® Reg. Trademark of Sociétié des Produits Nestlé S.A.

PURINA
Your Pet, Our Passion.®

WINALOT® Adult
With Iron for Vitality and protein for muscles

A key ingredient in **Winalot**® Adult food is iron. Your dog needs this to carry oxygen around his body and help him release the energy from the food he needs to get the most out of life.
Winalot® Adult also contains quality protein which is the key building block of muscle. It also helps his coat stay shiny and healthy.

For more information about how to feed your dog, go to
www.winalot-dog.co.uk

® Reg. Trademark of Sociétié des Produits Nestlé S.A.

Your Pet, Our Passion.®

Dogs**Trust**

Dogs**Trust**: A Dog is For Life

Are you thinking of going on holiday in the UK with your dog?

If so, the Dogs Trust has a free factsheet which will be of particular interest.

"Safe travel and happy holidays with your hound in the UK"

For this and any other of our free Dogs Trust factsheets please contact us at:

Dogs Trust,
17 Wakley St. London EC1V 7RQ.
Tel: 020 7837 0006

Website: www.dogstrust.org.uk
or e-mail us, info@dogstrust.org.uk

Last year Dogs Trust cared for over 16,000 stray and abandoned dogs at our network of 18 Rehoming Centres. So if you are looking for a companion for your dog or you have a friend who might like a dog, just contact your nearest Dogs Trust Rehoming Centre.

We care for around 1,600 dogs on any given day, so we are sure we will be able to find your perfect partner. The Dogs Trust never destroys a healthy dog.

For details of our Sponsor-a-Dog scheme please call **020 7837 0006**
or visit **www.sponsoradog.org.uk**

Dogs Trust Rehoming Centres

LONDON
Dogs Trust Harefield
0845 076 3647

ENGLAND
Dogs Trust Canterbury
01227 792 505

Dogs Trust Darlington
01325 333 114

Dogs Trust Evesham
01386 830 613

Dogs Trust Ilfracombe
01271 812 709

Dogs Trust Kenilworth
01926 484 398

Dogs Trust Leeds
01132 613 194

Dogs Trust Merseyside
0151 480 0660

Dogs Trust Newbury
01488 658 391

Dogs Trust Roden
01952 770 225

Dogs Trust Salisbury
01980 629 634

Dogs Trust Shoreham
01273 452 576

Dogs Trust Snetterton
01953 498 377

WALES
Dogs Trust Bridgend
01656 725 219

SCOTLAND
Dogs Trust Glasgow
0141 773 5130

Dogs Trust West Calder
01506 873 459

NORTHERN IRELAND
Dogs Trust Ballymena
028 2565 2977

IRELAND
Dogs trust Dublin
enquiries@dogstrust.ie

Registered Charity No. 227523

Donate £1 to your favourite Pets Charity

FHG has agreed to donate **£1** from the price of this
Pets Welcome! Guide to EITHER
The Royal Society For The Prevention of Cruelty to Animals,
Dogs Trust,
The Kennel Club,
or the Scottish Society for the Prevention of Cruelty to Animals

To allow the Charity of your choice to receive this donation simply
complete the slip below and return to FHG at

FHG Guides Ltd, Abbey Mill Business Centre
Seedhill, Paisley PA1 1TJ
Closing date end October 2012

Note: Original forms only please, do not send photocopies.

✂--

Please donate £1 from the price of this Pets Welcome! guide to:

RSPCA ☐   DOGS TRUST ☐   KENNEL CLUB ☐   SSPCA ☐

Name ....

Address ....

....

Postcode ....Date ....

FHG Guides may send readers details of discount offers for our holiday guides.

If you do not wish to receive this information please tick here ☐

Your details will not be passed on to any other organisation.

Readers' Pets Pictures

Send us your favourite Pet Photo!

On the following pages are a selection of pets' photos sent in by readers of

Pets Welcome!

If you would like to have a photo of your pet included in the next edition (published in OCTOBER 2012), send it along with a brief note of the pet's name and a few details such as age, breed etc.

Please remember to include your own name and address and let us know if you would like the pictures returned. FHG will give a FREE copy of the guide in which the picture appears.

We will be happy to receive prints, or pictures by e-mail to

editorial@fhguides.co.uk

All pictures should be forwarded by the middle of July 2012.
Thanks to everyone who sent in pictures of their pets and we regret that we were unable to include all of them. Pictures not included in this edition will be considered for use in the future. See the following pages for this year's selection.

Send your Pet photo to:
FHG Guides, Abbey Mill Business Centre,
Seedhill, Paisley PA1 1TJ

CERYS and PEPE
Wendy Halling, Colmworth

MAISIE
Andrea Ratcliffe, Poole

BUBBLES
Jaye Jones, Challacombe

JET
*Barbara Whitehorne,
Ross-on-Wye*

LUCY
Nicole Jones & Gareth Eveleigh, Barry

KODAH
Anya Eckleben, Poole

POPPY
Alison McLelland, Paisley

SHYLA & BILLY
Mags Thomson, Louth

MISTY
Moira Bryan, Ayr

ROBBIE
Mr & Mrs T. Milroy, Glasgow

MISHKA & BELLA
Meryl & Mark Dewolfreys, Newquay

STANLEY
Robert Ion, Johnstone

BONNIE & MAX
Mrs. M. Hylton, Hornsea

TOBY
Jo Stenning, Wrexham

PADDY
Sharon Symons, Bude

BRUNO
Jess Print, Alcester

BARNEY
Lesley Parr, St Helens

OZZY
*Ian Pearson,
Nether Stowey*

AMBER & SAPPHY
Jackie Goodwin

BESSIE & SALLY
Jennifer & Victor Gibbons, High Peak

The one-stop shop fc

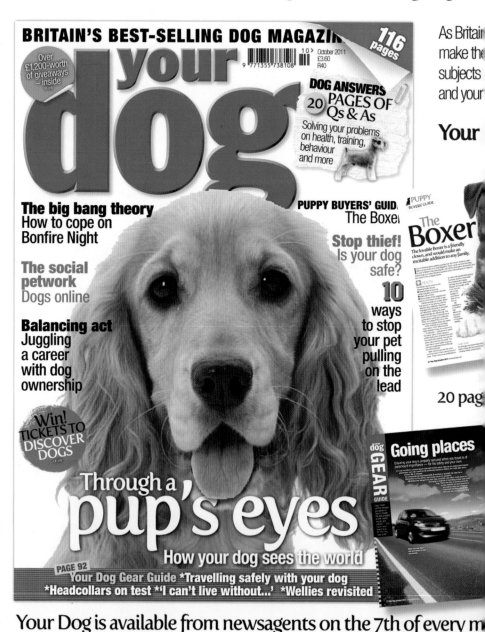

BRITAIN'S BEST-SELLING DOG MAGAZIN

Over £1,200-worth of giveaways – inside

your **dog**

116 pages

October 2011
£3.60
R40

9 771355 738108

DOG ANSWERS
20 PAGES OF Qs & As
Solving your problems on health, training, behaviour and more

The big bang theory
How to cope on Bonfire Night

The social petwork
Dogs online

Balancing act
Juggling a career with dog ownership

Win!
TICKETS TO DISCOVER DOGS

PUPPY BUYERS' GUID
The Boxer

Stop thief!
Is your dog safe?

10 ways to stop your pet pulling on the lead

PUPPY BUYERS' GUIDE
The **Boxer**
The lovable Boxer is a friendly clown, and would make an excitable addition to any family.

20 pag

Through a **pup's eyes**
How your dog sees the world

PAGE 92
Your Dog Gear Guide *Travelling safely with your dog *Headcollars on test *'I can't live without...' *Wellies revisited

Going places
Ensuring your dog is properly secured when you travel is of paramount importance — for his safety and your own.

dog GEAR GUIDE

As Britain make the subjects and your

Your

Your Dog is available from newsagents on the 7th of every m
a year for just £33.20, saving £10 on the full price. To

Visit www.

all your doggy needs

-selling dog magazine, Your Dog prides itself on giving you the best advice to help you
of life with your pet. Each month you'll find an extensive range of practical articles on
s training, behaviour, and your dog's health; the most important doggy news affecting you
id expert advice on topics like buying a new puppy.

Magazine — always putting its readers first.

Puppy Buyers' Guide

Everything you need to know about the UK's
most popular dog breeds — let us help you
decide which puppy would suit you best.

Dog Answers

Our experts solve your problems on a range
of issues,
including
training, health,
ehaviour, feeding, and grooming in
advice and guidance.

Gear Guide

Get help choosing
the best products
on the market —
the Your Dog testing panel
puts a selection of products through their
paces — and save £££s with our fantastic
money-off coupons.   **Plus lots more…**

h, priced at £3.60, or you can subscribe to the magazine for
r call 01858 438854 and quote source code PWII.

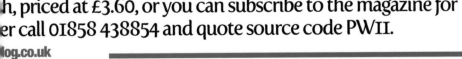

A dog-friendly walk in...
Loch Lomond and The Trossachs

The first beauty spot we are stopping off at on our dog-friendly tour of the UK is Loch Lomond and The Trossachs.

Balquhidder

This walk, which begins in Balquhidder, takes you along pine-scented forest paths where you will be able to enjoy fine views of Kirkton Glen and the surrounding scenery.
By Mary Welsh.

The lovely view of Loch Voil.

Majestic Loch Lomond is not far from Balquhidder.

Pic: Loch Lomond and The Trossachs National Park Authority.

Fact file

Distance: 9km/ 5½ miles.
Time: 3 hours.
Map: Explorer 365.
Start/parking: In Balquhidder; grid reference 536209.
Terrain: Good tracks throughout, may be muddy after rain.
Nearest town: Callander.
Refreshments: Kings House Hotel, Balquhidder; Monachyle Mhor, Balquhidder.
Public toilets: None en route.
Public transport: Call Traveline on 0871 200 2233.
Stiles: One.
Suitable for: All the family. Dogs should be on leads if there is livestock about.

1 Wind left of the new church (built in 1853) to take a tree-lined gravelled track, directing you towards a waterfall. Beside you hurries the Kirkton Burn. Ignore the path to the right, which is your onward route, to walk to a footbridge from where you have a fine view of the delectable fall. Return to the path you ignored earlier, now on your left, and signposted 'Creag an Tuirc and Kirkton Glen'. The pleasing path climbs uphill, through trees, to go over an easy stile, and then winds steadily through tall conifers. Watch out for the sign on the right directing you to Creag an Tuirc. After

0.5km go through a hurdle gate on the right, descend steps to cross a stream and climb up the other side. Ascend to a cairn and a seat on the top of a crag, with a lovely view of Loch Voil below.

2 Return from the crag and on through the hurdle. Continue left, down the path to the main track, where you turn right along a way that leads through Kirkton Glen. Go past a track coming in on the left and then another on the right. Go ahead into the glen to walk through an area where young conifers have been planted. Stride on through a fine stand of Scots pine and carry

on. Now that much of the forest has been felled it is possible to see the shape of the glen.

3 Follow the track to the head of the glen to reach a signpost. Bear right, still on the forestry track, and return down the glen. Because the

track is at a higher altitude you are able to see the glen stretching down below you. About a mile along you have another fine view of Loch Voil. Follow the track as it winds right and joins your outward route. Turn left and follow back to Balquhidder church and the parking area.

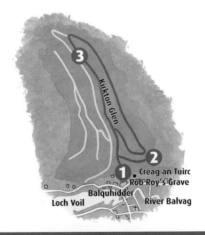

A dog-friendly walk in...
The Lake District

The Lake District has high mountains, sweeping views, wonderful woodlands and a myriad of becks and fine lakes.

Carlisle
Keswick
Penrith
Grasmere
Lake District National Park
Kendal
Barrow-in-Furness

Broughton-in-Furness

In 1859 Coniston village was linked by rail to the main west coast line. This line enabled slate quarried in the fells to be transported. The trains also carried goods, tourists and schoolchildren. In the late 1960s the nine-mile line was closed. In 2003, the national park resurfaced and refurbished the track, and the new trail was officially opened and is a very popular route with walkers. **By Mary Welsh.**

The second lake beside the railway track.

The Lake District offers fantastic views.

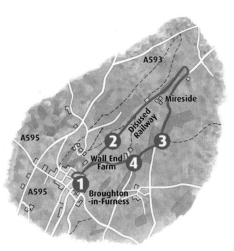

Fact file

Distance: 6.5km (4 miles).
Time: 2 – 3 hours.
Map: Explorer OL6.
Start/parking: Broughton-in-Furness square, just off the A595.
Terrain: Level, easy walking along railway track; a little quiet road walking; the track from Five Arches Road to the access track at the top of slope can be muddy in the dip.
Nearest towns: Ulverston, Millom.
Refreshments: In Broughton there is a good choice of inns and cafes, and one restaurant, all offering excellent food.
Public toilets: Just off the village square.
Public transport: Stagecoach bus service from Millom and Ulverston. For details, call Traveline on 0871 200 2233.
Stiles: Several.
Suitable for: All the family.

1 Leave Broughton's village square in the direction of the signed public toilets. Follow the track as it bends right to join the trackbed of the railway. Here, wind left, go round the barrier and dogs can start their 1¼ miles of freedom. Walk left, through the deep cutting. Just before the old bridge over the line, on the left, is the first of the two lakes. Go on under the bridge and up the short sloping path, on the left, to a seat overlooking the beautiful second lake.

2 Stroll the lovely way to cross a fine wooden bridge spanning a farm track. Carry on, soon to pass through another cutting shaded by tall forest trees, until you reach a fence supporting a 'no path' sign. Here bear right to descend through two gates on to Five Arches Road, named after a demolished bridge that carried the old railway line. Walk right to pass Mireside Farm and wind on along the narrow quiet road, through pastures and mixed woodland to come to a signposted bridleway on your right.

3 Pass between small plantations of firs, where dogs can have more freedom and then ascend the continuing steepish track that climbs through deciduous woodland to where it divides. Take the short right fork to the side of the access lane to Wall End Farm, which you cross.

4 Climb the stile, ascend a little slope and then descend the ongoing path over rough pasture, where there might be sheep or deer. This path keeps parallel with the wall on your right but keeping a short distance away from it. Press on until you can take the easy to miss gap stile in the wall, a 'fat man's agony'— two stone slabs that you have to squeeze between and which stout dogs may find difficult. Walk ahead beside another wall, also on your right, and go through the next gap stile or use the gate to its left, which is usually open. Walk ahead to the fenced edge of the railway cutting, high above where you walked earlier. Turn left and walk on through a gateless gap and on again to a step stile in the right corner on to the railway track. Cross and walk up the track ahead. Wind left to return to the village square.

A dog-friendly walk in...
The Brecon Beacon

The Brecon Beacons stretch from Llandeilo in the west to Hay-on-Wye in the east, and is one of three national parks in Wales. This stunning area is a popular destination for visitors who enjoy the freedom and remoteness of the Welsh countryside.

Enjoy the views at Blaen Llia.

Blaen Llia & Sarn Helen

The main sandstone mass of the Brecon Beacons meets a narrow strip of limestone just north of Ystradfellte, on the southern edge of Fforest Fawr (the Great Forest). This open-country walk cuts across these contrasting landscapes on moorland tracks, past a small Iron Age hill fort, and finally along a section of Roman road. **By Evelyne Sansot.**

Along the Roman road with Fan Llia in the background.

A derelict limekiln on the route.

Fact file

Distance: 8km (5 miles).
Time: Allow 3 hours.
Map: Explorer OL12 Brecon Beacons National Park, West and Central.
Start/parking: Blaen Llia car park; grid reference SN927166.
Terrain: Mainly good tracks and footpaths across pastures with gentle ascents and descents.
Nearest towns: Glyn-Neath, Merthyr Tydfil, Brecon.
Refreshments: None.
Public toilets: None.
Public transport: None.
Stiles: None.
Suitable for: All.

1 As you leave the car park, turn left on to the road and follow it for 0.8km (½ mile). At a sharp bend to the left, continue straight on to a walled track. After a gate, take the right fork as waymarked.

2 After the next gate take the left fork across the pasture, heading for the right of a limestone crag. Pass a derelict limekiln just below the crag and continue along the same path as it makes a curve to the left between the limestone escarpments of Carnau Gwynion. About 200m into the next field keep along this main track, ignoring another one shooting off to the right.

3 Make an elbow turn to the right in front of the gate in the bottom corner (at an angle between the wall and the track you have just followed). The path is not clearly defined at this point as it cuts across the rough pasture. Keep heading towards some scraggy hawthorn trees in the distance then, as you reach the brink of the field, aim for a small circular wire fence enclosure around a swallow-hole, cross a track and continue straight up the slope to a gate in the wall.

4 Bear left past the remains of an Iron Age hill fort on the crest on your right, suddenly emerging above the valley of Nedd Fechan, with views to the north over some of Fforest Fawr's sandstone summits (from right to left, Fan Nedd and Fan Gyhirych). Go through a gate and walk down several fields along the clearly waymarked footpath to the bottom of the valley.

5 Turn right on to the narrow road and enter Blaen-nedd-Isaf Farm. Walk past the farmhouse then turn immediately left across the farmyard to walk round the left-hand side of the barn. Cross the river over a footbridge and walk straight up a small wooded area, then a pasture.

6 Turn right at the top, on to Sarn Helen, the Roman road, thereby joining the Beacons Way. Cross the river again over a footbridge and continue straight up the other bank, later to pass the Maen Madoc standing stone.

7 Turn right on to the road to rejoin the car park on your left.

A dog-friendly walk in...
The Norfolk Broad

The Norfolk Broads National Park has rich history and unique wildlife. Restored windmills, medieval churches, charming villages, and peaceful waterways are just a few of the delights that visitors discover when they explore the Broads.

Horsey Windpump

Recognised as an internationally important wildlife site, the Horsey Estate is also a superb destination for anyone who enjoys birdwatching. This route allows visitors to enjoy the peace and tranquillity of the area along with the chance to walk by the sea. **By Anita Delf.**

The 'big Norfolk skies' at Horsey Beach.

Pic: The Broads Authority.

The Broads offers visitors a peaceful and tranquil holiday destination.

and the end of the path. Turn right, climb the stile and walk on the field edge to the houses ahead. Climb the stile at the end of the path to reach a lane. If you wish to take the shorter walk turn right by the footpath sign and follow the lane round to the church and main road. The Nelson Head public house is then directly opposite on the main road or you can turn right to return to the car park. Otherwise at the lane turn left and walk to the main road. Turn right along this road walking with care as it can be busy.

3 At the sharp bend turn left down the gravel track taking you back into the Horsey Estate, to reach a small car parking area. There is a choice of route here, you can turn right going through the kissing gate and along the path by the dunes or, if you prefer, you can continue ahead through Horsey Gap to reach the sea and turn right to walk along the beach.

1 From the car park at the Horsey Windpump walk to the steps and footpath sign and then turn right along the towpath. Follow the path and boardwalk until it reaches a gate. To the left are wonderful views of Horsey Mere. From here on dogs will need to be kept on a lead as sometimes there is livestock in the fields. Go through the gate and cross the field diagonally left to a further gate. Pass through this and continue along the path and boardwalk to reach the cut.

2 Continue alongside the water's edge to the ruined windpump ahead

Horsey Mill is owned by The National Trust.

4 Turn right at the next concrete gap on to a wide fenced track. If you choose the beach walk then you will need to turn right away from the beach, climbing the short sand hill. The track is then directly ahead of you. Continue on this track to arrive at the Nelson Head pub. From the Nelson Head turn right to the road, then turn left along it, following it back to the car park. This road is busy and must be walked with care, using the grass verge as much as possible.

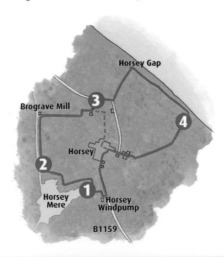

Fact file

Distance: 8 km (5 miles) or 4.8 km (3 miles).
Time: Allow 2½ hours.
Map: Explorer OL 40, The Broads.
Start/parking: The National Trust car park at Horsey Windpump on the B1159. It costs 30p per hour; grid reference TQ457224.
Terrain: Good paths; flat except for the climb through the sand dunes to the beach.
Nearest town: Great Yarmouth.
Refreshments: Nelson Head pub — dogs welcome inside on a lead. Seasonal shop/tea room at Horsey Mill, open Wednesday to Sunday, 10am – 4.30pm, with outside tables.
Public toilets: Horsey Mill car park — seasonal only.
Public transport: None.
Stiles: Two low wooden stiles — dogs may need to be lifted over.
Suitable for: All the family.

A dog-friendly walk on...

Dartmoor

Dartmoor has wild dramatic vistas and a colourful history steeped in folklore.

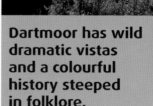

Lustleigh Cleave

This exploration of Lustleigh Cleave combines a fine ridge walk with a woodland and riverside ramble through a deep and sequestered valley, with a lovely boulder-strewn waterfall. The views over eastern Dartmoor, including Hound Tor and Haytor Rocks, are superb and there is a good deal of off-lead walking. We start and end at Lustleigh, one of Dartmoor's prettiest villages. **By Robert Hesketh.**

A Dartmoor mare and foal on Hunter's Tor.

There is plenty to see from Hunter's Tor.

1 From Lustleigh's church, turn left. Follow the lane signed for Rudge. Cross the bridge and keep right when the lane forks. Turn first right at the chapel and walk uphill before turning left by Oakehurst on to the signed path. Follow this uphill past houses and gardens to a group of three stone and thatched houses. Turn left and then turn right at the T-junction. About 50m ahead, turn left on to the bridlepath for Lustleigh Cleave.

2 Continue ahead through Heaven's Gate. At the junction of paths, follow the bridlepath ahead signed Manaton via Water. Bear right and uphill when the path forks. Continue uphill for Hammerslake at the next fingerpost. Turn left at the following fingerpost, signed Bridge (originally Foxworthy Bridge but the fingerpost has been damaged). Ignore the side turnings and then about 1.5km (1 mile) ahead divert left for 200m on the path for Horsham to see Horsham Steps, a beautiful boulder-strewn waterfall. Be careful of slippery moss, which grows thickly on trees and boulders in the clean, moist air of the Cleave. Return to the main path and turn left for Foxworthy. Pass behind the house and through a gate. Just beyond the converted barn take the path right signed Peck Farm.

3 When the path meets a concrete track turn right. Bypass Peck Farm, taking the signed public bridlepath through the gate to the right. Carry on to the top of the ridge. Hunter's Tor, a superb viewpoint, includes the eroded ramparts of an Iron Age fort — easily missed unless you look for them.

4 Follow the fine and clearly defined ridge path on to Harton Chest, a massive granite boulder, which can be climbed with care. Looking down nearly 500ft to the floor of the Cleave gives a dramatic impression of its size and steepness.

5 Entering woodland, littered with boulders, the path descends gently at first and then sharply. At the fingerpost, ignore the sign for Heaven's Gate and go straight ahead through the gate in front of you.

6 Turn right on to the metalled lane and first left after 250m. Follow the lane down past Ellimore Farm. At the bottom of the hill, take the signed public footpath left. Walk down through the woods, ignoring the first gated path on the left. Leave the wood by a gate and cross the brook via a wooden bridge. The large boulder in the centre of Lustleigh Orchard is surmounted by a stone seat, the May Queen's throne. Walk straight on through the orchard back to the start of the route at Lustleigh's church.

Fact file

Distance: 8.5km (5 miles).
Time: Allow 3 hours.
Maps: Landranger 191, Explorer OL 28 or Harvey's Dartmoor.
Start/parking: Roadside parking in Lustleigh; grid reference SX785813.
Terrain: Footpaths, bridlepaths and lanes well-signed; some short but steep ascents and descents.
Nearest towns: Moretonhampstead and Bovey Tracey.
Refreshments: Both Primrose Cottage Tearooms (home-made cakes) and the Cleave Hotel (real ales and a good menu) in Lustleigh welcome dogs.
Public toilets: Lustleigh.
Public transport: Bus no. 178 from Newton Abbot to Moretonhampstead via Bovey Tracey (Monday to Saturday).
Stiles: None.
Suitable for: Anyone who is fairly fit.

England and Wales • Counties

NORTHUMBERLAND

TYNE & WEAR

DURHAM
43
CUMBRIA   42 41 40 39

ISLE OF MAN

NORTH YORKSHIRE

38
LANCASHIRE   EAST RIDING OF YORKSHIRE
34
WEST YORKSHIRE   37
33
36
GREATER   35
MANCHESTER   S. YORKSHIRE
32 30
31
LINCOLNSHIRE

ISLE OF ANGLESEY

CONWY   b   CHESHIRE   DERBYSHIRE
a
c   NOTTINGHAMSHIRE
29
GWYNEDD   STAFFORDSHIRE   27   26
28
SHROPSHIRE   LEICESTERSHIRE
WEST   25 RUTLAND 24   NORFOLK
MIDLANDS
CEREDIGION   POWYS   NORTHAMPTONSHIRE
WARWICKSHIRE   CAMBRIDGESHIRE
WORCESTERSHIRE   SUFFOLK
HEREFORDSHIRE   23 BEDFORDSHIRE
CARMARTHENSHIRE   22
PEMBROKESHIRE   BUCKINGHAMSHIRE   ESSEX
GLOUCESTERSHIRE   HERTFORDSHIRE
d   e   g   k   m   o
f   i   l   n   OXFORDSHIRE
21   17   12 11   GREATER   9   10
20   16   15   14 13   LONDON   8
19 18
WILTSHIRE   SURREY   KENT
HAMPSHIRE
SOMERSET   WEST SUSSEX
EAST SUSSEX
DEVON   DORSET   5   6   7
3   4
CORNWALL   ISLE OF WIGHT
1   2

1. Plymouth	12. Windsor & Maidenhead	23. Milton Keynes	34. Blackpool	NORTH WALES
2. Torbay	13. Bracknell Forest	24. Peterborough	35. N.E. Lincolnshire	a. Denbighshire
3. Poole	14. Wokingham	25. Leicester	36. North Lincolnshire	b. Flintshire
4. Bournemouth	15. Reading	26. Nottingham	37. Kingston-upon-Hull	c. Wrexham
5. Southampton	16. West Berkshire	27. Derby	38. York	SOUTH WALES
6. Portsmouth	17. Swindon	28. Telford & Wrekin	39. Redcar & Cleveland	d. Swansea
7. Brighton & Hove	18. Bath & Northeast Somerset	29. Stoke-on-Trent	40. Middlesborough	e. Neath & Port Talbot
8. Medway	19. North Somerset	30. Warrington	41. Stockton-on-Tees	f. Bridgend
9. Thurrock	20. Bristol	31. Halton	42. Darlington	g. Rhondda Cynon Taff
10. Southend	21. South Gloucestershire	32. Merseyside	43. Hartlepool	h. Merthyr Tydfil
11. Slough	22. Luton	33. Blackburn with Darwen		i. Vale of Glamorgan
				j. Cardiff
				k. Caerphilly
				l. Blaenau Gwent
				m. Torfaen
				n. Newport
				o. Monmouthshire

COTTAGE IN THE COUNTRY COTTAGE HOLIDAYS (01608 646833). Lovely locations with superb walks in some of England's most picturesque countryside. Small friendly company with personal knowledge of the area.
e-mail: enquiries@cottageinthecountry.co.uk   website: www.cottageinthecountry.co.uk

HELPFUL HOLIDAYS (01647 434067). Variety of cottages and holiday homes all over the West Country. Ideal for countryside rambles. Many welcome pets.
website: www.helpfulholidays.co.uk

THE INDEPENDENT TRAVELLER, ORCHARD COTTAGE, THORVERTON, EXETER EX5 5NG (01392 860807). For a wide choice of cottages and apartments throughout England, Scotland & the Isles. Pets welcome in many properties. Quality Cottages in coastal, country and mountain location. Property finding service.
e-mail: help@gowithit.co.uk   website: www.gowithit.co.uk

Should have booked with Blue Chip Holidays

With the largest selection of luxury pet-friendly holiday homes in Devon, Cornwall, Somerset, Dorset, Wales and Isle of Wight, my owners should have booked with Blue Chip Holidays.

blue chip HOLIDAYS | www.bluechipholidays.co.uk/pets | 0844 7041694

BLUE CHIP HOLIDAYS. Choose from the largest selection of pet-friendly holiday homes in Devon, Cornwall, Dorset, Somerset, Wales and the Isle of Wight with outstanding views the whole family can enjoy. (0844 704 1694).
website: www.bluechipholidays.co.uk/pets

HOSEASONS. Over 200 pet-friendly countryside and seaside locations in the best areas of Britain. Peaceful, stylish lodges and lively holiday parks, some with pools, bars and restaurants. Price match guaranteed. Call 0844 847 1103 Quote GA150 or book on-line.
website: www.hoseasons.co.uk/fhgpets

THE FOUR SEASONS HOTEL, ST FILLANS PH6 2NF (01764 685333). Ideal holiday venue for pets and their owners. Spectacular Highland scenery, walking, fishing, watersports. Wonderful food. Full details on request. STB ★★★ Hotel, AA ★★★ and 2 Red Rosettes, Signpost, Best Loved Hotels. [pw! 🐾]
e-mail: sham@thefourseasonshotel.co.uk   website: www.thefourseasonshotel.co.uk

HOLIDAY COTTAGES. Choose from over 1000 pet-friendly cottages. Superb locations in England, Scotland and Wales. Contact us for a brochure or visit our website. Tel: 01228 406761 (lines open 7 days 9am-9pm (5.30pm Sat).
website: www.regional-cottages.co.uk

CLAYMOORE NARROWBOATS. Canal Holidays from base in Cheshire. Boats sleep 2-10. Fully equipped. Fuel included in hire. Full instruction. Day and Short Break hire. Car parking. Pets welcome. [🐾]
website: www.claymoore.co.uk

Bodmin

Bude, Crackington Haven, Crafthole

Crantock, Falmouth

Helston, Launceston, Liskeard

Liskeard, Longrock

Looe

Newquay

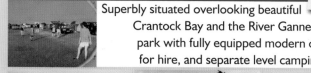

Newquay, Padstow, Penzance, Perranporth, Polruan

Polperro

PEAK HOUSE
POLPERRO • CORNWALL PL13 2RY

A lovely, comfortable property, around 250 years old, with terraced gardens, directly overlooking the picturesque fishing harbour of Polperro, with sea views.

VIEW FROM PEAK HOUSE

Located between Looe and Fowey, on South Cornish coast, 25 miles city of Plymouth, 12 miles A38 and 15 miles Eden Project

Let for 30 years for family holidays, as well as for friends and couples to enjoy. Sleeping 2-8. Pets and children are very welcome.

Situated in a really good position in the village, directly overlooking the harbour, 14 miles sea views stretching to the Eddystone Lighthouse.

Only 3 minute walk from shops, restaurants, tea rooms, olde-worlde pubs, small sandy beach, quay, pier and rock fishing and the beginning of miles of unspoilt National Trust cliff walks along stunning coastal paths, leading to outlying hamlets, beaches, coves and 13th century churches.

NO CHARGE FOR PETS • PRIVATE PARKING FREE

For details, please telephone GRAHAM WRIGHTS on

01579 344080

Portwrinkle

Redruth, St Agnes

The Links

Lelant, St Ives Cornwall TR26 3HY

If it's views, golf or walking you want, this is the place for you!

- Magnificent location alongside and overlooking West Cornwall Golf Course, Hayle Estuary and St Ives Bay.

- Both flats have lovely views. Wonderful spot for walking.

- Five minutes from the beach and dogs are allowed there all year round.

- Two well-equipped flats which are open all year.

Your hosts are Bob and Jacky Pontefract
Phone 01736 753326
e-mail: bobandjackyp@btinternet.com

Dalswinton House

St. Mawgan-in-Pydar, Cornwall TR8 4EZ. Tel: 01637 860385
www.dalswinton.com • dalswintonhouse@btconnect.com

HOLIDAYS FOR DOGS AND THEIR OWNERS

Overlooking the village of St Mawgan, Dalswinton House stands in 10 acres of gardens and meadowland midway between Padstow and Newquay with distant views to the sea at dog-friendly Mawgan Porth.

- Dogs free of charge and allowed everywhere except the restaurant
- 8 acre meadow for dog exercise. Nearby local walks. Beach 1.5 miles
- Heated outdoor pool (May-Sep). Off street car parking
- All rooms en suite with tea/coffee fac., digital TV and clock radios
- Wifi access in public rooms and all bedrooms (except the lodge)
- Residents' bar and restaurant serving breakfast and dinner
- Bed and breakfast from £46 per person per night
- Weekly rates available and special offers in Mar/Apr/May/Oct
- Self-catering lodge sleeps 3 adults
- Easy access to Padstow, Eden Project, Newquay Airport & Coastal Path

Regret no children under 16
Maximum 3 dogs per room at proprietor's discretion

Tregarne, Truro, Wadebridge

Truro

FARM & COTTAGE HOLIDAYS (01237 459897). An inspiring collection of holiday cottages throughout Cornwall, Devon, Somerset and Dorset in stunning rural and coastal locations. [Pets £20 per week]. website: www.holidaycottages.co.uk

TOAD HALL COTTAGES (01548 853089 24 hrs). Over 250 outstanding, dog friendly coastal, waterside and rural holiday cottages throughout Devon, Cornwall and Exmoor. Some superb beaches await your stroll. Well behaved people welcome too!
e-mail: thc@toadhallcottages.co.uk   website: www.toadhallcottages.co.uk

CORNISH TRADITIONAL COTTAGES. A fine selection of self-catering cottages on both coasts of Cornwall and on Scilly. Pets welcome in many cottages. Free colour brochure: 01208 821666 or visit our website. [Pets £18 per week (£20 in 2013)]
website: www.corncott.com

CORNISH SEAVIEW COTTAGES (01428 723819). Ideal for walking coastal paths and accessing beaches. Pets welcome at most. Furnished and equipped to high standard; all have central heating, dishwashers etc. Visit our website for photos and virtual tours. [Pets £20 per week].
e-mail: enquiries@cornishseaviewcottages.co.uk   website: www.cornishseaviewcottages.co.uk

WEST CORNWALL COTTAGE HOLIDAYS, 4 ALBERT STREET, PENZANCE TR18 2LR (01736 368575). Coastal and country cottages, town houses and apartments. Pets with well behaved owners welcome in many of our properties. [🐾]
website: www.westcornwallcottageholidays.com

Bodmin

Quaint county town of Cornwall, standing steeply on the edge of Bodmin Moor. Pretty market town and touring centre. Plymouth 31 miles, Newquay 20, Wadebridge 7.

PENROSE BURDEN, ST BREWARD, BODMIN PL30 4LZ (01208 850277 & 850617; Fax: 01208 850915). Holiday Care Award Winning Cottages featured on TV. Open all year. Outstanding views over wooded valley. Free Salmon and Trout fishing. Superb walking area. Dogs welcome, wheelchair accessible. [Pets £15 per week]
website: www.penroseburden.co.uk

Bodmin Moor

Superb walking area attaining a height of 1375 feet at Brown Willy, the highest point in Cornwall.

DARRYNANE COTTAGES, DARRYNANE, ST BREWARD, BODMIN MOOR PL30 4LZ (Tel & Fax: 01208 850885). Absolutely fabulous detached cottages. Set in private gated gardens. Unique moorland valley setting. Waterfalls, woods, river. Woodburning stoves, four-poster beds, Eden Project and Camel Trail close by. [Pets £15 per week, £7 per short break]
e-mail: enquiries@darrynane.co.uk   website:www.darrynane.co.uk

HENWOOD BARNS HOLIDAY COTTAGES, HENWOOD, LISKEARD PL14 5BP (01579 363576/07956 864263). Three stone barns set around original courtyard on the edge of Bodmin Moor, with stunning views. Tranquil, village location, horse riding two minutes' walk. Woodburning stoves; sleep 2/5; within easy reach of North Cornwall and Devon. [Pets £15 per week]
e-mail: henwoodbarns@tiscali.co.uk   website: www.henwoodbarns.co.uk

Bude

Popular seaside resort overlooking a wide bay of golden sand and flanked by spectacular cliffs. Ideal for surfing; sea water swimming pool for safe bathing.

HEDLEY WOOD CARAVAN & CAMPING PARK, BRIDGERULE, (NR BUDE), HOLSWORTHY EX22 7ED (01288 381404). 16 acre woodland family-run site; children's adventure areas, bar, clubroom, shop, laundry, meals & all amenities. Static caravans for hire, Caravan Storage available. Dog walk nature trail. See main advertisement under Bude. [pw! 🐕]
website: www.hedleywood.co.uk

IVYLEAF BARTON HOLIDAY COTTAGES, NEAR BUDE EX23 9LD. Five cottages sleeping 2-8 in converted stone barns, well equipped with all modern conveniences. Laundry. Tennis court. Certain cottages welcome pets. ★★★★/★★★★★★ Contact: ROBERT B. BARRETT (07525 251773). [Pets £20 per week].
e-mail: info@ivyleafbarton.co.uk   website: www.ivyleafbarton.co.uk

WILLOW VALLEY HOLIDAY PARK, DYE HOUSE, BUSH, BUDE EX23 9LB (01288 353104). Two bedroom lodges equipped to high standard. Colour TV, bathroom, fully equipped kitchen. Two miles from beach and town. Brochure on request. Lodges from £270 per week plus £20 per dog.
e-mail: willowvalley@talk21.com   website: www.willowvalley.co.uk

GRANARY COTTAGE, ROSECARE, BUDE EX23 0BE. Self- catering ground floor cottage (sleeps 4). Lots of doorstep walking. Good dog and child-friendly pubs and beaches nearby. Short breaks available out of season. Contact: L. HUNT (01384 878287 or 07941 148340). [🐕]
e-mail: lynneh@ethicaltraining.co.uk   website: www.cottagenearbude.com

Crackington Haven

Small coastal village in North Cornwall set amidst fine cliff scenery. Small sandy beach, Launceston 18 miles, Bude 10, Camelford 10.

MINESHOP, CRACKINGTON HAVEN, BUDE EX23 0NR. Cornish Character Cottages, sleep 1 to 8, in tranquil location. Footpath leads through fields/woods to beach/pub. Excellent walking, breathtaking scenery. Open all year. Proud to be inspected and featured in The Good Holiday Cottage Guide. For more details phone CHARLIE or JANE (01840 230338). [£20 per pet per week.]
e-mail: info@mineshop.co.uk   website: www.mineshop.co.uk

Five 18th century converted barns, beamed ceilings, log fires and secluded rural setting. Ideal touring base. Five miles to coast at Crackington Haven. Sleep 2/5. Pets welcome. Open all year. From £110 short breaks, £210 per week. ETC ★★★★. APPLY: LORRAINE HARRISON, TRENANNICK COTTAGES, WARBSTOW, LAUNCESTON PL15 8RP (01566 781443). [pw! Pets £10 per stay]
e-mail: trenannick–1@tiscali.co.uk   website: www.trenannickcottages.co.uk

Crafthole

Village near sea at Portwrinkle. Fine views over Whitsand Bay and River Lynner. Golf course nearby. Torpoint 6 miles..

THE LISCAWN, CRAFTHOLE, NEAR TORPOINT PL11 3BD (01503 230863). Charming, family-run 14th Century Inn. Close to Coastal Path in the forgotten corner of Cornwall. En suite accommodation; bar meals available. Open all year. Self-catering suites available. AA ★★★★ [🐕]
e-mail: enquiries@liscawn.co.uk   website: www.liscawn.co.uk

Crantock

Village near the coast 2 miles/3 km SW of Newquay across the River Gannel.

CORNWALL HOLIDAY COTTAGES. Luxury cottages, some with spectacular sea veiws. We have period and modern properties, some with log burners or open fires. Sleeping from 2-10 people in great comfort. Alll equipped to a very high standard. Most have gardens and are within easy reach of a beach. CORNWALL HOLIDAY COTTAGES, APPENSLEIGH, FEOCK TR3 6SD (01872 870889). ETC ★★★★/★★★★★★ Self Catering. [Pets £30 per week]
e-mail: rentals@cwlcot.com   website: www.cwlcot.com

Falmouth

Well-known port and resort on Fal estuary, ideal for boating, sailing and fishing; safe bathing from sandy beaches. Of interest is Pendennis Castle (18th century). Newquay 26, Penzance 26, Truro 11.

CREEKSIDE COTTAGES offer a fine selection of individual water's edge, village and rural cottages, sleeping from 2-8. All offer peaceful, comfortable and fully equipped accommodation. Just come and relax. For a colour brochure phone 01326 375972. [Pets £20 per week]
website: www.creeksidecottages.co.uk

PENMORVAH MANOR HOTEL & COURTYARD COTTAGES, BUDOCK WATER, NEAR FALMOUTH TR11 5ED (01326 250277; Fax: 01326 250509). Situated in 6 acres of mature gardens and woodland. Ideal for visiting Cornwall's superb gardens.Close to Falmouth and Coastal Paths. Well behaved dogs welcome. AA ★★★ Hotel, ETC ★★★★ Self-catering. [Pets £7.50 per night.]
e-mail: reception@penmorvah.co.uk   website: www.penmorvah.co.uk

SUE & DICK BARRETT, TUDOR COURT, 55 MELVILL ROAD, FALMOUTH TR11 4DF (01326 312807) Strikingly stylish, mock-Tudor family-run guest house, in award-winning gardens. Comfortable, friendly, non-smoking accommodation, a short walk from town and beaches. Open all year incl. Christmas. AA★★★ [Pets £2 per night].
e-mail: enquiries@tudorcourthotel.com   website: www.tudorcourtguesthouse.co.uk

GOOD-WINDS HOLIDAY APARTMENTS. Six fully self-contained apartments, each with two bedrooms, lounge/diner, bathroom and fully fitted kitchen, balconies, central heating. Sleep 2/5 people. Marvellous views over Falmouth Harbour. One well behaved pet welcome. ETC ★★★. CONTACT: MRS JEAN GOODWIN, 13 STRATTON TERRACE, FALMOUTH TR11 2SY (Tel/Fax: 01326 313200; mobile: 07772 890999).
e-mail: alanandnancy@goodwind64.orangehome.co.uk

PETER WATSON, CREEKSIDE HOLIDAY HOUSES, RESTRONGUET, FALMOUTH TR11 5ST (01326 372722). Spacious houses sleep 2/4/6/8. Peaceful, picturesque water's edge hamlet. Boating facilities. Use of boat. Own quay, beach. Secluded gardens. Near Pandora Inn. Friday bookings. Dogs welcome. [Pets £15 per week]. Letting at Restronguet since 1956.
website: www.creeksideholidayhouses.co.uk

PARKLANDS - SELF-CATERING BUNGALOW. Sleeps 6. Walking distance of harbour and town. Dogs welcome. For prices and availability contact MRS J.A. SIMMONS (01326 312076) or see our website. ETC ★★★. [Pets £10 per week]
website: www.parklandsbungalow.co.uk

Fowey

Historic town, now a busy harbour, Regatta and Carnival Week in August.

TREVANION GUEST HOUSE, 70 LOSTWITHIEL STREET, FOWEY PL23 1BG (01726 832602). A warm welcome awaits in this spacious 4 star guesthouse. Walkers, cyclists and pets welcome. Farmhouse breakfasts. Parking. Open all year round. AA ★★★★.
email: alisteve@trevanionguesthouse.co.uk   website: www.trevanionguesthouse.co.uk

FOWEY HARBOUR COTTAGES. Sleep 2-6. Selection of cottages and flats situated around Fowey Harbour on the South Cornish Coast. All properties registered with VisitBritain and personally vetted. Short breaks and weekend bookings accepted subject to availability Brochure and details from W.J.B. HILL & SON, 3 FORE STREET, FOWEY PL23 1AH (01726 832211; Fax: 01726 832901)
e-mail: hillandson@talk21com   website: www.foweyharbourcottages.co.uk

OLD FERRY INN, BODINNICK-BY-FOWEY PL23 1LX (01726 870237; Fax: 01726 870116). Family-run Inn, ideal for many varied walks. Excellent à la carte menu; bar meals available. Comfortable bedrooms with colour TV and tea/coffee. Rate £90-£130 per night for two people sharing. ETC ★★★★ Inn [Pets £3.50 per night per pet]
e-mail: royce972@aol.com   website: www.oldferryinn.com

A useful index of towns/counties appears on pages 415-421

Helford

Village on inlet South side of Helford River, 6 miles East of Helston.

Enchanting creekside cottages in a timeless and tranquil hamlet. Stunning coastal and riverside walks, country inns, local food, warm and comfortable with cosy log fires. Boat hire, moorings. Short breaks. Open all year. ST ANTHONY HOLIDAY COTTAGES LTD, MANACCAN, HELSTON TR12 6JW (01326 231 357). [Pets £3 per night, £21 per week].
e-mail: info@stanthony.co.uk   website: www.StAnthony.co.uk

Helston

Ancient Stannary town and excellent touring centre, noted for the annual "Furry Dance". Nearby is Looe Pool, separated from the sea by a bar. Truro 17 miles, St Ives 15, Redruth 11, Falmouth & Penzance 12.

BOSCREGE CARAVAN & CAMPING PARK, ASHTON, HELSTON TR13 9TG (01736 762231) Award-winning, quiet, family park close to beaches and attractions. No bar or clubs. Laundry. Static vans available. Pets welcome. AA Three Pennants. [🐕]
e-mail: enquiries@caravanparkcornwall.com   website: www.caravanparkcornwall.com

SILVER SANDS HOLIDAY PARK, GWENDREATH, KENNACK SANDS, RUAN MINOR, HELSTON TR12 7LZ (01326 290631). Quiet, family-run park. Pets welcome with well-trained owners. Short walk through woodland path to award-winning dog beach. Choice of holiday homes, touring and camping. ETC ★★★★, AA 3 Pennants. [Pets £4 per night, £25 per week]
e-mail: info@silversandsholidaypark.co.uk   website: www.silversandsholidaypark.co.uk

Launceston

Town on hill above River Kensey, 20 miles NW of Plymouth.

THE SPRINGER SPANIEL, TREBURLEY, NEAR LAUNCESTON PL15 9NS (01579 370424). Country pub specialising in home cooked, fresh, locally sourced food. Meats from owner's organic farm. Cornish ales and fine wine.
e-mail: enquiries@thespringerspaniel.org.uk   website: www.thespringerspaniel.org.uk

SIMON HIRSH, BAMHAM FARM COTTAGES, HIGHER BAMHAM, LAUNCESTON PL15 9LD (01566 772141). Eight well equipped cottages in converted 18th century farmhouse and outbuildings. Heated indoor swimming pool with paddling pool. Country location with superb views. Pets welcome. VisitBritain ★★★★[🐕].
e-mail:simon@bamhamfarm.co.uk   website: www.bamhamfarm.co.uk

Liskeard

Pleasant market town and good centre for exploring East Cornwall. Bodmin Moor and the quaint fishing villages of Looe and Polperro are near at hand. Plymouth 19 miles, St Austell 19 miles, Launceston 16, Fowey (via ferry) 15, Bodmin 13, Looe 9.

LISTED LUXURY, OLD LANWARNICK, NEAR LISKEARD (01503 221003/07889 298642). Luxury holiday hamlet 3 miles from dog- friendly beach and South West Coastal Path. 3D TV and Blu-Ray players, beauty treatments, champagne breakfasts, hot tub barn. Dogs and horses free of charge. EnjoyEngland ★★★★★, Gold Award.
website: www.listedluxury.co.uk

BUTTERDON MILL HOLIDAY HOMES, MERRYMEET, LISKEARD PL14 3LS (01579 342636) Two-bedroom detached bungalows on idyllic rural site. Sleep up to six. Games barn; children's play areas. Ideal for touring coasts & moors. Discounts for Senior Citizens/couples Sept to June. Brochure available. [🐕]
e-mail: butterdonmill@btconnect.com   website: www.bmhh.co.uk

CUTKIVE WOOD HOLIDAY LODGES, ST IVE, LISKEARD PL14 3ND (01579 362216). Six well-equipped comfortable cedar-clad lodges on country estate with wonderful views. Great for children, dogs welcome. Ideal for coasts, beaches, moors etc. Short breaks. Open all year. [pw! Pets £20 per week].
e-mail: holidays@cutkivewood.co.uk   website: www.cutkivewood.co.uk

LINDA & NEIL HOSKEN, HOPSLAND HOLIDAYS, HOPSLAND COMMONMOOR, LISKEARD PL14 6EJ (01579 344480). Come and stay with your pets at our converted barn cottages. Fully equipped, all with TV/DVD. Own field to exercise in or 150 yards from open moorland. [pw! 🐕]
e-mail: hopslandholidays@btinternet.com   website: www.hopslandholidays.co.uk

CELIA HUTCHINSON, CARADON COUNTRY COTTAGES, EAST TAPHOUSE, NEAR LISKEARD PL14 4NH (Tel & Fax: 01579 320355). Luxury cottages in the heart of the Cornish countryside. Ideal centre for exploring Devon and Cornwall, coast and moor and Eden Project. Meadow and paddock (enclosed). Central heating and log burners for cosy off-season breaks. [pw! Pets £15 per week.]
e-mail: celia@caradoncottages.co.uk   website: www.caradoncottages.co.uk

CLIVE & JULIE FFITCH, REDGATE SMITHY B&B, REDGATE, ST CLEER, LISKEARD PL14 6RU (01579 321578). 200-year-old converted smithy, situated on the southern edge of Bodmin Moor. Extensive and tasty breakfast menu. Excellent pubs and restaurants locally. AA ★★★★ [pw! 🐾]
e-mail: enquiries@redgatesmithy.co.uk   website: www.redgatesmithy.co.uk

SUE JEWELL, BOTURNELL FARM COTTAGES, ST PINNOCK, LISKEARD PL14 4QS (01579 320880). Cosy character cottages set in 25 acres of fields and woodland between Looe and Bodmin. Linen, electricity included. Well equipped. Dog creche. Pets welcome free. [🐾]
e-mail: sue@dogs-holiday.co.uk   website: www.dogs-holiday.co.uk

Lizard

The most southerly point in England, with fine coastal scenery and secluded coves. Sandy beach at Housel Bay. Truro 28 miles, Helston 11.

MULLION COVE HOTEL, MULLION COVE, THE LIZARD TR12 7EP (01326 240328). Located on the Cornish Coastal Path in a spectacular position on the Lizard Peninsula. Stunning country and coastal walks. Dog-friendly lounge, comfortable bedrooms, excellent food. AA ★★★ [pw! Pets £7 per night – free in low season]
e-mail: enquiries@mullion-cove.co.uk   website: www.mullion-cove.co.uk

Longrock

Hamlet to the east of Penzance. Submerged forest to the east.

MRS DOREEN CAPPER, MOUNT VIEW HOTEL, LONGROCK, PENZANCE TR20 8JJ (01736 710416) A family-run pub with comfortable accommodation, situated 100 yards from Mount's Bay in Longrock village. Three en suite rooms and two with shared bathroom. Breakfast in dining room, lunch and dinner available. Dogs welcome by arrangement. Prices from £22 pppn. [🐾]

Looe

Twin towns linked by a bridge over the River Looe. Capital of the shark fishing industry; nearby Monkey Sanctuary is well worth a visit.

COLDRINNICK COTTAGES, DULOE, NEAR LOOE. Attractively converted barns set in large secluded gardens. Excellent locality for walking and relaxing. Sleep 2/4 people. Ideal place for families and dogs alike. For a brochure contact BILL AND KAYE CHAPMAN, COLDRINNICK FARM, DULOE, LISKEARD PL14 4QF (01503 220251). [Pets £15 per week, per dog].
website: www.cornishcottage.net

WRINGWORTHY COTTAGES, LOOE (01503 240685). 8 luxury stone cottages set in peaceful countryside offer you and your pet space for the perfect break. A friendly welcome awaits in our fully equipped, centrally heated cottages, sleeping 2-8. Linen included, walks from our door and more! 7 acre exercise field. ETC ★★★★. [pw! Pets £20 per week, maximum 3 dogs per cottage]
e-mail: holidays@wringworthy.co.uk   website: www.wringworthy.co.uk

BADHAM FARM, ST KEYNE, LISKEARD PL14 4RW (01579 343572). Farmhouse and farm buildings converted to a high standard. Sleep 2-10. All well furnished/equipped; prices include electricity, bed linen and towels. Well behaved dogs welcome (not in high season). Prices from £120 per week. ETC ★★★★. [Pets £4 per night, £20 per week].
e-mail: badhamfarm@yahoo.com   website: www.badhamfarm.co.uk

VALLEYBROOK, PEAKSWATER, LANSALLOS, LOOE PL13 2QE. Peaceful nine acre site with six superb villas and two delightful cottages, all dog friendly. Individual fenced gardens, dog walks, dog friendly beaches nearby. Short breaks. Open all year. 2 dogs max. ETC ★★★/★★★★. Contact DENISE, KEITH or BRIAN HOLDER (01503 220493). [pw! Pets £3 per night]
website: www.valleybrookholidays.com

MRS BARBIE HIGGINS, TREWITH HOLIDAY COTTAGES, TREWITH, DULOE PL14 4PR (01503 262184; mobile: 07968 262184). Four refurbished cottages in peaceful location with panoramic views near Looe. Fully equipped, 1-3 bedrooms, tastefully furnished. Full central heating. Well behaved dogs welcome.VisitBritain ★★★★ Self-catering. [Pets from £18 per week]
e-mail: info@trewith.co.uk   website: www.trewith.co.uk

TREMAINE GREEN COUNTRY COTTAGES, PELYNT, NEAR LOOE PL13 2LT (01503 220333). A beautiful hamlet of 12 award-winning traditional cosy craftsmen's cottages. Clean, comfortable and well equipped. Set in lovely grounds with country/coastal walks and The Eden Project nearby. [pw! Pets £20 per week]
e-mail: stay@tremaine-green.co.uk   website: www.tremaine-green.co.uk

Idyllic 18th century country cottages for romantics and animal lovers. Looe three miles. Wonderful walks from your cottage. Cottages warm and cosy in winter. Personal attention from: MRS LAING, TREWORGEY COTTAGES, DULOE, LISKEARD PL14 4PP (01503 262730). VisitBritain ★★★★★ Quality Assurance Scheme. [Pets £21 per week.]
e-mail: stay@cornishdreamcottages.co.uk   website: www.cornishdreamcottages.co.uk

FOX VALLEY COTTAGES, LANLAWREN, TRENEWAN, LOOE PL13 2PZ (01726 870115). Set in beautiful countryside, just three miles from Polperro. Indoor heated pool and spa. Open all year round. Field for dogs to run around. Contact Andy & Linda for details. [pw! Pets £20 per week]
e-mail: info@foxvalleycottages.co.uk   website: www.foxvalleycottages.co.uk

MOUNT BRIONI SELF CATERING APARTMENTS, LOOE HILL, SEATON, NEAR LOOE PL11 3JN (01503 250251). Along the quiet coastline of South Cornwall, a cluster of 24 luxury Mediterranean-style self-catering apartments, set in beautiful south-facing gardens. Many are dog-friendly. The beach, ocean and coastal path are just yards away. EnjoyEngland ★★★/★★★★.
e-mail: holidays@mountbrioni.co.uk   website: www.mountbrioni.co.uk

NEAR LOOE. Five miles along the coast from the town of Looe, in the picturesque Cornish fishing village of Polperro, a lovely comfortable property for 2-8, for family holidays, as well as for friends and couples to enjoy. Located in a really good position in the village, directly overlooking the picturesque harbour with 14 miles sea views stretching to the Eddystone Lighthouse. 3 minute walk from shops, restaurants, tea rooms, olde-worlde pubs, small sandy beach, quay, pier and rock fishing, and the start of miles of unspoilt National Trust cliff walks, along stunning coastal paths. Located between Looe and Fowey on the South Cornish coast. 25 miles city of Plymouth, 12 miles A38 and 15 miles Eden Project. For details, please telephone Graham Wrights on 01579 344080. [🐾]

GEOFF & STEPH BOWYER, CARTOLE COTTAGES, PELYNT, LOOE PL13 2QH (01503 220956). Small group of self-catering holiday cottages in a private setting. Large open grounds, children's play area, hot tub and sauna, Wi-Fi. Dogs welcome, field walk. EnjoyEngland ★★★/★★★★ [🐾]
email: info@cartole.co.uk   website: www.cartole.co.uk

Marazion

Quaint little village, the oldest town in Britain. Good beach and splendid fishing, sailing waters.

THE GODOLPHIN ARMS, WEST END, MARAZION TR17 0EN (01736 710202) Perched on the edge of the sand, facing St Michael's Mount. Ten en suite bedrooms, most with breathtaking sea views. Relaxing bars. Perfect for exploring coast and coves. AA ★★★★ Inn [Pets £10 per night].
e-mail: enquiries@godolphinarms.co.uk   website: www.godolphinarms.co.uk

Mawgan Porth

Modern village on small sandy bay. Good surfing. Inland stretches the beautiful Vale of Lanherne. Rock formation of Bedruthan Steps is nearby. Newquay 6 miles west..

BLUE BAY, TRENANCE, MAWGAN PORTH TR8 4DA (01637 860324). Guest accommodation, restaurant and lodges in fantastic location between Padstow and Newquay, overlooking Mawgan Porth beach. ETC ★★★★ Guest Accommodation, ★★★ Self-catering. [pw! Pets £5 per night, max. £20 per visit].
e-mail: bluebaycornwall@googlemail.com   website: www.bluebaycornwall.co.uk

Mevagissey

Central for touring and walking. Eden Project nearby.

KILBOL COUNTRY HOUSE HOTEL & COTTAGE, POLMASSICK, MEVAGISSEY PL26 6HA (01726 842481). 'Perfect Peace in Hidden Cornwall'. Small country hotel two miles from the coast. Eight rooms, and one self-catering cottage. No children under 12 years in hotel. [pw! Pets £10 per week].
e-mail: info@kilbol-hotel.co.uk   website: www.kilbol-hotel.co.uk

MRS M.R. BULLED, MENAGWINS, GORRAN PL26 6HP (MEVAGISSEY 01726 843517). Traditional cottage, sleeps two to five. Linen, towels, electricity supplied. Beach one mile. Large garden. Central for touring/walking. Near Eden Project and Heligan Gardens. Pets welcome. [🐾]

Mousehole

Picturesque fishing village with sand and shingle beach. Penzance 3 miles.

POLVELLAN HOLIDAY FLAT. In Mousehole, a quaint and unspoilt fishing village, a fully equipped self-catering flat with full sea views. Sleeps two. Microwave, cooker, fridge, TV, all bedding and towels provided. Open all year. Apply: MR A.G. WRIGHT, LEAFIELDS FARM, UTTOXETER ROAD, ABBOTS BROMLEY, STAFFS WS15 3EH (01283 840651)[🐾]
e-mail: alang23@hotmail.com

Newquay

Popular family holiday resort surrounded by miles of golden beaches. Semi-tropical gardens, zoo and museum. Ideal for exploring all of Cornwall.

MRS DEWOLFREYS, DEWOLF GUEST HOUSE, 100 HENVER ROAD, NEWQUAY TR7 3BL (01637 874746). Single, double or family rooms, two chalets in rear garden. All rooms non-smoking with en suite facilities, colour TV and tea/coffee making facilities. AA ★★★★ [Pets £5 per night]
e-mail: holidays@dewolfguesthouse.com   website: www.dewolfguesthouse.com

TRETHIGGEY TOURING PARK, QUINTRELL DOWNS, NEWQUAY TR8 4QR (01637 877672). Friendly, family-run park minutes from surfing beaches. Touring caravans, tent and campervans welcome. Luxury holiday homes for hire. Shop, off-licence, free showers, electric hook-ups, laundry, children's play area, TV/games room, fishing, licensed bar, Bistro, take-away food in summer. ETC ★★★★ [Pets £2.90 per night]
e-mail: enquiries@trethiggey.co.uk   website: www.Trethiggey.co.uk

QUARRYFIELD CARAVAN & CAMPING PARK, CRANTOCK, NEWQUAY TR7 2RE (Tel & Fax: 01637 872792). Fully equipped modern caravans overlooking beautiful Crantock Bay. Separate camping field. Bar, pool, children's play area.   [Pets £10 per week, £1.50 per night (camping); £20 per week, £3.50 per night in caravan]
e-mail: quarryfield@crantockcaravans.orangehome.co.uk   website: www.quarryfield.co.uk

SUMMER LODGE HOLIDAY PARK, WHITECROSS, NEWQUAY TR8 4LW (0844 272 1138). Just minutes from beach in landscaped park. Outdoor heated pool. Country Club and restaurant. Sports Bar and family entertainment area. Children's play area. Launderette. Touring guest facilities.
e-mail: info@summerlodge.co.uk   website: www.summerlodge.co.uk

THE GRANARY, RETORRICK MILL, ST MAWGAN, NEWQUAY TR8 4BH (01637 860460). Set in 30 acres, self-catering Retorrick Mill offers two cottages, six chalets, traditional camping and licensed bar. Pets including horses very welcome. For a brochure or further assistance contact Chris Williams.
website: www.retorrickmill.co.uk

Padstow

Bright little resort with pretty harbour on Camel estuary. Extensive sands. Nearby is Elizabethan Prideaux Place. Newquay 15 miles, Wadebridge 8.

SHANICE, PADSTOW (01473 327479 OR 07973 538670). Modern home, sleeps four (one double, two singles). Wonderful views, patio, barbecue. Short walk to Stein's and Camel Trail. Heating, gas wood-burner, TV+DVD. Open all year. [🐾]
website: www.brookfarm.demon.co.uk

Penzance

Well-known resort and port for Scilly Isles, with sand and shingle beaches. Truro 27 miles, Helston 13, Land's End 10, St Ives 8.

BOLANKAN COTTAGE, CROWS-AN-WRA, ST BURYAN, PENZANCE TR19 6HU (01736 810168). Fully modernised B&B approximately halfway between Penzance and Land's End. Double, twin and family rooms, all en suite with central heating, colour TV, hairdryer and tea/coffee making facilities. Dog-friendly beaches within a short drive. [🐾]
e-mail: bolankancottage@talktalk.net   website: www.bolankan-cottage.co.uk

Perranporth

North Coast resort 6 miles SW of Newquay.

GREENMEADOW COTTAGES, NEAR PERRANPORTH. Spacious, clean luxury cottages. Sleep six. Open all year. Short breaks out of season. Non-smoking. Ample off road parking. Pets welcome in two of the cottages. ETC ★★★ For brochure and bookings: 01872 540483. [Pets £25 per week]. website: www.greenmeadow-cottages.co.uk

Polperro

Picturesque and quaint little fishing village and harbour. Of interest is the "House of the Props". Fowey 9 miles, Looe 5..

PEAK HOUSE, POLPERRO PL13 2RY. In the picturesque Cornish fishing village of Polperro, directly overlooking the harbour with sea views, a lovely comfortable 250-year-old property, for 2-8. Terraced gardens and private parking, 3 minutes' walk shops, restaurants, tea rooms, olde-worlde pubs, small sandy beach, quay, pier and rock fishing and the start of miles of unspoilt National Trust cliff walks. Located between Looe and Fowey on the South Cornish coast, 25 miles city of Plymouth, 12 miles A38 and 15 miles Eden Project. For details, please telephone Graham Wrights on 01579 344080. [🐾]

Polruan

Village at mouth of River Fowey, opposite the town of Fowey.

POLRUAN-BY-FOWEY, Superb views. A number of properties allowing pets. Enjoy sailing, fishing, walking or just watching. Small unspoilt friendly village. People will say "Good Morning!". JANE BRENNAN, POLRUAN COTTAGES, 1 FOWEY VIEW, POLRUAN PL23 1PA (01726 870582)
e-mail: info@polruancottages.co.uk   website: www.polruancottages.co.uk

Port Gaverne

Hamlet on east side of Port Isaac, near Camel Estuary.

GREEN DOOR COTTAGES. PORT GAVERNE. A delightful collection of 18C Cornish buildings built around a sunny enclosed courtyard, and 2 lovely apartments with stunning sea views. Situated in a picturesque, tranquil cove ideal for children. Dogs allowed on the beach year round. Half a mile from Port Isaac, on the Cornish Coastal Path. Traditional pub directly opposite. ETC ★★★★. For brochure: (01208 880293) [🐾]
e-mail: enquiries@greendoorcottages.co.uk   website: www.greendoorcottages.co.uk

Porthleven

Small town with surprisingly big harbour. Grand woodland walks. 2 miles SW of Helston.

MRS NEAL, TAMARIND, SHRUBBERIES HILL, PORTHLEVEN, HELSTON TR13 9EA (01326 574303 or 07814 911532). Situated close to beach and coastal path. Five minutes' walk from shops, harbour, restaurants and inns. Garden. Off-road parking. Sea views. Continental and English breakfast served. House also available to let. [🐾]
website: www.web-direct.co.uk/porthleven

PORTHLEVEN. "Kernow agas dynargh" - "Cornwall welcomes you". Fishermen's cottages. Harbour, bay or country views. 3 minutes to beach, coast path, harbourside eating places. Open fires. Pets welcome. Please contact: MRS KERNO (01209 860410). [Pets welcome at a charge]

Port Isaac

Attractive fishing village with harbour. Much of the attractive coastline is protected by the National Trust. Camelford 9 miles. Wadebridge 9.

DAVID AND JENNY OLDHAM, THE GARDEN HOUSE, MICHAELSTOW (01208 850529). Secure garden for dogs. Doggy shower. Lovely far reaching views. Full central heating and electric inc. Bed linen and towels inc. One bedroom with twin or double. Central location in small quiet hamlet. From £188 pw.[🐾]
e-mail: david.trevella@btconnect.com   website: www.trevellacornwall.co.uk

Homes from home around our peaceful courtyard garden 100 yards from sea in bygone fishing hamlet. Each sleeps six and has full CH, fridge/freezer, washer/dryer, dishwasher, Freeview HD TV, HD PVR, Blu-ray, PC plus broadband, £220 (February), £820 (August) weekly. Resident owner. APPLY:- MALCOLM LEE, GULLROCK, PORT GAVERNE, PORT ISAAC PL29 3SQ (01208 880106). [🐾]
e-mail: gullrockportgaverne@btinternet.com   website: www.gullrock-port-gaverne.co.uk

LONGCROSS HOTEL & VICTORIAN GARDENS, TRELIGHTS, PORT ISAAC PL29 3TF (01208 880243). Lovely Victorian country house hotel with four acres of restored gardens. Close to the area's best beaches, golf courses and other attractions. Newly refurbished en suite bedrooms and suites. [Pets £5.00 per night.]
website: www.longcrosshotel.co.uk

Portreath

Coastal village 4 miles north west of Redruth.

Charming, elegantly furnished, self-catering cottages between Newquay and St Ives. Sleep 2 to 6. Fully equipped including linen. Beautiful beaches. Laundry and games room. Ample parking. Colour brochure – FRIESIAN VALLEY COTTAGES, MAWLA, CORNWALL TR16 5DW (01209 890901) [🐾]

Portwrinkle

Village on Whitsand Bay, 6 miles west of Torpoint.

WHITSAND BAY SELF-CATERING (01579 345688). Twelve cottages sleeping 4-10, all with sea views and situated by an 18-hole clifftop golf course. Children and pet-friendly. [Pets £20 per week].
e-mail: ehwbsc@hotmail.com   website: www.whitsandbayselfcatering.co.uk

Redruth

Market town 9 miles west of Truro, 12 miles east of St Ives.

THE LAURELS & LANYON HOLIDAY PARK, LOSCOMBE LANE, FOUR LANES, REDRUTH TR16 6LP (01209 313474) Superb central location surrounded by beautiful countryside. Indoor heated pool. Games room. Bar/ Restaurant/Takeaway/Free entertainment. Play area. Spacious level pitches and short grass. Pets welcome. EnjoyEngland ★★★★. AA Three Pennants.
websites: www.lanyonholidaypark.co.uk   www.thelaurelsholidaypark.co.uk

St Agnes

Patchwork of fields dotted with remains of local mining industry. Watch for grey seals swimming off St Agnes Head.

CHIVERTON PARK, BLACKWATER, TRURO TR4 8HS (01872 560667). Caravan and touring holidays only a short drive from magnificent beaches. Quiet, spacious; exclusive gym, sauna, steamroom; laundry, play area and games room. All amenities. [Dogs £18 per week; £2.50 per night camping]
e-mail: info@chivertonpark.co.uk   website: www.chivertonpark.co.uk

THE DRIFTWOOD SPARS, TREVAUNANCE COVE, ST AGNES TR5 0RT (01872 552428). Take a deep breath of Cornish fresh air at this comfortable B&B ideally situated for a perfect seaside holiday. Dogs on leads allowed on beach. Miles of footpaths for 'walkies'. Children and pets welcome. AA ★★★★ [Pets £3 per night].
e-mail: info@driftwoodspars.co.uk   website: www.driftwoodspars.co.uk

PENKERRIS, PENWINNICK ROAD, ST AGNES TR5 0PA (01872 552262). B&B/Guest House/Hotel with lawned garden, picnic tables, barbeque, ample parking. Comfortable rooms, "real" food. Country/cliff walks, beaches (dog-friendly). B&B £25-£35pppn. Open all year. ETC ★★ [🐾]
e-mail: penkerris@gmail.com   website: www.penkerris.co.uk

St Austell

Old Cornish town and china clay centre with small port at Charlestown (1½ miles). Excellent touring centre. Newquay 16 miles, Truro 14, Bodmin 12, Fowey 9, Mevagissey 6.

BOSINVER FARM COTTAGES, ST MEWAN, ST AUSTELL PL26 7DT (01726 72128). Award-winning individual cottages in peaceful garden surroundings. Close to major holiday attractions. Short walk to shop and pub. Phone for brochure. No pets during Summer School holidays. ETC ★★★★ [pw!, Pets £30 per week].
e-mail: reception@bosinver.co.uk   website: www.bosinver.co.uk

SUN VALLEY HOLIDAY PARK, PENTEWAN ROAD, ST AUSTELL PL26 6DJ (Tel & Fax: 01726 843 266) Holiday Park and Campsite with landscaped grounds, indoor heated swimming pool, well equipped caravans and campsite, bar and restaurant, refurbished shower block and holiday apartments. Open all year. EnjoyEngland ★★★★★.
e-mail: reception@sunvalleyholidays.co.uk   website: www.sunvalleyholidays.co.uk

St Ives

Picturesque resort, popular with artists, with cobbled streets and intriguing little shops. Wide stretches of sand.

BOB & JACKY PONTEFRACT, THE LINKS, LELANT, ST IVES TR26 3HY (01736 753326). Magnificent location overlooking golf course and beach. Wonderful spot for walking. Five minutes from beach where dogs allowed all year. Two well-equipped flats open all year. [🐾]
e-mail: bobandjackyp@btinternet.com

SANDBANK HOLIDAYS, ST IVES BAY, HAYLE (01736 752594). High quality Apartments and Bungalows for 2-6 persons. Heated, Colour TV, Microwave etc. Dogs welcome. [🐾]
website: www.sandbank-holidays.co.uk

St Mawgan

Delightful village in wooded river valley. Ancient church has fine carvings.

DALSWINTON HOUSE, ST MAWGAN TR8 4EZ (01637 860385). Old Cornish house standing in ten acres of secluded grounds. All rooms en suite, colour TV, tea/coffee facilities. Solar heated outdoor swimming pool. Restaurant and bar. Out-of-season breaks. No children under 16. ETC ★★★★ Silver Award. [🐾 pw!]
e-mail: dalswintonhouse@btconnect.com   website: www.dalswinton.com

St Tudy

Village 5 miles north east of Wadebridge.

MAYMEAR COTTAGE. Comfortable end of terrace cottage in picturesque and friendly village. Enclosed garden and parking. Ideal location for exploring all Cornwall. Short Breaks and brochure available. Contact: MRS R REEVES, POLSTRAUL, TREWALDER, DELABOLE PL33 9ET (Tel & Fax: 01840 213120). [🐾]
e-mail: ruth.reeves@hotmail.co.uk   website: www.maymear.co.uk

Tregarne

On the Lizard peninsula, 8 miles east of Helston.

THE HEN HOUSE, TREGARNE, NEAR HELFORD TR12 6EW (01326 280236). Idyllic peaceful country setting a mile from the sea. Superb walks in all directions with year-round dog-friendly beaches Delightful spacious barns each open onto courtyard garden. Wild flower meadow, bird song and complete relaxation. Complimentary Tai-chi. Award Winners for Green Ethos and Quality. AA ★★★★. [pw! Pets £5 per night]
e-mail: henhouseuk@aol.com   website: www.thehenhouse-cornwall.co.uk

Truro

Bustling Cathedral City with something for everyone. Museum and Art Gallery with interesting shop and cafe is well worth a visit.

KING HARRY COTTAGES, FEOCK, TRURO TR3 6QJ (01872 861917). Two comfortable, well equipped cottages in own charming gardens. Dogs welcome. Beautiful woodland walks. Perfect for fishing and bird watching. Free use of boat. [🐕]
e-mail: beverley@kingharry.net   website: www.kingharrycottages.co.uk

MRS PAMELA CARBIS, TRENONA FARM, RUAN HIGH LANES, TRURO TR2 5JS (01872 501339). Enjoy a relaxing stay on the unspoilt Roseland Peninsula between Truro and St Austell. Self-catering in three renovated barns, B&B in Victorian farmhouse. Children and pets welcome. Brochure available. [Pets £10 per stay, 🏠]
e-mail: info@trenonafarmholidays.co.uk   website: www.trenonafarmholidays.co.uk

HIGHER TREWITHEN, STITHIANS, TRURO TR3 7DR (01209 860863; mobile: 07966 794562) The ideal centre for your pet and your family. We are surrounded by public footpaths and have 3½ acres of fields. ETC ★★★[🐕]
e-mail: trewithen@talk21.com   website: www.trewithen.com

Wadebridge

Town on River Camel, 6 miles north-west of Bodmin

Three barn converted luxury cottage-style self catering homes near Wadebridge. Found along a leafy drive, with wonderful views, beside the lazy twisting Camel River with its "Trail" for walking and cycling. CORNWALL TOURISM AWARDS 2002 - Self Catering Establishment of the Year - "Highly Commended". Sleep 2-7 plus cot. Two dogs per cottage welcome. GARY NEWMAN, COLESENT COTTAGES, ST TUDY, WADEBRIDGE PL30 4QX (Tel & Fax: 01208 850112). [pw! 🐕]
e-mail: relax@colesent.co.uk   website: www.colesent.co.uk

Ashburton, Axminster

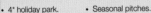

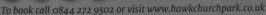

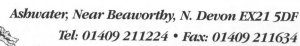

Welcome to North Hill

deep in the rolling hills of Devon, close to beaches and the best North Devon has to offer.

Carol Ann and Adrian Black, North Hill, Shirwell, Barnstaple EX31 4LG
Tel: 01271 850611
Mobile: 07834 806434
www.north-hill.co.uk

17th century farm buildings, sympathetically converted into nine cottages sleeping 2-6, with exposed beams, wood stoves and central heating. Set in 9 acres of pastures and gardens with a children's play area. Facilities include: indoor heated swimming pool, jacuzzi, sauna, all-weather tennis court and games room.

This area of North Devon offers some of the finest beaches in the country and the National Park of Exmoor offers thousands of acres of moorland to explore.

Terms from £235 to £1025

Lower Yelland Farm Guest House

Winner Golden Achievement Award of Excellence for Devon Retreat of the Year

Situated half way between Barnstaple and Bideford, this delightfully modernised 17th Century farmhouse accommodation is part of a working farm. The farm is centrally located for easy access to the many attractions of North Devon, its beautiful beaches, varied walks and sports facilities including golf, surfing, fishing, riding etc. Its proximity to both Exmoor and Dartmoor makes this location perfect for those who wish to explore. Instow with its sandy beach, pubs and restaurants is a just mile away. It lies adjacent to the Tarka Trail, part of the South West Coastal Footpath, and RSPB bird sanctuary. The bed and breakfast accommodation comprises 2 twin/super king-size and 1 room with four-poster bed, 2 double rooms and 2 single rooms; all rooms en suite, with TV and tea/coffee making facilities. Breakfast includes eggs from our free-range chickens, home-made bread, jams and marmalade. The delightful sitting room has a large selection of books for those who want to relax and browse.
Please visit our website for further details   **www.loweryellandfarm.co.uk**
Lower Yelland Farm Guest House, Fremington, Barnstaple EX31 3EN
Tel: 01271 860101 • e-mail: peterday@loweryellandfarm.co.uk

Martinhoe Cleave Cottages
Martinhoe, Parracombe, Barnstaple, Devon EX31 4PZ
Overlooking the beautiful Heddon valley and close to the dramatic coast of the Exmoor National Park, these delightful cottages, equipped to a very high standard throughout, offer perfect rural tranquillity. Open all year. Sleep 1-2. • **Tel: 01598 763313**
e-mail: info@exmoorhideaway.co.uk • www.exmoorhideaway.co.uk

www.holidayguides.com
for pet-friendly accommodation in Britain

Bideford, Bigbury-on-Sea, Bradworthy, Broadwoodwidger

FHG Guides publish a large range of well-known accommodation guides. We will be happy to send you details or you can use the order form at the back of this book.

Brixham

Budleigh Salterton, Chittlehamholt, Chulmleigh, Combe Martin

Combe Martin

Combe Martin, Cullompton, Dartmoor

Dartmoor

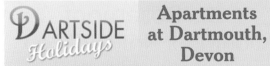

Station Lodge, Doddiscombsleigh, Exeter, Devon

Comfortably furnished apartment for two people in the beautiful Teign River valley. Excellent location for exploring Devon's moors, coasts and villages. Kitchen, lounge/diner, en suite bedroom with double bed. Private garden, extensive grounds. Pubs, shops and walks nearby, golf, fishing, horseriding, tennis and swimming pools within 10 miles. Central heating. Colour TV. All linen provided. Parking. Non-smokers only. Well behaved dogs welcome.
From £240 per week.
Short Breaks welcome Oct-April. For further details contact:

Ian West, Station House, Doddiscombsleigh, Exeter EX6 7PW • Tel: 01647 253104
e-mail: enquiries@station-lodge.co.uk • www.station-lodge.co.uk

---

Challacombe, Barnstaple, Devon EX31 4TT

Twitchen Farm

Tel: 01598 763568
e-mail: holidays@twitchen.co.uk
www.twitchen.co.uk

Welcome to Twitchen Farm, a small, family-run business. Anybody who loves the countryside and excellent food will enjoy their stay here. We have eight large en suite rooms that can accommodate most requirements, including family rooms, a wheelchair accessible room, ground floor rooms and rooms suitable for groups. Several good food pubs nearby. Well behaved dogs are welcome. ETC ★★★★

Staghunters Inn/Hotel • Brendon, Exmoor EX35 6PS

A friendly, family-run Exmoor village inn with frontage to the East Lyn River. Beautiful landscaped garden to the rear; 12 en suite rooms. Varied menu of home-made food using fresh local produce. Log fires, fine wines and local cask ales. A walkers' paradise in the Doone Valley, close to Watersmeet, Lynton and Lynmouth. Ample off-road parking. B&B from £32.50. *New owners: The Wyburn Family.*

e-mail: stay@staghunters.com • www.staghunters.com • Tel: 01598 741222 • Fax: 01598 741352

Tinney Waters

Coarse Fishing Holidays
Self Catering • Bed & Breakfast
No closed Season
Beautiful setting where you will be able to enjoy peace and tranquillity in the heart of rural Devon.
Lots of non-fishing activities.
Telephone: 01409 271362
www.tinneywaters.co.uk

Taking your pet on holiday?

for quality properties where pets will be warmly welcomed visit:

www.pets-welcome.co.uk

Hope Cove, Ilfracombe

Kingsbridge

Blue Ball Inn

formerly The Exmoor Sandpiper Inn

is a romantic Coaching Inn dating in part back to the 13th century, with low ceilings, blackened beams, stone fireplaces and a timeless atmosphere of unspoilt old world charm. Offering visitors great food and drink, a warm welcome and a high standard of accommodation.

The inn is set in an imposing position on a hilltop on Exmoor in North Devon, a few hundred yards from the sea, and high above the twin villages of Lynmouth and Lynton, in an area of oustanding beauty.

The spectacular scenery and endless views attract visitors and hikers from all over the world.

We have 16 en suite bedrooms, comfortable sofas in the bar and lounge areas, and five fireplaces, including a 13th century inglenook. Our extensive menus include local produce wherever possible, such as locally reared meat, and locally caught game and fish, like Lynmouth Bay lobster; specials are featured daily. We also have a great choice of good wines, available by the bottle or the glass, and a selection of locally brewed beers, some produced specially for us.

Stay with us to relax, or to follow one of the seven circular walks through stunning countryside that start from the Inn. Horse riding for experienced riders or complete novices can be arranged. Plenty of parking. Dogs (no charge), children and walkers are very welcome!

Blue Ball Inn formerly The Exmoor Sandpiper Inn

Countisbury, Lynmouth, Devon EX35 6NE

01598 741263

www.BlueBallinn.com • www.exmoorsandpiper.com

Paignton

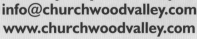

Paignton, Salcombe, Seaton, Sidmouth

Sidmouth

Sidmouth, South Molton, Tavistock

TAVISTOCK • EDGE OF DARTMOOR

Comfortably furnished studio cottage five miles from the market town of Tavistock. Ideal for two. Private walled garden. Pets welcome. Private parking, free coal for open fire. All linen provided. Wonderful walking, riding, fishing country with excellent local pubs. Terms £240 per week.

Higher Quither

Milton Abbot, Tavistock, Devon PL19 0PZ
Contact: Mrs P.G.C. Quinton
Tel: 01822 860284 • www.higherquither.2day.ws/

Cutaway Cottage • Thurlestone, Kingsbridge TQ7 3NF
Self-catering cottage within fenced garden in the middle of the village, on private road. • 5 minutes to pub and shop. • 20 minutes' walk to beaches and sea • Ideal for children, dog walkers and bird watchers.
Pets free of charge ° Phone Pat on 01548 560688

NEWHOUSE FARM COTTAGES

Superior Quality
Self-catering Accommodation

Nine beautifully converted, well equipped, Grade II Listed stone barns, with a choice of accommodation ranging from a one-bedroom cottage with four-poster bed through to our spacious five-bedroom barn sleeping 10. Take a stroll through 23 acres of flower-filled meadows and woodland, or simply relax in our heated indoor swimming pool and games room.

For long or short breaks and more information, please call us on
01884 860266 or visit our website at www.newhousecottages.com
Newhouse Farm, Witheridge, Tiverton, Devon EX16 8QB

Visit www.holidayguides.com
for pet-friendly accommodation in Britain

Torrington, Totnes, Tuckenhay, Woolacombe

Woolacombe, Yelverton

COAST & COUNTRY COTTAGES (01548 843773). Over 425 self-catering properties in and around Salcombe, Dartmouth and Hope Cove and throughout the beautiful South Devon coast and countryside, the ideal destination for a holiday or short break with your dog all year round. Free brochure. One pet free when quoting PET12.
website: www.coastandcountry.co.uk

FARM & COTTAGE HOLIDAYS (01237 459897). An inspiring collection of holiday cottages throughout Cornwall, Devon, Somerset and Dorset in stunning rural and coastal locations. [Pets £20 per week]
website: www.holidaycottages.co.uk

TOAD HALL COTTAGES (01548 853089 24 hrs). Over 250 outstanding, dog friendly coastal, waterside and rural holiday cottages throughout Devon, Cornwall and Exmoor. Some superb beaches await your stroll. Well behaved people welcome too!
e-mail: thc@toadhallcottages.co.uk   website: www.toadhallcottages.co.uk

HELPFUL HOLIDAYS (01647 434067). Variety of cottages and holiday homes all over the West Country. Ideal for countryside rambles. Many welcome pets.
website: www.helpfulholidays.co.uk

PORT LIGHT, BOLBERRY DOWN, MALBOROUGH, NEAR SALCOMBE TQ7 3DY (01548 561384 or 07970 859992). A totally unique location set amidst acres of National Trust coastline. Luxury en suite rooms. Superb home-cooked fare, specialising in local seafood. Licensed bar. Pets welcome throughout the hotel. Short Breaks throughout the year. Contact: Sean and Hazel Hassall. [🐾]
e-mail: info@portlight.co.uk   website: www.portlight.co.uk

Ashburton

Delightful little town on southern fringe of Dartmoor. Centrally placed for touring and the Torbay resorts. Plymouth 24 miles, Exeter 20, Kingsbridge 20, Tavistock 20, Teignmouth 14, Torquay 14, Totnes 8, Newton Abbot 7.

PARKERS FARM HOLIDAY PARK, HIGHER MEAD FARM, ASHBURTON TQ13 7LJ (01364 654869; Fax: 01364 654004). Static caravans to let, also level touring site with two toilet/shower blocks and electric hook-ups. Central for touring; 12 miles Torquay. ETC ★★★★, AA Four Pennants. [pw! Pets £1.50 per night touring, £17 per week static caravans]
e-mail: parkersfarm@btconnect.com   website: www.parkersfarmholidays.co.uk

MRS A. BELL, WOODER MANOR, WIDECOMBE IN THE MOOR, NEAR ASHBURTON TQ13 7TR (Tel & Fax: 01364 621391). Cottages nestled in picturesque valley. Surrounded by unspoilt woodland and moors. Clean and well equipped, colour TV/DVD, central heating, laundry room. Two properties suitable for disabled visitors. Colour brochure available. Please telephone. ETC ★★★ to ★★★★ [pw! £20 per week].
website: www.woodermanor.com

PARKERS FARM COTTAGES & CARAVANS, MEAD, ALSTON CROSS, ASHBURTON TQ13 7LJ (01364 653008). Farm Cottages and Static Caravans to let surrounded by beautiful countryside. Perfect for children and pets. Central for touring; 12 miles Torquay. ETC★★★★ [pw! Pets £17 per week]
e-mail: parkerscottages@btconnect.com   website: www.parkersfarmcottages.co.uk

Ashwater

Village 6 miles south-east of Holsworthy.

BLAGDON MANOR RESTAURANT WITH ROOMS, ASHWATER, NORTH DEVON EX21 5DF (01409 211224; Fax: 01409 211634). Beautifully restored Grade II Listed building in peaceful location 20 minutes from Bude. 7 en suite bedrooms, three-acre gardens. No children under 12 years. AA ★★★★★ Restaurant with Rooms, 2 Rosettes. [pw! Dogs £8 per night]
email: stay@blagdon.com   website: www.blagdon.com

🐾 Pets are welcome free of charge.

£   A charge is made for pets: nightly or weekly.

pw! Special provision for pets; exercise facility, feeding or accommodation arrangement.

⌂   Separate pets' accommodation.

Classified Symbols

Axminster

Small friendly market town, full of old world charm, set in the beautiful Axe Valley. Excellent centre for touring Devon, Somerset and Dorset. 5 miles from coast.

HAWKCHURCH COUNTRY PARK, HAWKCHURCH, AXMINSTER EX13 5UL (0844 272 9502). A peaceful and tranquil caravan park situated in beautiful East Devon. Convenience shop. Licensed bar and restaurant. Children's play area. Mains electricity and waste disposal points. Enjoy England ★★★★.
e-mail: enquiries@hawkchurchpark.co.uk   website: www.hawkchurchpark.co.uk

LEA HILL, MEMBURY, AXMINSTER EX13 7AQ (01404 881881). Tranquil location. Wonderful scenery. Close to World Heritage Coast. Eight acres of grounds and gardens. Walks, footpaths and exercise fields. Hot tub and barbecue. Comfortable, well equipped self-catering cottages with en suite bedrooms and own gardens. Green Tourism Silver Award. [pw! Pets £15 per week]
e-mail: reception@leahill.co.uk   website: www.leahill.co.uk

LILAC COTTAGE. Detached cottage, furnished to a high standard, sleeps six plus cot. Children and pets are welcome. Walled garden and garage. On borders of Devon, Dorset, and Somerset; many seaside towns within 10 miles. Wi-Fi. Contact: MRS J.M. STUART, 2 SANDFORD HOUSE, KINGSCLERE RG20 4PA (Tel & Fax: 01635 291942; Mobile: 07700 036648). [Pets £10 per week].
e-mail: jm.stuartb@gmail.com   www.chateau-rentals.com/lilac.htm

THE FAIRWATER HEAD HOTEL, HAWKCHURCH, NEAR AXMINSTER EX13 5TX (01297 678349; Fax: 01297 678459). Located in the tranquil Devon countryside and close to Lyme Regis, this beautiful Edwardian Country House Hotel has all you and your dog need for a peaceful and relaxing holiday. Dogs most welcome free of charge. Countryside location with panoramic views. AA ★★★, Rosette. [🐾, 🏠]
e-mail: e-mail: stay@fairwaterheadhotel.co.uk   website: www.fairwaterheadhotel.co.uk

Barnstaple

Market town at head of River Taw estuary, 34 miles north west of Exeter.

NORTH HILL COTTAGES, NORTH HILL, SHIRWELL, BARNSTAPLE EX31 4LG (01271 850611; mobile: 07834 806434). 9 cottages sleeping 2-6. 17th century farm buildings, sympathetically converted into cottages. Indoor heated swimming pool, jacuzzi, sauna, all-weather tennis court and games room. [Pets £25 per week]
website: www.north-hill.co.uk

LOWER YELLAND FARM GUEST HOUSE, FREMINGTON, BARNSTAPLE EX31 3EN (01271 860101). Delightfully modernised farmhouse accommodation on working farm. Central for North Devon attractions. All rooms en suite, with TV and tea/coffee making. Breakfast includes free-range eggs and home-made bread etc. ETC ★★★★ [Pets £5 per night, £25 per week]
e-mail: peterday@loweryellandfarm.co.uk   website: www.loweryellandfarm.co.uk

MARTINHOE CLEAVE COTTAGES, MARTINHOE, PARRACOMBE, BARNSTAPLE EX31 4PZ (01598 763313). Perfect rural tranquillity overlooking the beautiful Heddon valley and close to the Exmoor National Park. Delightful cottages, equipped to a very high standard throughout. Open all year. Sleep 1-2. [🐾].
e-mail: info@exmoorhideaway.co.uk   website:www.exmoorhideaway.co.uk

Bideford

Neat port village overlooking the beautiful Sterridge Valley has a 17th century pub and even older church, and is half-a-mile from the coast road between Combe Martin and Ilfracombe.

THE PINES AT EASTLEIGH, NEAR BIDEFORD EX39 4PA (01271 860561). Luxury B&B and cottages. Log-fires, king-size beds, garden room bar with library, maps and a warm welcome await our guests. B&B from £35pp. No smoking. AA ★★★★ [pw! Pets £5 per night]
e-mail: pirrie@thepinesateastleigh.co.uk   website: www.thepinesateastleigh.co.uk

Bigbury-on-Sea

A scattered village overlooking superb coastal scenery and wide expanses of sand.

MRS J. TUCKER, MOUNT FOLLY FARM, BIGBURY-ON-SEA, KINGSBRIDGE TQ7 4AR (01548 810267). Cliff top position, with outstanding views of Bigbury Bay. Spacious, self-catering wing of farmhouse, attractively furnished. Farm adjoins golf course and River Avon. Lovely coastal walks, ideal centre for South Hams and Dartmoor. Always a warm welcome, pets too! EnjoyEngland ★★★ [Pets £15 per week]
e-mail: info@bigburyholidays.co.uk   website: www.bigburyholidays.co.uk

Bradworthy

Village to the north of Holsworthy. Well placed for North Devon and North Cornish coasts.

PETER & LESLEY LEWIN, LAKE HOUSE COTTAGES AND B&B, LAKE VILLA, BRADWORTHY, DEVON EX22 7SQ (01409 241962). Four well equipped cottages sleeping two to five/six. Quiet rural position; one acre gardens and tennis court. 6 acre meadow for dog exercising, plus 2 lakes and fishing. Half-a-mile from village shops and pub. Dog-friendly beaches eight miles. Also two lovely en suite B&B rooms with balcony, all facilities, from £31. [🐾]
e-mail: lesley@lakevilla.co.uk   website: www.lakevilla.co.uk

Brixham

Lively resort and fishing port, with quaint houses and narrow winding streets. Ample opportunities for fishing and boat trips.

DEVONCOURT HOLIDAY FLATS, BERRYHEAD ROAD, BRIXHAM TQ5 9AB (01803 853748 or 07802 403289 after office hours). 24 self-contained flats with private balcony, colour television, heating, private car park, all-electric kitchenette, separate bathroom and toilet. Open all year. Pets welcome.
website: www.devoncourt.info

BRIXHAM HOLIDAY PARK, FISHCOMBE COVE, BRIXHAM TQ5 8RB (01803 853324). Situated on coastal path. Choice of one and two-bedroomed chalets. Indoor heated pool, free club membership, comfortable bar offering meals and takeaway service, launderette. 150 yards from beach with lovely walks through woods beyond. ETC ★★★★. [Pets £30 per week]
e-mail: enquiries@brixhamholpk.fsnet.co.uk   website: www.brixhamholidaypark.co.uk

Broadwoodwidger

Village 6 miles north-east of Launceston.

WEST BANBURY FARM COTTAGES, BROADWOODWIDGER (01566 780423). 10 charming cottages, set around two courtyards. Sleep 2-8 (dogs welcome in all). Large indoor pool, sauna, games room etc. Ideal for exploring Devon and Cornwall. [Pets £20 per week].
e-mail: info@westbanbury.co.uk   website: www.westbanbury.co.uk

Budleigh Salterton

South Devon resort of dignified charm. Attractive sea front, shingle beach, pleasant walks in vicinity. Good fishing in sea and River Otter. Taunton 16 miles, Exeter 14, Sidmouth 7, Exmouth 5.

BADGER'S DEN, DALDITCH LANE, KNOWLE, BUDLEIGH SALTERTON EX9 7AH (01395 443282) A thatched, Grade II listed cottage which has been furnished and equipped to a very high standard. Surrounded by coastal paths and countryside. Pets welcome. ETC ★★★★ [Pets £10 per week]
e-mail: info@holidaycottagedevon.com   website: www.holidaycottagedevon.com

Chittlehamholt

Village 5 miles south west of South Molton.

GRANGE HOLIDAY COTTAGES, CHITTLEHAMHOLT, UMBERLEIGH EX37 9NS (01769 540748). Two self catering cottages, sleep 2 to 11 people. Fully furnished. Enclosed lawn area. BBQ facilities. Set in charming village between Taw and Mole valleys. Short breaks available. Well behaved pet by arrangement. [Pets £12 per week]

Chulmleigh

Mid-Devon village set in lovely countryside, just off A377 Exeter to Barnstaple road. Exeter 23 miles, Tiverton 19, Barnstaple 18.

SANDRA GAY, NORTHCOTT BARTON FARM COTTAGE, NORTHCOTT BARTON, ASHREIGNEY, CHULMLEIGH EX18 7PR (Tel & Fax: 01769 520259). Three bedroom character cottage, large enclosed garden, log fire. Special rates low season, couples and short breaks. Near golf, riding, Tarka Trail and RHS Rosemoor. ETC ★★★★ [🐾]
e-mail: sandra@northcottbarton.co.uk   website: www.northcottbarton.co.uk

Combe Martin

Coastal village with harbour set in sandy bay. Good cliff and rock scenery. Of interest is the Church and "Pack of Cards" Inn. Barnstaple 14 miles, Lynton 12, Ilfracombe 6.

NORTHCOTE MANOR FARM HOLIDAY COTTAGES, NEAR COMBE MARTIN EX31 4NB (01271 882376). Five self-catering holiday cottages grouped around a courtyard. Dogs are warmly welcomed in all of the cottages, three of which have enclosed gardens. 34 acres of fields, woods and rivers to explore. Indoor heated pool, games room and playground. [Pets £25 per week]
e-mail: info@northcotemanorfarm.co.uk   website: www.northcotemanorfarm.co.uk

WATERMOUTH COVE COTTAGES, WATERMOUTH, NEAR COMBE MARTIN EX34 9SJ (0845 029 1958 or 01271 883931). 8 beautiful cottages, most with four-poster and log burner, set beside grounds of Watermouth Castle, 200 yards from sea, cove and coastal path. Pets welcome. Open all year. [Pets £25 per week]
e-mail: cottages@watermouthcove.co.uk   website: www.watermouth-cove-cottages.co.uk

YETLAND FARM COTTAGES, BERRY DOWN, COMBE MARTIN EX34 0NT (01271 883655). 6 well equipped cottages surrounding a pretty paved courtyard. Ideally situated for North Devon beaches, Exmoor, the South West Coastal Path and many tourist and leisure attractions. Linen and towels supplied. Sleep 3-6 plus cot. Well behaved pets welcome. ETC ★★★★ [Pets £15 per week]
e-mail: enquiries@yetlandfarmcottages.co.uk   website: www.yetlandfarmcottages.co.uk

GRASSMERE HOUSE LUXURY HOLIDAY APARTMENT, KING STREET, COMBE MARTIN EX34 0BS (01746 780902 or 07929656239). Luxurious Four Bedroomed Apartment. Sleeps nine, ideal for large families. Air conditioned and non smoking. Small to medium pet dogs welcome. [🐾]
e-mail paulinetaft@msn.com   website: www.grassmerehouse.net

Cullompton

Small market town off the main A38 Taunton - Exeter road. Good touring centre. Noted for apple orchards which supply the local cider industry. Taunton 19 miles, Exeter 13, Honiton 11, Tiverton 9.

FOREST GLADE HOLIDAY PARK (PW), KENTISBEARE, CULLOMPTON EX15 2DT (01404 841381; Fax: 01404 841593). Country estate surrounded by forest with modern 6-berth holiday caravans, all well-equipped. Free indoor heated swimming pool. Tents, touring caravans and motor homes welcome. ETC ★★★★, AA 4 Pennants, David Bellamy Gold Award. [Pets £2 per night, pw!]
e-mail: enquiries@forest-glade.co.uk   website: www.forest-glade.co.uk

Dartmoor

365 square miles of National Park with spectacular unspoiled scenery, fringed by picturesque villages.

PRINCE HALL HOTEL, DARTMOOR PL20 6SA (01822 890403). Small, friendly, relaxed country house hotel with glorious views onto open moorland. Walks in all directions. Eight en suite bedrooms. Log fires. Excellent seasonal local food, freshly prepared daily. Fishing, riding, golf nearby. Three-Day Break from £100pppn. [🐾]
e-mail: info@princehall.co.uk   website: www.princehall.co.uk

DARTMOOR COUNTRY HOLIDAYS, MAGPIE LEISURE PARK, DEPT PW, BEDFORD BRIDGE, HORRABRIDGE, YELVERTON PL20 7RY (01822 852651). Purpose-built pine lodges in peaceful woodland setting. Sleep 2-7. Furnished to very high standard (microwave, dishwasher etc). Easy walk to village and shops. Launderette. Dogs permitted. [Pets £20 per week].
website: www.dartmoorcountryholidays.co.uk

THE CHERRYBROOK, TWO BRIDGES PL20 6SP (01822 880260). In the middle of Dartmoor National Park with seven comfortable en suite bedrooms. Excellent quality home-made meals. See our website for details, tariff and sample menu. [🐾]
e-mail: info@thecherrybrook.co.uk   website: www.thecherrybrook.co.uk

ILSINGTON COUNTRY HOUSE HOTEL, NEAR HAYTOR, DARTMOOR TQ13 9RR (01364 661452). Don't leave them behind...we welcome your four-legged furry friends too! 10 acres of grounds. Extensive leisure facilities. 2 AA Rosette Restaurant. [pw! Pets £8 per night].
website: www.ilsington.co.uk

COLLAVEN MANOR HOTEL, SOURTON, OKEHAMPTON EX20 4HH (01837 861522). An elegant 15thC manor house set in 4 acres. The nine en suite rooms have glorious views and are individually furnished. Beamed residents' lounge, restaurant featuring local and home-grown produce. AA ★★ [Pets £5 per night]
e-mail: collavenmanor@supanet.com   website: www.collavenmanor.co.uk

THE EDGEMOOR COUNTRY HOUSE HOTEL, HAYTOR ROAD, LOWERDOWN CROSS, BOVEY TRACEY TQ13 9LE (01626 832466; Fax: 01626 834760). Country House Hotel in peaceful wooded setting adjacent Dartmoor National Park. Many lovely walks close by. All rooms en suite. Dogs welcome. See our website for further details. ETC ★★★ Silver Award [pw! 🐾]
e-mail: reservations@edgemoor.co.uk   website: www.edgemoor.co.uk

CHRIS & JULIE EASTAUGH, THE ROSEMONT, YELVERTON PL20 6DR (01822 852175). Four star quality B&B in village. Open access to moorland. Excellent walking country. Modern, spacious en suite rooms. B&B per room per night: Single £45, Double £65-75. [🐾].
e-mail: office@therosemont.co.uk   website: www.therosemont.co.uk

TWO BRIDGES HOTEL, DARTMOOR PL20 6SW (01822 892300) and THE BEDFORD HOTEL, TAVISTOCK PL19 8BB (01822 613221). Two superb hotels, ideally placed for exploring Dartmoor. Comfortable bedrooms, award-winning food. Well behaved dogs especially welcome.
websites: www.twobridges.co.uk / www.bedford-hotel.co.uk

Dartmouth

Historic port and resort on the estuary of the River Dart, with sandy coves and pleasure boat trips up the river. Car ferry to Kingswear.

WATERMILL COTTAGES, HIGHER NORTH MILL, HANSEL, NEAR SLAPTON, DARTMOUTH TQ6 0LN (01803 770219). Five comfy old stone cottages in 13 acres of unspoilt valley close to dog-friendly beaches and coastal path. Walks from your cottage door, enclosed gardens, log burners. We really welcome pets! [pw!, Pets £25 per week]
e-mail: christine@watermillcottages.co.uk   website: www.watermillcottages.co.uk

MRS S.R. RIDALLS, THE OLD BAKEHOUSE, 7 BROADSTONE, DARTMOUTH TQ6 9NR (Tel & Fax: 01803 834585). Four cottages (one with four-poster bed). Sleep 2–6. Near river, shops, restaurants. Blackpool Sands 15 minutes' drive. TV/DVD, free wireless internet, linen free. Open all year. Free parking. Non-smoking. ETC ★★★/★★★★★ [🐾]
e-mail: oldbakehousecottages@yahoo.com   website: www.oldbakehousedartmouth.co.uk

DARTSIDE HOLIDAYS, RIVERSIDE COURT, SOUTH EMBANKMENT, DARTMOUTH TQ6 9BH (01803 832093; Fax: 01803 835135). Comfortable holiday apartments with private balconies and superb river and harbour views. Available all year with colour TV, linen and parking. Free Colour Brochure on request. [Pets £50 per week.]
website: www.dartsideholidays.com

THE ROYAL CASTLE HOTEL, 11 THE QUAY, DARTMOUTH TQ6 9PS. (01803 833033; Fax: 01803 835445). Award-winning 17th century Hotel located in the heart of Dartmouth. 25 unique en suite bedrooms, many with four-poster beds and spa baths, restaurant 'Grill Room', two bars; parking. Dogs welcome. AA/Enjoy England ★★★.
e-mail: enquiry@royalcastle.co.uk   website: www.royalcastle .co.uk

Dunsford

Attractive village in upper Teign valley with Dartmoor to the west. Plymouth 35 miles, Okehampton 16, Newton Abbot 13, Crediton 9, Exeter 8.

ROYAL OAK INN, DUNSFORD, NEAR EXETER EX6 7DA (01647 252256). Welcome to our Victorian country inn with real ales and home-made food. All en suite rooms are in a 300-year-old converted barn. Well behaved children and dogs welcome. [🐾]
e-mail: mark@troid.co.uk   website: www.royaloakd.com

Exeter

Chief city of the South-West with a cathedral and university. Ample shopping, sports and leisure facilities.

THORVERTON ARMS, THORVERTON EX5 5NS (01392 860205). Traditional coaching inn just 7 miles north of Exeter. Small, well behaved dogs welcome. 6 en suite bedrooms. Award-winning restaurant. Excellent choice of real ales. Ideal touring base for Dartmoor, Exmoor and Devon's beaches. [Pets £5 per night, pw!]
website: www.thethorvertonarms.co.uk

MRS SALLY GLANVILL, RYDON FARM, WOODBURY, EXETER EX5 1LB (01395 232341). 16th Century Devon Longhouse on working dairy farm. Open all year. 4 Star Silver Award. From £37 to £60pppn. ETC ★★★★ [🐾]
website: www.rydonfarmwoodbury.co.uk

STATION LODGE, DODDISCOMBSLEIGH, EXETER (01647 253104). Comfortably furnished apartment for two people in beautiful Teign River valley. Excellent location for exploring Dartmoor. From £240 per week. For further details contact: IAN WEST, STATION HOUSE, DODDISCOMBSLEIGH, EXETER EX6 7PW. [pw! 🐾]
e-mail: enquiries@station-lodge.co.uk   website: www.station-lodge.co.uk

Exmoor

265 square miles of unspoiled heather moorland with deep wooded valleys and rivers, ideal for a walking, pony trekking or fishing holiday

JAYE JONES AND HELEN ASHER, TWITCHEN FARM, CHALLACOMBE, BARNSTAPLE EX31 4TT (01598 763568). Comfort for country lovers in Exmoor National Park. High quality en suite rooms. Breakfast prepared with local and organic produce. Farm walk through fields to village pub. ETC ★★★★ [One dog free, two dogs £8]
e-mail: holidays@twitchen.co.uk   website: www.twitchen.co.uk

THE STAGHUNTERS INN/HOTEL, BRENDON, EXMOOR EX35 6PS (01598 741222; Fax: 01598 741352). Family-run village inn with river frontage. Beautiful gardens. 12 en suite rooms. Varied menu, log fires, fine wines and cask ales. A walkers' paradise. [Pets £2.50 per night]
e-mail: stay@staghunters.com   website: www.staghunters.com

Holsworthy

Town 9 miles east of Bude.

TINNEY WATERS, PYWORTHY. Self-catering. Three beautiful lakes - carp, tench, bream. No day tickets, no close season. Ideal for birdwatching. Contact: J. MASON (01409 271362).
e-mail: bookings@tinneywaters.co.uk   website: www.tinneywaters.co.uk

Hope Cove

Attractive fishing village with flat sandy beach and safe bathing. Kingsbridge 6 miles.

HOPE BARTON BARNS, HOPE COVE, NEAR SALCOMBE TQ7 3HT (01548 561393). 17 stone barns in two courtyards and four luxury apartments in farmhouse. Farmhouse meals. Free range children and well behaved dogs welcome. For full colour brochure please contact: MELANIE POPE. [pw! Pets £20 per week]
e-mail: info@hopebarton.co.uk   website: www.hopebarton.co.uk

Ilfracombe

This popular seaside resort clusters round a busy harbour. The surrounding area is ideal for coastal walks.

WIDMOUTH FARM COTTAGES, NEAR ILFRACOMBE EX34 9RX (01271 863743). Comfortable, well equipped cottages on South West coastal footpath with private beach, gardens and woodland. Ideal for young families, dog owners, walkers, fishing and golf. Dogs welcome. Contact: MRS E. SANSOM. AA ★★★/★★★★. [pw! Pets £25 per week each].
e-mail: holiday@widmouthfarmcottages.co.uk   website: www.widmouthfarmcottages.co.uk

THE FOXHUNTERS INN, WEST DOWN, NEAR ILFRACOMBE EX34 8NU (01271 863757; Fax: 01271 879313). 300 year-old coaching Inn conveniently situated for beaches and country walks. En suite accommodation. Pets welcome by prior arrangement.[🐾]
website: www.foxhuntersinn.co.uk

BEACHSIDE HOLIDAY PARK, HELE BAY, ILFRACOMBE EX34 9QZ (0844 272 9500). A tranquil holiday park between cliffs at beautiful Hele Bay. One and two bedroomed caravans for hire, sleeping up to six. Superb sea views. Bed linen free of charge. Laundry facilities. Car park. Enjoy England ★★★★★.
e-mail: enquiries@beachsidepark.co.uk   website: www.beachsidepark.co.uk

THE DARNLEY HOTEL, 3 BELMONT ROAD, ILFRACOMBE EX34 8DR (01271 863955). A small family-run hotel with a warm and friendly atmosphere. The distinctive Victorian building is set within attractive gardens. Car park. Pets are welcome free of charge. VisitBritain/AA ★★ [🐾]
e-mail: info@darnleyhotel.co.uk   website: www.darnleyhotel.co.uk

Kingsbridge

Pleasant town at head of picturesque Kingsbridge estuary. Centre for South Hams district with its lush scenery and quiet coves.

DITTISCOMBE HOLIDAY COTTAGES, SLAPTON, NEAR KINGSBRIDGE, SOUTH DEVON TQ7 2QF (01548 521272). Nature trail and 20 acres of open space. Perfect holiday location for dogs and owners. All cottages have gardens and views of surrounding valley. ETC ★★★★. [Pets £20 per week]
e-mail: info@dittiscombe.co.uk   website: www.dittiscombe.co.uk

MRS B. KELLY, BLACKWELL PARK, LODDISWELL, KINGSBRIDGE TQ7 4EA (01548 821230). 17th century Farmhouse, five miles from Kingsbridge. Ideal centre for Dartmoor, Plymouth, Torbay, Dartmouth and many beaches. Some bedrooms en suite. Bed and Breakfast. Evening meal optional. Dogsitting. Pets welcome free of charge. [pw! 🐾]

MOUNTS FARM TOURING PARK, THE MOUNTS, NEAR EAST ALLINGTON, KINGSBRIDGE TQ9 7QJ (01548 521591). Family-run site in the heart of South Devon. We welcome tents, touring caravans and motor caravans. Children and pets welcome. Many safe, sandy beaches nearby.
website: www.mountsfarm.co.uk

ASHBURTON ARMS, NEAR KINGSBRIDGE TQ7 2AH (01548 531242). Cosy and welcoming Village Inn, ideal base for exploring beautiful South Hams. Three very comfortable en suite bedrooms. Well behaved pets welcome in bar and as overnight guests. Excellent home-made food. [Pets £5 per night; £25 per week].
email: info@ashburtonarms.co.uk   website: www.ashburtonarms.co.uk

King's Nympton

3 miles north of Chulmleigh.

COLLACOTT FARM, KING'S NYMPTON, UMBERLEIGH, NORTH DEVON EX37 9TP (01769 572491). Eight Country Cottages sleeping from 2 to 12 in rural area; lovely views, private patios and gardens. Well furnished and equipped. Heated pool, tennis court, BHS approved riding school. Laundry room. Open all year. [pw!, Pets £20 per week]
e-mail: info@collacott.co.uk   website: www.collacott.co.uk

Lynton/Lynmouth

Picturesque twin villages joined by a unique cliff railway (vertical height 500 ft). Lynmouth has a quaint harbour and Lynton enjoys superb views over the rugged coastline.

RIVER LYN VIEW, 26 WATERSMEET ROAD, LYNMOUTH EX35 6EP (01598 753501). Well presented en suite bedrooms with TV and tea/coffee facilities.Full English breakfast served in the dining area. Comfortable lounge. Exmoor National Park is a short drive away. Pets welcome. [🐾]
website: www.riverlynview.com

CLOONEAVIN HOLIDAY APARTMENTS, CLOONEAVIN PATH, LYNMOUTH EX35 6EE (01598 753334). Eight well equipped self contained apartments and chalet. A short walk to the harbour. Numerous coastal and river walks through idyllic countryside. ETC ★★★. [Pets £15 per week].
e-mail: relax@clooneavinholidays.co.uk   website: www.clooneavinholidays.co.uk

BATH HOTEL, LYNMOUTH EX35 6EL (01598 752238). Great views of harbour. Quality rooms and service. Ideal for moors. Pets welcome. Off-season discounts available. AA ★★ [🐾]
e-mail: info@bathhotellynmouth.co.uk   website: www.bathhotellynmouth.co.uk

MOORLANDS. Where countryside and comfort combine. Two self-contained apartments within a family-run guesthouse, within the Exmoor National Park. Hotel amenities available for guests' use. Contact: MR I. CORDEROY, MOORLANDS, WOODY BAY, PARRACOMBE, NEAR LYNTON EX31 4RA (01598 763224). ETC ★★★★ [🐾]
website: www.moorlandshotel.co.uk

BLUE BALL INN (formerly The Exmoor Sandpiper Inn), COUNTISBURY, LYNMOUTH EX35 6NE (01598 741263). Romantic coaching inn on Exmoor. 16 en suite bedrooms, extensive menus with daily specials, good wines. Horse riding, walking. No charge for dogs. [🐾]
website: www.BlueBallinn.com or www.exmoorsandpiper.com

JIM AND SUSAN BINGHAM, NEW MILL FARM, BARBROOK, LYNTON EX35 6JR (01598 753341). Exmoor Valley. Two delightful genuine modernised XVII century cottages by stream on 100-acre farm with A.B.R.S. Approved riding stables. Free fishing. ETC ★★★★. [pw! Pets £15 per week.]
e-mail: info@outovercott.co.uk   website: www.outovercott.co.uk

LYNHURST, LYNTON. Self-catering - elegant Victorian house, sleeps up to 22 in 10 bedrooms. Two lounges, dining room, large kitchen, laundry room, large garden. Dogs welcome. Short breaks available. For bookings ring Jane on 01598 753757 or 07592 870929. [pw! 🐾]
website: www.thelynhurst.com

THE NORTH CLIFF HOTEL, NORTH WALK, LYNTON EX35 6HJ (01598 752357). On the South West Coastal Path, the North Cliff is an ideal base for discovering Exmoor and the North Devon Coast. Delicious home cooking. We welcome pets, children and groups. [Pets £4 per night, £20 per week].
e-mail: holidays@northcliffhotel.co.uk   website: www.northcliffhotel.co.uk

MR AND MRS I. RIGBY, BRENDON HOUSE, BRENDON, LYNTON EX35 6PS (01598 741206). Licensed country guesthouse in beautiful Lyn Valley. Ideal walking, fishing, riding. Award winning restaurant serving local food. Weekly discounts and short breaks. VisitBritain ★★★★ [Pets £5 per night]
email: brendonhouse4u@aol.com   website: www.brendonhouse4u.com

PRIME SPOT CHARACTER COTTAGES. Spectacular area for dog walking and mountain biking. Riverbank cottage for 1-6 at Lynmouth harbour. Romantic thatched cottage for two at Lynton. Seaside cottage for 1-4 at Combe Martin harbour. Available all year. Cosy winter breaks. ★★★/★★★★. Details/ brochures from MRS WOLVERSON (01271 882449).[one pet 🐾]
website: www.primespotcottages.co.uk

Mortehoe

Adjoining Woolacombe with cliffs and wide sands. Interesting rock scenery beyond Morte Point. Barnstaple 15 miles.

THE SMUGGLERS REST INN, NORTH MORTE ROAD, MORTEHOE EX34 7DR (Tel & Fax: 01271 870891). In the pretty village of Mortehoe. The Smugglers offers luxury accommodation from twin rooms to family suites. En suite rooms, TV, full English breakfast, licensed bar, beer garden, home-cooked meals. Well trained pets welcome. [Pets £5 per week].
e-mail: thesmugglersrest@gmail.com   website: www.thesmugglersrest.co.uk

Noss Mayo

Village 3 miles south west of Yealmpton, on south side of creek running into River Yealm estuary, opposite Newton Ferrers.

CRAB COTTAGE, NOSS MAYO. Charming fisherman's cottage, 50 yards from the quay. Fantastic walks, beaches and dog-friendly pubs on the doorstep. Close to the South Devon Coastal Path. Sleeps 5. Phone 01425 675021 for a brochure. [🐾]
e-mail: 07enquiries@crab-cottage.co.uk   website: www.crab-cottage.co.uk

Ottery St Mary

Pleasant little town in East Devon, within easy reach of the sea. Many interesting little buildings including 11th century parish church. Birthplace of poet Coleridge.

MRS A. FORTH, FLUXTON FARM, OTTERY ST MARY EX11 1RJ (01404 812818). Charming 16th Century farmhouse. B&B from £32.50. Peace and quiet. Cat lovers' paradise. Masses of dog walks. AA ★★ [🐾 pw!]
website: www.fluxtonfarm.co.uk

Paignton

Popular family resort on Torbay with long, safe sandy beaches and small harbour. Exeter 25 miles, Newton Abbott 9, Torquay 3.

BROADSHADE HOLIDAY APARTMENTS, 9 ST ANDREWS ROAD, PAIGNTON, TORBAY TQ4 6HA . An ideal holiday location for families and couples of all ages. All fully equipped for self-catering. Close to Paignton and Goodrington beaches. For bookings and information call 01803 559647. [Pets £15 per week]
e-mail: info@broadshade.co.uk   website: www.broadshade.co.uk

THE COMMODORE, 14 ESPLANADE ROAD, PAIGNTON TQ4 6EB (01803 553107). Ideally situated on Paignton sea front, sea view rooms. Luxury en suites, refreshments, sea view guest lounge, bar, gift shop. Excellent breakfast. Close to harbour, bus and rail stations. AA ★★★★ [Pets £5 per night, £20 per week].
e-mail: info@commodorepaignton.com   website: www.commodorepaignton.com

MERRITT HOUSE, 7 QUEENS ROAD, PAIGNTON TQ4 6AT (01803 528959). Traditional Victorian townhouse 5 minutes from town centre and beach. Small dogs welcome in ground floor rooms. En suite shower rooms. Free Wi-Fi. On-site parking. AA ★★★★. [pw!, Pets £10 per week].
e-mail: bookings@merritthouse.co.uk   website: www.merritthouse.co.uk

Plymouth

Historic port and resort, impressively rebuilt after severe war damage. Large naval docks at Devonport. Beach of pebble and sand.

CHURCHWOOD VALLEY, WEMBURY BAY, NEAR PLYMOUTH PL9 0DZ (01752 862382). Relax in one of our comfortable log cabins, set in a peaceful wooded valley near the beach. Enjoy wonderful walks in woods and along the coast. Abundance of birds and wildlife. Up to two pets per cabin. [Pets £5 per week each]
e-mail: info@churchwoodvalley.com   website: www.churchwoodvalley.com

Salcombe

Fishing and sailing centre in sheltered position. Fine beaches and coastal walks nearby.

PORT LIGHT, BOLBERRY DOWN, MALBOROUGH, NEAR SALCOMBE TQ7 3DY (01548 561384 or 07970 859992). A totally unique location set amidst acres of National Trust coastline. Luxury en suite rooms. Superb home-cooked fare, specialising in local seafood. Licensed bar. Pets welcome throughout the hotel. Short Breaks throughout the year. Contact: Sean and Hazel Hassall. [🐾]
e-mail: info@portlight.co.uk   website: www.portlight.co.uk

Seaton

Bright East Devon resort near Axe estuary. Shingle beach and chalk cliffs; good bathing, many lovely walks in vicinity. Exeter 23 miles, Sidmouth 11.

MILKBERE COTTAGE HOLIDAYS, 3 FORE STREET, SEATON EX12 2LE (01297 20729). Specialising in coast/country holidays on the Devon/Dorset border. Cottages, bungalows, houses, apartments and caravans, ideally situated for walking and exploring the Jurassic Coast. VisitBritain ★★★/★★★★★. [Pets £20 per week.]
e-mail: info@milkberehols.com   website: www.milkberehols.com

AXEVALE CARAVAN PARK, COLYFORD ROAD, SEATON EX12 2DF (0800 0688816). A quiet, family-run park with 68 modern and luxury caravans for hire. Laundry facilities, park shop. All caravans have a shower, toilet, fridge and TV. Wi-Fi is available in every caravan. Relaxing atmosphere. ETC ★★★★ [Pets £15 per week]
website: www.axevale.co.uk

Sidmouth

Sheltered resort, winner of many awards for its floral displays. Good sands at Jacob's Ladder beach.

LEIGH COTTAGES, WESTON, SIDMOUTH EX10 0PH. Cottages and bungalows for couples and families close to SW Coast path, Weston Combe and Donkey Sanctuary. Dog friendly beaches and pubs nearby. Peaceful location. ETC ★★★★ Contact: ALISON CLARKE (01395 516065/514764; Fax: 01395 512563). [pw! Pets £20 per week]
e-mail: Alison@leighcottages.co.uk   website: www.leighcottages.co.uk

SWEETCOMBE COTTAGE HOLIDAYS, ROSEMARY COTTAGE, WESTON, NEAR SIDMOUTH EX10 0PH (01395 512130). Selection of Cottages, Farmhouses and Flats in Sidmouth and East Devon, all personally selected and very well-equipped. Gardens. Pets welcome. Please ask for our colour brochure.
e-mail: enquiries@sweetcombe-ch.co.uk   website: www.sweetcombe-ch.co.uk

THE PIGGERY, HOPPINS FARM, EAST DEVON (01395 568182). Contemporary accommodation in idyllic rural setting. Ideal couples retreat with modern kitchen/living room, one spacious bedroom with shower room. Walled decked area with barbeque. Fourteen acres for your dog to roam.[🐕]
website: http://thepiggerydevon.weebly.com

WOODLANDS HOTEL, STATION ROAD, SIDMOUTH EX10 8HG 01395 513120; Fax: 01395 513348). 20-bedroom hotel just a few minutes' easy walk from both Sidmouth town centre and seafront; spacious bar and lounge. Well behaved pets welcome. AA ★★.
e-mail: info@woodlands-hotel.com   website: www.woodlands-hotel.com

OAKDOWN HOLIDAY PARK, WESTON, SIDMOUTH EX10 0PT (01297 680387; Fax: 01297 680541). Sidmouth's multi-award-winning holiday park. Welcome to Oakdown, set near the "Jurassic Coast" World Heritage Site, and a winner of "Caravan Holiday Park of The Year". Oakdown is level, sheltered and landscaped into groves to give privacy. Luxurious amenities. Enjoy our Field Trail to the famous Donkey Sanctuary. Free colour brochure with pleasure. ETC ★★★★★, David Bellamy Gold Award, Loo of the Year Award, Best of British, Excellence in England 2007.
e-mail: enquiries@oakdown.co.uk   website: www.oakdown.co.uk

OTTERFALLS HOLIDAY COTTAGES & LODGES, NEW ROAD, UPOTTERY, HONITON EX14 9QD (01404 861634 ; Fax: 01404 861706). Luxurious fully equipped self-catering cottages and lodges set in 120 acres. Fishing lakes, heated indoor pool. Wonderful walking, including special pet "off-lead" walkways. [pw! Pets £30 per week]
e-mail: hols@otterfalls.co.uk   website: www.otterfalls.co.uk

South Molton

Busy market town, ideally situated as a base to explore the beautiful countryside of North and Mid Devon, and Exmoor and Dartmoor National Parks

PARTRIDGE ARMS FARM, YEO MILL, WEST ANSTEY, SOUTH MOLTON EX36 3NU (01398 341217; Fax: 01398 341569) Converted, self-catering railway carriage. Situated on the old Taunton to Barnstaple railway line. Fully equipped, sleeps up to 6 people. Children and dogs welcome. Prices start from £490 per week (no hidden extras). Daily rates also available. [🐕]
e-mail: bangermilton@gmail.com

LITTLE KIDLAND, KNOWSTONE, SOUTH MOLTON EX36 4RT. A beautiful thatched house in peaceful and tranquil surroundings. Set within 10 acres with own stream and adjacent to extensive woodland. 4 bedrooms, sleeps up to 7. Perfectly located for visiting Exmoor, beaches and local market towns. Call Brian 07788 421311 or Jodi 07921 909803
website: www.littlekidland.co.uk

Tavistock

Birthplace of Sir Francis Drake and site of a fine ruined Benedictine Abbey. On edge of Dartmoor, 13 miles north of Plymouth

LANGSTONE MANOR HOLIDAY PARK, MOORTOWN, TAVISTOCK PL19 9JZ (Tel & Fax 01822 613371). Peaceful Holiday Park, offering camping, cottages, apartment, static caravans. Ideal location outside Tavistock with direct access onto Dartmoor. Bar and evening meals. Excellent location. ETC ★★★★, AA 4 Pennants [Pets £20 per week in self-catering.]
e-mail: jane@langstone-manor.co.uk   website: www.langstone-manor.co.uk

MRS P.G.C. QUINTON, HIGHER QUITHER, MILTON ABBOT, TAVISTOCK PL19 0PZ (01822 860284). Modern self-contained barn conversion. Own private garden. Terms from £240 inc. linen, coal and logs. Electricity metered. [pw! 🐕]
website: www.higherquither.2day.ws/

Thurlestone

Village resort above the cliffs to the north of Bolt Tail, 4 miles west of Kingsbridge.

CUTAWAY COTTAGE, THURLESTONE, KINGSBRIDGE TQ7 3NF. Self-catering cottage within a fenced garden in the middle of the village. Private road, 5 minutes to pub and shop, 20 minutes' walk to beaches & sea. Ideal for children, dog walkers and bird watchers. Phone Pat on 01548 560688 [🐾]

Tiverton

Busy market town situated north of Exeter on the A396.

NEWHOUSE FARM COTTAGES, WITHERIDGE, TIVERTON EX16 8QB (01884 860266). Nine well equipped Grade II Listed stone barns, with accommodation ranging from a one bedroom cottage to a 5- bedroom barn. 23 acre grounds, heated indoor pool and games room. [Pets £20 per week, pw!]. website: www.newhousecottages.com

Torbay

An east-facing bay and natural harbour at the western end of Lyme Bay, midway between the cities of Exeter and Plymouth.

J. AND E. BALL, DEPARTMENT P.W., HIGHER WELL FARM HOLIDAY PARK, STOKE GABRIEL, TOTNES TQ9 6RN (01803 782289). Within 4 miles Torbay beaches and one mile of River Dart. Central for touring. Dogs on leads. Tourist Board Graded Park ★★★★. [pw! Pets £2 per night, £15 per week in statics, free in tents and tourers] website: www.higherwellfarmholidaypark.co.uk

Torquay

Popular resort on the English Riviera with a wide range of attractions and entertainments. Yachting and watersports centre with 10 superb beaches and coves.

REDHOUSE HOTEL AND MAXTON LODGE HOLIDAY APARTMENTS, ROUSDOWN ROAD, CHELSTON, TORQUAY TQ2 6PB (01803 607811; Fax: 01803 605357). Choose either the friendly service and facilities of a hotel or the privacy and freedom of self-catering apartments. The best of both worlds! AA/ETC ★★ Hotel & ★★★ Self-catering. [🐾 in flats; £3 per night in hotel] e-mail: stay@redhouse-hotel.co.uk   website: www.redhouse-hotel.co.uk

THE DOWNS HOTEL, 41-43 BABBACOMBE DOWNS ROAD, TORQUAY TQ1 3LN (01803 328543/ 0845 051 0989). Fully licensed family-run establishment with 12 en suite rooms, eight with private balconies and superb views. Family rooms, reduced rates for under 12s. Dog-friendly. [Pets £5 per night]. website: www.downshotel.co.uk

THE NORWOOD, 60 BELGRAVE ROAD, TORQUAY TQ2 5HY (01803 294236, Fax: 01803 294224). Just a stroll from the seafront, town centre and all local attractions. A quality holiday experience focussing on old-fashioned hospitality, clean comfortable rooms and beautifully presented, home-cooked food. VisitBritain ★★★★. e-mail: enquiries@norwoodhoteltorquay.co.uk   website: www.norwoodhoteltorquay.co.uk

Torrington

Pleasant market town on River Torridge. Good centre for moors and sea. Exeter 36 miles, Okehampton 20, Barnstaple 12, Bideford 7.

RICH AND DIANA JONES, STOWFORD LODGE, LANGTREE, GREAT TORRINGTON EX38 8NU (01805 601487). Sleep 4/6. Picturesque and peaceful. Four delightful cottages and log cabin set within 6 acres of private land with heated indoor pool. Magnificent countryside. Convenient North Devon coast and moors. Phone for brochure. VisitBritain ★★★/★★★★ [Pets £15 per week, pw!] e-mail: enq@stowfordlodge.co.uk   website: www.stowfordlodge.co.uk

CLOISTER PARK COTTAGES, FRITHELSTOCK, TORRINGTON EX38 8JH (01805 622518). Three recently converted cottages (sleep 6/4/2), all fully equipped, with own patio areas. The attractive market town of Great Torrington is just 2 miles away. Tarka Trail and North Devon beaches close by. ETC ★★★★. [First pet free, additional pets £15 per week] website: www.cloisterpark.co.uk

Totnes

Town at tidal estuary of River Dart 7 miles west of Torquay.

THE KINGSTON ESTATE, KINGSTON HOUSE, STAVERTON, TOTNES TQ9 6AR (01803 762235). Luxury holidays in Devon. Self-catering Estate cottages created from restored period outbuildings. Perfect for a family holiday or weekend escape. Leisure facilities. ETC ★★★★★ Self Catering.[pw!, Pets £20 per week].
e-mail : bookingsenquiries@kingston-estate.co.uk   website: www.kingston-estate.co,uk

Tuckenhay

Hamlet at head of Bow Creek, 3 miles south of Totnes.

THE MALTSTERS ARMS, TUCKENHAY TQ9 7EQ (01803 732350). Bar food served daily at lunchtimes and evenings. Separate restaurant. Accommodation available. Charcoal barbecue on quay during summer. Pets welcome.
e-mail: maltsters@tuckenhay.com   website: www.tuckenhay.com

Woolacombe

Favourite resort with long, wide stretches of sand. Barnstaple 15 miles, Ilfracombe 6.

SUNNYMEADE COUNTRY HOTEL, WEST DOWN, NEAR WOOLACOMBE EX34 8NT (01271 863668; Fax: 01271 866061). Small country hotel set in beautiful countryside. A few minutes away from Ilfracombe, Exmoor and Woolacombe's Blue Flag Beach. 12 en suite rooms, 4 on the ground floor. Deaf accessible. Pets welcome. [pw!]
e-mail: holidays@sunnymeade.co.uk   website: www.sunnymeade.co.uk

WOOLACOMBE BAY HOLIDAY PARKS (0844 770 0385). Four award-winning Holiday Parks set in delightful surroundings, all beside three miles of golden Blue Flag sandy beach in Devon. Pet-friendly holiday homes with pet pack and "Woof" Guide to Woolacombe.
website: www.woolacombe.com/fpw

EUROPA PARK, BEACH ROAD, WOOLACOMBE (01271 871425). Static caravans, chalets, camping, surf lodges and surf cabins. Full facilities. Pets welcome. Indoor heated swimming pool, sauna, site shop. [Pets £3 per night]
e-mail: holidays@europapark.co.uk   website: www.europapark.co.uk

MRS JOYCE BAGNALL, CHICHESTER HOUSE, THE ESPLANADE, WOOLACOMBE EX34 7DJ (01271 870761). Holiday apartments on sea front. Fully furnished, sea and coastal views. Watch the sun go down from your balcony. Open all year. SAE Resident Proprietor. [pw! Pets £12 per week]
website: www.chichesterhouse.co.uk

Yelverton

Large village on edge of Dartmoor. Nearby attractions include Buckland Abbey.

SAMPFORD MANOR, SAMPFORD SPINEY, YELVERTON PL20 6LH (01822 853442). Bed and Breakfast (on the edge of Dartmoor near Tavistock). Double or twin bedded rooms with private bathroom or shower. Dogs welcome. AA ★★★ [Pets £3 per night]
e-mail: manor@sampford-spiney.fsnet.co.uk   website: www.sampford-spiney.fsnet.co.uk

---

🐾   Pets are welcome free of charge.   Classified Symbols

£   A charge is made for pets: nightly or weekly.

pw!   Special provision for pets; exercise facility, feeding or accommodation arrangement.

⌂   Separate pets' accommodation.

Terms quoted in this publication may be subject to increase if rises in costs necessitate

Bournemouth

White topps

THE *REALLY* DOG-FRIENDLY PLACE
WHITE TOPPS

Guests enjoying the lounge

Small, friendly and catering only for guests with dogs. In a nice quiet position close to lovely walks on the beach (dogs allowed) and Hengistbury Head. Plus the New Forest isn't far away. There's no charge for pets, of course and the proprietor, MARJORIE TITCHEN, just loves dogs.

We're 100% dog orientated, all our guests bring at least one dog and you're equally welcome whether you have one Yorkie or six Alsatians. Dogs are allowed anywhere - in bedrooms, lounges, even in the dining room should they be unhappy being left alone in the bedroom. Bring your own dog food, we are happy to cook it, free of charge, if required.

We have five bedrooms on the first floor with bathroom and toilets opposite and one room on the ground floor, suitable for elderly or disabled dogs. We do not have any en suite rooms but all have washbasins and tea/coffee making facilities.

- DOG(S) ESSENTIAL - ANY SIZE, ANY NUMBER, ANYWHERE
- GROUND FLOOR ROOM FOR ELDERLY DOGS
- ADULTS ONLY (14yrs +)
- GENEROUS HOME COOKING
- VEGETARIANS WELCOME
- NOT SUITABLE FOR DISABLED
- CAR PARKING

WRITE (SAE APPRECIATED) OR PHONE FOR FACT SHEET.

**WHITE TOPPS, 45 CHURCH ROAD, SOUTHBOURNE, BOURNEMOUTH, DORSET BH6 4BB
TEL: 01202 428868**

No Credit Cards - Cheque or Cash only

e-mail: thedoghotel@aol.com • www.whitetopps.co.uk

IF YOU DON'T LOVE DOGS YOU WON'T LIKE WHITE TOPPS

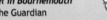

Bournemouth, Bridport

Bridport, Burton Bradstock, Charmouth, Christchurch

Dorchester, Evershot, Lulworth Cove

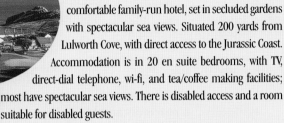

21 individually
decorated bedrooms

Superb food using
fresh local produce

Overlooking
Studland Bay

Private path to beaches

Pets welcome
& beautiful walks

2 all-weather
Tennis Courts

Golf Course
& Riding Stables nearby

Manor House Hotel
STUDLAND BAY DORSET

★ ★ ★

Old fashioned charm & service

3, 5 & 7 day Bargain Breaks

" *Welcome to one of the most beautiful places in England. I can't take the credit for the glorious views and the beaches. But I am proud to provide a comfortable and relaxing hotel with good food and attentive but informal service, to give you the break you deserve.* '   *Andrew Purkis*

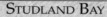

White Horse Farm

★ Self-Catering Holidays in Rural Dorset ★

Four self-catering barn conversion cottages,
a 4-star converted farmhouse annexe "The Willows",
and a luxury 4-star 3 bedroom lodge "Otter's Holt".

Our holiday cottages were formerly part of the old courtyard.
Tastefully converted with exposed stone walls and beams,
providing comfortable accommodation.

- **Toad Hall** sleeps 4 • **Ratty's** sleeps 2/4
- **Moley's** and **Badger's** sleep 2

The Willows, converted 4 star 3 bedroom self-catering annexe for up to six people.
Otter's Holt, 4 star luxury Wessex-built Milbourne lodge for 6 people in 3 bedrooms,

Surrounded by 2 acres of gardens and paddock with a large duck pond. Fully equipped recreation room. Delightful walks and many tourist attractions locally. Fishing, walking, horse-riding and golfing facilities within a short drive. Easy travelling distance to the Dorset coast, Weymouth and Lyme Regis.

White Horse Farm, Middlemarsh, Sherborne, Dorset DT9 5QN

e-mail: enquiries@whitehorsefarm.co.uk

Tel: 01963 210222 • www.whitehorsefarm.co.uk

The White Swan

The Square, 31 High Street, Swanage, Dorset BH19 2LT • 01929 423804

A pub with a warm and friendly atmosphere, three minutes from the beach. Traditional pub food, Sunday roasts. Large beer garden. En suite accommodation with parking. Free WiFi and internet access. TV and pool table. Children and dogs welcome. Best Beer Guide Pub CAMRA selected.

e-mail: info@whiteswanswanage.co.uk • www.whiteswanswanage.co.uk

THE LIMES

AA ★★★★ Guest House

A warm welcome awaits all dogs – and their owners – at the Limes, only a few hundred yards from wonderful coastal walks and beach, surrounded by the unspoilt Purbeck Hills. En suite rooms with colour TV, hospitality tray and free Wi-Fi. Pets come free!

Car Park • Families Welcome

48 Park Road, Swanage, Dorset BH19 2AE

Tel: 01929 422664 • info@limeshotel.net

www.limeshotel.net

Luckford Wood Farmhouse • Church Street, East Stoke, Wareham, Dorset BH20 6AW

AA ★★★★ Farmhouse

B&B classic farmhouse with style. Peaceful surroundings, delightful scenery. Breakfast served in conservatory, dining room or garden. All rooms en suite. Free Wi-Fi. Freeview TV. Our camping and caravanning site nearby. Caravan and boat storage available. Near Lulworth Cove, Tank Museum, Monkey World. Open all year. B&B from £35pp per night.

Tel: 01929 463098 / 07888 719002 • luckfordleisure@hotmail.co.uk • www.luckfordleisure.co.uk

West Bexington

DORSET COTTAGE HOLIDAYS. Self-catering cottages, town houses, bungalows and apartments. All within 10 miles of Heritage Coastline and sandy beaches. Excellent walking in idyllic countryside. Short breaks from £165, weekly from £220 (per cottage). Open all year. Free brochure tel: 01929 481547. [🐾]
e-mail: enq@dhcottages.co.uk   website: www.dhcottages.co.uk

DORSET COASTAL COTTAGES (0800 9804070). Carefully selected, traditional cottages in or near villages within ten miles of World Heritage Coast. Many are thatched; open fires or logburners; over half welcome dogs. Available all year. [🐾]
website: www.dorsetcoastalcottages.com

FARM & COTTAGE HOLIDAYS (01237 459897). An inspiring collection of holiday cottages throughout Cornwall, Devon, Somerset and Dorset in stunning rural and coastal locations. [Pets £20 per week]
website: www.holidaycottages.co.uk

ISLAND COTTAGE HOLIDAYS (01929 481555). Pet and dog friendly cottages in beautiful rural and coastal locations on the Isle of Purbeck. [Pets £29 per week]
website: www.purbeckcottageholidays.co.uk

Bere Regis

Village 7 miles north west of Wareham.

MR & MRS R. CARGILL, ROWLANDS WAIT TOURING PARK, RYE HILL, BERE REGIS BH20 7LP (01929 472727). Situated in an Area of Outstanding Natural Beauty. A good base for touring; direct access onto heathland and woodland walks. Ideal for nature lovers, bird watching and quiet family holidays. Tents also welcome. Dogs welcome. David Bellamy Gold Award. ETC ★★★.
website: www.rowlandswait.co.uk

Bournemouth

One of Britain's premier holiday resorts with miles of golden sand, excellent shopping and leisure facilities. .

BILL AND MARJORIE TITCHEN, WHITE TOPPS HOTEL, 45 CHURCH ROAD, SOUTHBOURNE, BOURNEMOUTH BH6 4BB (01202 428868). Situated in quiet position close to lovely walks and beach. Dogs essential. Free parking. [🐾 pw!]
e-mail: thedoghotel@aol.com   website: www.whitetopps.co.uk

IONA HOLIDAY FLAT (01202 460517, Mob: 07967 027025). Luxury Self-Catering accommodation in Bournemouth, close to sea and shops.Very well equipped ground floor studio apartment sleeping 2. Fully fitted kitchen. Shower room. Short distance to Blue Flag beaches. Small house-trained dogs welcome.
email: reservemyholiday@yahoo.co.uk   website: www.ionaholidayflat.co.uk

SOUTHBOURNE GROVE HOTEL, 96 SOUTHBOURNE ROAD, SOUTHBOURNE, BOURNEMOUTH BH6 3QQ (01202 420503; Fax: 01202 421953). Friendly, family-run hotel with parking. Close to beach and shops. Excellent breakfast. En suite rooms, four-poster, double, twin and family room on ground floor. B&B from £24pppn. [🐾]
e-mail: neil@pack1462.freeserve.co.uk   website: www.southbournegrovehotel.co.uk

LANGTRY MANOR, DERBY ROAD, EAST CLIFF, BOURNEMOUTH BH1 3QB (0844 371 3705 - local rate). A rare gem of a hotel where the building, food, service and history blend to form something quite exceptional. Midweek and weekend breaks. Pets welcome by arrangement. Bournemouth Tourism 'Best Small Hotel'. [🐾]
e-mail: lillie@langtrymanor.com   website: www.langtrymanor.co.uk

MIKE AND LYN LAMBERT, 16 FLORENCE ROAD, BOURNEMOUTH BH5 1HF (01202 304925). Modern Holiday Apartments sleeping up to ten persons, close to sea and shops. Clean, well-equipped flats. Car park. Phone or e-mail for brochure. [Pets from £45 per week]
e-mail: mikelyn_lambert@btinternet.com   website: www.selfcateringbournemouth.co.uk

THELMA AND ROY TURNER, DERWENT GUEST HOUSE, 103 SOUTHBOURNE OVERCLIFF DRIVE, BOURNEMOUTH BH6 3NW (01202 426262). Situated on the cliff top road with views of the sea and the Isle of Wight. All rooms fully en suite, with colour TV and complimentary tea/coffee tray. New Forest is only 5 miles away. Small dogs welcome. [🐾]
email: thelmaroy@derwenthouse82.fsnet.co.uk   website: www.derwentguesthouse.co.uk

STOURCLIFFE COURT HOLIDAY APARTMENTS. Two fully furnished apartments, sleep 2/5. Three minutes' walk to beach. Linen provided free. Forecourt parking. Terms from £200. MRS HAMMOND, STOURCLIFFE COURT, 56 STOURCLIFFE AVENUE, SOUTHBOURNE, BOURNEMOUTH BH6 3PX (01202 420698). [Pets £2 per night, £10 weekly]
e-mail: rjhammond1@hotmail.co.uk   website: www.stourcliffecourt.co.uk

ALUM DENE HOTEL, 2 BURNABY ROAD, ALUM CHINE, BOURNEMOUTH BH4 8JF (01202 764011) Renowned for good old fashioned hospitality and friendly service. Come and be spoilt at our licensed hotel. All rooms en suite, colour TV. Some have sea views. 200 metres sea. Parking. Christmas House party. No charge for pets. [🐾]
e-mail: alumdenehotel@hotmail.co.uk   website: www.alumdenehotel.com

Bridport

Market town of Saxon origin noted for rope and net making. Harbour at West Bay has sheer cliffs rising from the beach

MRS S. NORMAN, FROGMORE FARM, CHIDEOCK, BRIDPORT DT6 6HT (01308 456159). The choice is yours - Bed and Breakfast in charming farmhouse, OR self-catering Cottage equipped for five, pets welcome. Brochure and terms free on request. [1st dog free, 2nd dog £3 per night, £15 per week]
e-mail: bookings@frogmorefarm.com   website: www.frogmorefarm.com

LANCOMBES HOUSE, WEST MILTON, BRIDPORT DT6 3TN (01308 485375). Three cottages and farmhouse, two with enclosed gardens. Set in 9 acres in an area ideal for walking, riding and outdoor pursuits. Children and dogs welcome. Open all year. ETC ★★★★ [Pets £5 per night, £15 per week].
website: www.lancombes-house.co.uk

GOLDEN ACRE, EYPE, NEAR BRIDPORT DT6 6AL (01308 421521). Private peaceful park. Close to beach. Chalet bungalows (1 or 2 bedrooms), sleep 2-4. Wonderful walks, on the Jurassic Coast. [🐾]
website: www.golden-acre.com

EYPE HOUSE CARAVAN & CAMPING PARK, EYPE, BRIDPORT DT6 6AL (01308 424903) Small, quiet family-run park lying on the Heritage Coastal Path, 200 yards from the beach. Static vans for hire, tent pitches (all terraced with sea views). Sorry, no touring caravans. Children and dogs welcome. [Pets £2 per night.]
e-mail: enquiries@eypehouse.co.uk   website: www.eypehouse.co.uk

COGDEN COTTAGES, NEAR BRIDPORT, DORSET. Seven beautifully presented and equipped beachfront sea view cottages all with private sea facing decks or patios. Pets can take advantage of the South West Coastal Path which runs through the property or our private beach. £290-£650. Contact: KIM CONNELLY, OLD COASTGUARD HOLIDAY PARK, BURTON BRADSTOCK, NEAR BRIDPORT DT6 4RL (01308 897223).
website: www.cogdencottages.co.uk

Burton Bradstock

Village near coast, 3 miles SE of Bridport.

MRS JOSEPHINE PEARSE, TAMARISK FARM, BEACH ROAD, WEST BEXINGTON, DORCHESTER DT2 9DF (01308 897784). Self Catering properties sleep 2/6. Overlooking Chesil Beach: two large (MIMOSA FOR WHEELCHAIR DISABLED M3 (1)and THE MOAT), plus two small Cottages (ETC 3/4 Stars). Part of organic farm with arable, sheep, cattle, horses and market garden with organic vegetables, meat and wholemeal flour available. Good centre for touring, sightseeing, walking. Glorious sea views, very quiet. Lovely place for dogs. Terms from £215 to £900. Please telephone for details. [pw! 🐾]
e-mail: holidays@tamariskfarm.com   website: www.tamariskfarm.com/holidays

Charmouth

Small resort on Lyme Bay, 3 miles from Lyme Regis.

MR F. LOOSMORE, MANOR FARM HOLIDAY CENTRE, CHARMOUTH, BRIDPORT DT6 6QL (01297 560226). All units for four to six people. Ten minutes' level walk to beach, many fine local walks. Swimming pools, licensed bar with family room, shop, launderette. Sporting facilities nearby. Children and pets welcome. SAE for colour brochure. [Pets £30 per week]

Christchurch

Residential town near coast, 5 miles east of Bournemouth.

COUNTRY HOLIDAY CHALET on small, quiet, secluded woodland park. Sleeps four. Fenced private garden. Dogs welcome. Car parking. £150 to £350 per week. BH & HPA Member. Write enclosing SAE or telephone: MRS L.M. BOWLING, OWLPEN CARAVANS, OWLPEN, 148 BURLEY ROAD, BRANSGORE, NEAR CHRISTCHURCH, DORSET BH23 8DB (01425 672875; mobile 07860 547391). [🐾 pw!]
website: www.owlpen-caravans.co.uk

Dorchester

Busy market town steeped in history. Roman remains include Amphitheatre and villa.

GREYGLES, MELCOMBE BINGHAM, NEAR DORCHESTER. Spacious, well-equipped house just 10 miles from Dorchester. Sleep 7. Heating, electricity, linen and towels incl. No smoking. ETC ★★★★
Booking: P. SOMMERFELD, 22 TIVERTON ROAD, LONDON NW10 3HL (020 8969 4830; Fax: 020 8960 0069). [Pets £10 per booking]
e-mail: enquiry@greygles.co.uk   website: www.greygles.co.uk

CHURCHVIEW GUEST HOUSE, WINTERBOURNE ABBAS, DORCHESTER DT2 9LS (Tel & Fax: 01305 889296). Beautiful 17th Century Licensed Guest House set in the heart of West Dorset, character bedrooms, two lounges, licensed bar and patio garden. Non-smoking. B&B £39-£44pp. Short breaks available. ETC ★★★★ [🐾]
e-mail: stay@churchview.co.uk   website: www.churchview.co.uk

GRACE COTTAGE. Charming cottage with enclosed garden. Lounge/dining room, study/bedroom, two bedrooms, well-equipped kitchen, two bathrooms. Pub nearby. Non-smokers only. Good touring centre. Contact Nicky Willis (01308 863868). [🐕]
e-mail: veronicawillis@tiscali.co.uk   website: www.grace-cottage.com

MRS JACOBINA LANGLEY, THE STABLES B&B, HYDE CROOK (OFF A37), FRAMPTON DT2 9NW (01300 320075; Fax: 01300 321718). Comfortable country house in 20 acres with uninterrupted country views. Guest accommodation in separate wing, fully double-glazed, with central heating. Dogs most welcome (must have own beds and be kept under control). [Pets £4 per night]
e-mail: coba.stables@tiscali.co.uk   website: www.framptondorset.com

THE BREWERS ARMS, MARTINSTOWN, DORCHESTER DT2 9LB (01305 889361). Country pub with lovely garden. Pub food. Large car park and a large grassed area (which may be suitable for tents). Area in the pub where customers can eat and sit with their dogs.
e-mail: jackie_smith54@hotmail.com   website: www.thebrewersarms.com

Evershot

Village 5 miles north of Maiden Newton.

THE ACORN INN, EVERSHOT, DORCHESTER DT2 0JW (01935 83228). Lovely old stone-built 16th Century coaching inn, with individually decorated en suite bedrooms. Excellent meals using the best fresh local ingredients. Two oak-panelled bars. Well behaved dogs welcome. AA ★★★★ Rosette. [pw! Pets £10 per night]
e-mail: stay@acorn-inn.co.uk   website: www.acorn-inn.co.uk

Lulworth Cove (Near Wareham)

Village and Cove on the World Heritage Jurassic Coastline. Good beaches and numerous guided boat trips leaving from the cove showing the highlights of the area.

THE CASTLE INN, LULWORTH COVE BH20 5RN (01929 400311). Family-run, dog-friendly inn with good food, local real ales and B&B accommodation in a wonderful dog walking area. Half a mile from the coast in the heart of the Purbecks. [🐕, pw!]
website: www.lulworthinn.com

CATRIONA AND ALISTAIR MILLER, CROMWELL HOUSE HOTEL, LULWORTH COVE BH20 5RJ (01929 400253/400332; Fax: 01929 400566). Comfortable family-run hotel, set in secluded gardens with spectacular sea views. Heated swimming pool, 20 en suite bedrooms. Restaurant, bar wine list. Self-catering. Disabled access. ETC/AA ★★ [Pets £6 per night, £28 per week]
website: www.lulworthcove.co.uk

Lyme Regis

Picturesque little resort with harbour, once the haunt of smugglers. Shingle beach with sand at low tide. Fishing, sailing and water ski-ing in Lyme Bay. Taunton 28 miles, Dorchester 24, Seaton 8.

JON SNOOK AND AMANDA HUNT, WESTOVER FARM COTTAGES, WOOTTON FITZPAINE, NEAR LYME REGIS DT6 6NE (01297 560451, 07979 265064, 07979 595850). Within walking distance of the sea. Two beautiful cottages, sleep 6/8, with large secluded gardens. Car parking. Logs supplied. 3 bedrooms, 2 bathrooms. Well behaved pets welcome. VisitBritain ★★★★ [Pets £22 per week]
e-mail: wfcottages@aol.com   website: www.westoverfarmcottages.co.uk

LYME BAY HOLIDAYS. Over 200 VisitBritain 3, 4, or 5 Star self catering holiday properties in beautiful country and coastal locations in and around Lyme Regis, many of which welcome pets.
e-mail: email@lymebayholidays.co.uk   website: www.lymebayholidays.co.uk

Marnhull

Village in the Blackmore Vale, 3 miles from Sturminster Newton.

SPRING COTTAGE, MILL LANE, MARNHULL DT10 1JT (01258 820519). Newly refurbished, dog and child friendly B&B in pretty village. Private entrance to own sitting room. Access to patio and off-road parking. Picturesque, relaxing walks from the door.
e-mail: jan.roper76@btinternet.com

North Perrott

Village 2 miles east of Crewkerne.

MRS E NEVILLE, WOOD DAIRY, WOOD LANE, NORTH PERROTT TA18 7TA (Tel & Fax: 01935 891532). Three well-appointed stone holiday cottages set around courtyard in two and a half acres of Somerset/Dorset countryside. Close to Lyme Bay and Jurassic Coast, excellent base for walking, trails and historic properties. Wheelchair friendly. Pets welcome by arrangement. [🐾]
e-mail: liz@acountryretreat.co.uk   website: www.acountryretreat.co.uk

Poole

Flourishing port and market town. Three museums with interesting collections and lively displays.

PEAR TREE HOLIDAY PARK, ORGANFORD ROAD, HOLTON HEATH, POOLE BH16 6LA (0844 272 9504). A peaceful touring caravan park in beautiful Dorset. Convenience shop. Local pub just a short walk away. Children's play area. Mains electricity and waste disposal points. Enjoy England ★★★★.
e-mail: enquiries@peartreepark.co.uk   website: www.peartreepark.co.uk

HARBOUR HOLIDAYS. QUAY COTTAGE in quiet area with sea views. Sky TV and DVD. Dogs welcome. WYCHCOTT - detached bungalow 6 minutes' drive from beaches at Sandbanks. Fenced rear garden. Barbecue. Safe for young children and dogs. Sky TV/DVD. MRS SAUNDERS, 15 WHITE CLIFF ROAD, POOLE BH14 8DU (01202 741637). [🐾]

Portland

Connected to the Dorset mainland by a road bridge. Spectacular cliff views of the World Heritage coastline.

PORTLAND HIDEAWAY (07957 138054 / 01475 689541. Spacious, well-equipped, tastefully decorated and furnished studio accommodation. Sleeps 2. Fully enclosed patio. Off-road parking. Near Portland Bill, an ideal location for coastal holidays and sightseeing.
e-mail: howard@bestlimited.co.uk   website: www.portlandhideaway.co.uk

Sherborne

Town with abbey and two castles, one of which was built by Sir Walter Raleigh with lakes and gardens by Capability Brown.

FOLKE MANOR FARM COTTAGES. Four comfortable, spacious cottages in converted barns. Sleep 4-8. Peaceful location, outstanding views, walking. Near Sherborne. Open all year. ETC ★★★★. JOHN & CAROL PERRETT, FOLKE MANOR FARM, FOLKE, SHERBORNE DT9 5HP (01963 210731).
e-mail: stay@folkemanorholidays.co.uk   website: www.folkemanorholidays.co.uk

WHITE HORSE FARM, MIDDLEMARSH, SHERBORNE DT9 5QN. The Willows sleeps 4/6; Otters Holt sleeps 6/8; Toad Hall sleeps 4; Badger's & Moley's sleep 2; Ratty's sleeps 2/4. Character self-catering holiday cottages in rural location. Well equipped and comfortable. Digital TV. video, free films. 2 acres of paddock, garden and duck pond. Inn 100 yards. ETC ★★★/★★★★. AUDREY & STUART WINTERBOTTOM (01963 210222) [pw!] [🐾]
e-mail: enquiries@whitehorsefarm.co.uk   website: www.whitehorsefarm.co.uk

Studland Bay

Unspoilt seaside village at south western end of Poole Bay, 3 miles north of Swanage.

THE MANOR HOUSE HOTEL, STUDLAND BAY BH19 3AU (01929 450288; Fax: 01929 452255). National Trust hotel set in 20 acres on cliffs overlooking Studland Bay. Superb food and accommodation. Log fires and four-posters. Tennis, horse-riding, golf and walking. [Pets £5 per night] e-mail: info@themanorhousehotel.com   website: www.themanorhousehotel.com

THE KNOLL HOUSE, STUDLAND, DORSET BH19 3AH (01929 450450). Country house hotel within National Trust reserve. Golden beach. 100 acre grounds. Family suites of connecting rooms. Tennis, golf, swimming, games rooms, health spa. See our Full Page Advertisement under Studland Bay. [pw! Pets £5 per night, including food] e-mail: info@knollhouse.co.uk   website: www.knollhouse.co.uk

Swanage

Traditional family holiday resort set in a sheltered bay ideal for water sports. Good base for a walking holiday.

THE WHITE SWAN, THE SQUARE 31 HIGH STREET, SWANAGE BH19 2LT (01929 423804). A pub with warm and friendly atmosphere, three minutes from the beach. Traditional pub food, Sunday roasts. Large beer garden. En suite accommodation. Parking. Free WiFi and internet access. TV and pool table. Children welcome. [Pets £5 per night]. e-mail: info@whiteswanswanage.co.uk   website: www.whiteswanswanage.co.uk

THE LIMES, 48 PARK ROAD, SWANAGE BH19 2AE (01929 422664). Informal and friendly, with en suite rooms, TV, tea/coffee making facilities, free Wi-Fi. Children and pets welcome. Car park. Licensed bar. AA ★★★★ [🐾] e-mail: info@limeshotel.net   website: www.limeshotel.net

Wareham

Picturesque riverside town almost surrounded by earthworks, considered pre-Roman. Nature reserves of great beauty nearby. Weymouth 19 miles, Bournemouth 14, Swanage 10, Poole 6.

MRS L. S. BARNES, LUCKFORD WOOD FARMHOUSE, EAST STOKE, WAREHAM, NEAR LULWORTH BH20 6AW (01929 463098; Mobile: 07888719002). Peaceful surroundings, delightful scenery. B&B classic farmhouse with style. Breakfast served in conservatory, dining room or garden. All rooms en suite. Free Wi-Fi. Freeview TV. Also our camping and caravanning site nearby includes showers, toilets. Caravan and boat storage available. Near Lulworth Cove, Swanage, Studland, Tank Museum and Monkey World. Open all year. B&B from £35pp per night. Please phone for details. AA ★★★★. [Pets £5 per night, £30 per week] e-mail: luckfordleisure@hotmail.co.uk   website: www.luckfordleisure.co.uk

West Bexington

Seaside village with pebble beach. Chesil beach stretches eastwards. Nearby is Abbotsbury with its Benedictine Abbey and famous Swannery. Dorchester 13 miles, Weymouth 13, Bridport 6.

GORSELANDS CARAVAN PARK, DEPT PW, WEST BEXINGTON-ON-SEA DT2 9DJ (01308 897232; Fax: 01308 897239). Holiday Park. Fully serviced and equipped 4/6 berth caravans. Shop and launderette on site. Glorious sea views. Good country and seaside walks. One mile to beach. Holiday apartments with sea views and private garden. Pets most welcome. Colour brochure on request. ETC ★★★★.[🐾] e-mail: info@gorselands.co.uk   website: www.gorselands.co.uk

Bibury, Bourton-on-the-Water, Cheltenham, Cirencester

Forest of Dean, Longhope, Moreton-in-Marsh, Nailsworth

While every effort is made to ensure accuracy, we regret that FHG Guides cannot accept responsibility for errors, misrepresentations or omissions in our entries or any consequences thereof. Prices in particular should be checked. We will follow up complaints but cannot act as arbiters or agents for either party.

Painswick, South Cerney, Stow-on-the-Wold, Stroud

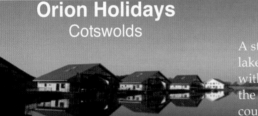

Stroud, Symonds Yat

Bibury

Village on the River Colne, 7 miles NE of Cirencester.

CAROLINE MANN, HARTWELL FARM COTTAGES, READY TOKEN, NEAR BIBURY, CIRENCESTER GL7 5SY (01285 740210). Two comfortable, fully equipped cottages with country views. Ideally located for touring. Stabling available. Glorious walks, excellent pubs. Non-smoking. Children and well-behaved dogs welcome. ETC ★★★★ [pw! Pets £15 per week]
e-mail: ec.mann@btinternet.com   website: www.selfcateringcotswolds.com

A useful index of towns/counties appears on pages 415-421

Bourton-on-the-Water

Delightfully situated on the River Windrush which is crossed by miniature stone bridges. Stow-on-the-Wold 4 miles.

CHESTER HOUSE HOTEL, VICTORIA STREET, BOURTON-ON-THE-WATER GL54 2BU (01451 820286). All rooms en suite, all with central heating, colour TV, phone, tea/coffee making facilities. Wheelchair friendly. Ideal for touring Cotswolds. [🐾]
e-mail: info@chesterhousehotel.com   website: www.chesterhousehotel.com

THE GARDEN ROOM AT STRATHSPEY, LANSDOWNE, BOURTON-ON-THE-WATER GL54 2AR (01451 810321). Just a short stroll from the village centre, and with its own private entrance, the Garden Room offers relaxing accommodation in quiet and secluded surroundings. This ground floor room with en suite shower makes for the perfect getaway. One small dog welcome by prior arrangement. ETC ★★★ [Pets £5 per night]
e-mail: strathspeybandb@hotmail.co.uk   website: www.strathspeybandb.co.uk

Cheltenham

Large residential town, formerly a spa, 8 miles East of Gloucester.

CHARLTON KINGS HOTEL & RESTAURANT, LONDON ROAD, CHELTENHAM GL52 6UU (01242 231061). Ideally located for Cheltenham and the Cotswolds. Close to Cotswold Way. Friendly resident owners. [🐾]
e-mail: enquiries@charltonkingshotel.co.uk   website: www.charltonkingshotel.co.uk

HOPE ORCHARD, GLOUCESTER ROAD, STAVERTON, CHELTENHAM GL51 0TF (01452 855556). Comfortable and attractive family run bed and breakfast, providing ground floor en suite accommodation with own separate entrances. Pets are welcome at no charge. Pubs and restaurants close by. AA ★★★★. [🐾]
e-mail: info@hopeorchard.com   website: www.hopeorchard.com

Cirencester

Market town which lies on River Chum, a tributary of the River Thames. Largest town in the Cotswolds, 93 miles from London.

POLLY AND NICK HANDOVER, GLEBE FARM, BARNSLEY ROAD, CIRENCESTER GL7 5DY (01285 659226; Fax: 01285 642622). Restored barn cottages. Fully equipped, some en suite. Patios, communal garden and ample parking. Utility room. Children under 2 years only. Pets welcome by arrangement. Enjoy England ★★★★/★★★★★. [Pets £20 per week]
e-mail: enquiries@glebefarmcottages.co.uk   website: www.glebefarmcottages.co.uk

THE TUNNEL HOUSE INN. COATES, CIRENCESTER GL7 6PW (01285 770280) A traditional Cotswold pub, a perfect haven for families. Home-cooked pub food, traditional ales and ciders. Pets are welcome in all areas inside and out. Camping available for tents and camper vans in our grounds.
e-mail: info@tunnelhouse.com   website: www.tunnelhouse.com

Fairford

Small town 8 miles east of Cirencester.

THE BULL HOTEL, MARKET PLACE, FAIRFORD GL7 4AA (01285 712535/712217; Fax: 01285 713782). 15thC family-run coaching inn with 27 fully equipped bedrooms; four-poster beds available. A la carte restaurant. Ideal for touring; many leisure facilities within easy reach. ETC/AA ★★ [Pets £5 per night, £20 per week]
e-mail: info@thebullhotelfairford.co.uk   website: www.thebullhotelfairford.co.uk

Forest of Dean

Formerly a royal hunting ground, this scenic area lies between the rivers Severn and Wye.

DRYSLADE FARM, ENGLISH BICKNOR, COLEFORD GL16 7PA (01594 860259; Mobile: 07766 631988). Daphne & Phil ensure a warm welcome for yourself and your dog. A relaxed, friendly atmosphere awaits you at their farmhouse, which dates back to 1880, on their 184-acre beef farm. In the small village of English Bicknor in the Royal Forest of Dean, with Symonds Yat only 2 miles. AA ★★★★ Highly Commended. [pw! 🐾]
e-mail: daphne@drysladefarm.co.uk   website: www.drysladefarm.co.uk

THE SPEECH HOUSE HOTEL, COLEFORD, FOREST OF DEAN GL16 7EL (01594 822607). A friendly Hotel set in the heart of the Forest of Dean. The perfect place for pets. 35 en suite bedrooms. Assorted menus using local produce. AA ★★★. [Pets £10 per night]
e-mail: relax@thespeechhouse.co.uk   website: www.thespeechhouse.co.uk

THE WYNDHAM ARMS HOTEL, CLEARWELL, NEAR COLEFORD, THE ROYAL FOREST OF DEAN GL16 8JT (01594 833 666; Fax: 01594 836 450). Between the beautiful Wye Valley and the Royal Forest of Dean. Eighteen en suite bedrooms including four poster bedrooms and a sumptuous suite. Pets welcome in bedrooms, bar and hotel grounds. AA ★★★ [pw! Pets £5 per night]
e-mail: res@thewyndhamhotel.co.uk   website: www.thewyndhamhotel.co.uk

ANTHONY & INEZ MIDGLEY, HIGHBURY COACH HOUSE, BREAM ROAD, LYDNEY GL15 5JH (01594 842 339 or 07834 408 550). Come and stay in one or more of the three spacious flats in the Coach House of Highbury House, situated on the southern edge of the Royal Forest of Dean. EnjoyEngland ★★★. [pw! ✻]
e-mail: info@highburycoachhouse.co.uk   website: www.highburycoachhouse.co.uk

WHARTON LODGE COTTAGES, WESTON-UNDER-PENYARD, NEAR ROSS-ON-WYE HR9 7JX (Tel & Fax: 01989 750140). Two beautifully furnished, fully equipped self-catering retreats overlooking Herefordshire countryside, sleeping 2, 3 or 4 guests. Dog paradise. Tourist Board ★★★★★ Gold Award. [pw! Pets £4 per night, £20 per week]
e-mail: ncross@whartonlodge.co.uk   website: www.whartonlodge.co.uk

Longhope (near Forest of Dean)

Village situated just outside the Forest of Dean. Longhope means 'long, enclosed valley' which describes the aspect of the village.

THE OLD FARM, BARREL LANE, LONGHOPE GL17 0LR (01452 830252) Character-packed, timber framed, converted 450-year-old barns. Set around an old farmyard leading onto paddocks, woodland and play orchard. Dog and babysitting services. Properties sleep 2/3 and 5/6. ETC ★★★★ [pw! ✻]
e-mail: mattandliza@aol.com   website: www.oldfarmcottages.co.uk

Moreton-in-Marsh

Principal market town in the northern Cotswolds, situated on the Fosse Way.

THE WHITE HART ROYAL HOTEL, MORETON-IN-MARSH GL56 0BA (01608 650731). Historic old coaching inn full of character, quality and comfort. Beautifully furnished throughout to maintain its old world charm while offering 21st century facilities. Wide variety of bedrooms. AA ★★★. [Pets £10 per night]
e-mail: whr@bpcmail.co.uk   website: www.whitehartroyal.co.uk

Nailsworth

Hilly town 4 miles south of Stroud

THE LAURELS, INCHBROOK, NAILSWORTH GL5 5HA (01453 834021; Fax: 01453 835190). A lovely rambling house, cottage and secluded garden where dogs and their owners are encouraged to relax and enjoy. Ideally situated for touring all parts of the Cotswolds and West Country; splendid walks. Brochure. [✻]
e-mail: lesley@laurelsinchbrook.plus.com   website: www.laurelsinchbrook.co.uk

Painswick

Beautiful little Cotswold town with characteristic stone-built houses.

MRS E. WARLAND, HAMBUTTS MYND, EDGE ROAD, PAINSWICK GL6 6UP (01452 812352). Bed and Breakfast in an old converted Corn Mill. Very quiet with superb views. Three minutes to the centre of the village. Field nearby for exercising dogs. Central heating. One double room, one twin, one single, all with TV. £36 single, £66 double or twin, 10% discount for 4 nights or more. ALL ROOMS EN SUITE. AA ★★★ [✻]
e-mail: ewarland@supanet.com   website: www.accommodation.uk.net/hambutts.htm

South Cerney

4 miles from Cirencester in the Cotswold Waterpark, an area of 40 square miles.

ORION HOLIDAYS, COTSWOLDS (01285 861839). A stunning collection of 4/5 ★ lakeside homes. Perfect retreat with pets - Thames Footpath on the doorstep and idyllic countryside to explore. [Pets £20 per week].
e-mail: contact@orionholidays.com   website: www.orionholidays.com

Stow-on-the-Wold

Charming Cotswold hill-top market town with several old inns and interesting buildings. Birmingham 45 miles, Gloucester 26, Stratford-upon-Avon 21, Cheltenham 18, Chipping Norton 9.

THE LIMES, EVESHAM ROAD, STOW-ON-THE-WOLD GL54 1EN (01451 830034/831056). Large Country House. Attractive garden, overlooking fields, 4 minutes town centre. Television lounge. Central heating. Car park. Bed and Breakfast from £30 to £40pppn. Twin, double or family rooms, all en suite. Children and pets welcome. ETC ★★★. [Pets £5 per visit]
e-mail: gkeyte@sky.com   website: www.thelimescotswolds.co.uk

THE OLD STOCKS HOTEL, RESTAURANT & BAR, THE SQUARE, STOW-ON-THE-WOLD GL54 1AF (01451 830666; Fax: 01451 870014). Ideal base for touring this beautiful area. Tasteful guest rooms (including three 'garden' rooms) with modern amenities. Mouth-watering menus. Special bargain breaks also available. HETB/AA ★★ [Pets £5 each per stay]
e-mail: fhg@oldstockshotel.co.uk   website: www.oldstockshotel.co.uk

Stroud

Cotswold town on River Frome below picturesque Stroudwater Hills, formerly renowned for cloth making. Bristol 32 miles, Bath 29, Chippenham 25, Cheltenham 14, Gloucester 9.

MRS A. RHOTON, HYDE CREST, CIRENCESTER ROAD, MINCHINHAMPTON GL6 8PE (01453 731631). Beautiful country house with enclosed acre garden. All rooms on ground floor opening on to patios and lawns. 500 acres of commons, plus country walks nearby. AA ★★★★ [pw! 🐕]
e-mail: stay@hydecrest.co.uk   website: www.hydecrest.co.uk

MRS UNA PEACEY, THE WITHYHOLT GUEST HOUSE, PAUL MEAD, EDGE, NEAR STROUD GL6 6PG (01452 813618: Mobile: 07798 712407: Fax: 01452 812375) Modern guesthouse in Gloucestershire close to Gloucester Cathedral, Tetbury, Stroud. Many lovely country walks. En suite bedrooms, large lounge. Large garden. ETC ★★★★ [🐕]
e-mail: info@thewithyholtbedandbreakfast.com   website: www.thewithyholtbedandbreakfast.com

TOM AND LESLEY WILLIAMS, ORCHARDENE, CASTLE STREET, KINGS STANLEY, STONEHOUSE GL10 3JA (01453 822684; Fax: 01453 821554). Warm welcome at Cotswold Stone cottage. Ideal location to explore undiscovered Cotswolds and Severn Vale. Glorious walks. Evening Meal optional. Local and organic food. Pets welcome.
e-mail: info@orchardene.co.uk   website: www.orchardene.co.uk

Symonds Yat

Well known beauty spot on River Wye, 4 miles from Monmouth.

SYMONDS YAT ROCK LODGE, HILLERSLAND, NEAR COLEFORD GL16 7NY (01594 836191). Family-run B&B and Self catering in Forest of Dean near Wye Valley. All rooms en suite, flat screen TV, Freeview, DVD and CD. 4 poster and family rooms. Brochure available on request. Dogs welcome. [pw! 🐕]
e-mail: info@rocklodge.co.uk   website: www.rocklodge.co.uk

FREE or **REDUCED RATE** entry to Holiday Visits and Attractions –
see our **READERS' OFFER VOUCHERS** on pages 409-414

Duddings
COUNTRY COTTAGES

Thatched longhouse and 12 cottages for 2-16 persons, beautifully converted from old stone barns and stables. Original beams and exposed stonework retain the character of the buildings. Two miles from the picturesque village of Dunster in the Exmoor National Park.

Luxury Cottages

Indoor Heated Pool • Tennis Court

Duddings Country Cottages
Timberscombe, Dunster, Somerset TA24 7TB

Tel: 01643 841123
e-mail: richard@duddings.co.uk
www.duddings.co.uk

As resident owners, we personally guarantee immaculate presentation of cottages on arrival. Each cottage has tasteful decor with matching, highest quality fabrics and is fully central heated. Amenities include comfortable lounges with colour TV/video/DVD, fully fitted modern kitchens with fridge-freezer, cooker and microwave. Our facilities include heated indoor pool, hard tennis court, putting green, pool and table tennis, trampoline, football net and play centre. Trout stream in 8.5 acres for fishing or picnics. Families and pets welcome, walking, riding, beaches nearby. Short breaks available off season, open all year. Full details and plans of the cottages together with up to date prices and availablity can be found on our website, or please call for brochure.

The Yarn Market Hotel is a comfortable, family-run hotel which provides a friendly, relaxed atmosphere. Situated at the centre of a quaint English village it is an ideal location for walking and exploring Exmoor, the surrounding coastline and the many local attractions. All rooms are en suite, with tea and coffee making facilities and colour TV. Some have four-poster beds while others have spectacular views over the surrounding countryside. Family rooms are also available. The restaurant offers a mouth watering selection of dishes featuring local produce whenever possible. Packed lunches and drying facilities are also available. Non-smoking. Well behaved pets are welcome. Party bookings and midweek breaks a speciality. B&B from £50.

THE YARN MARKET HOTEL
High Street, Dunster TA24 6SF

Tel: 01643 821425   Fax: 01643 821475
e-mail: hotel@yarnmarkethotel.co.uk
www.yarnmarkethotel.co.uk

Burnells Gardens   Knowle Lane, Dunster TA24 6TX

Quality Exmoor farmhouse bed and breakfast, near Dunster. Pets very welcome, multiple pets no problem; superb breakfasts, wonderful walking; the essence of peace and comfort. Prices start from £32 pppn, discounts available for stays of 3 nights or more.

01643 822045 • 07796 833183 • libbyportch@yahoo.co.uk • www.burnellsgardens.moonfruit.com

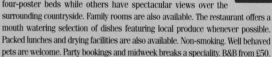

CHAPEL COTTAGE, EXFORD TA24 7PY • 01788 810275

Enjoy walking or riding on the moors, by the rivers or the beach. Return to our cosy cottage, log fire and beams. Two bedrooms (sleeps 4+2), two bathrooms. Excellent inns within 100 yards. Open all year.

e-mail: stay@chapelcottage-exmoor.co.uk
www.chapelcottage-exmoor.co.uk

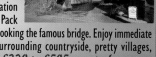

Exmoor

Sunfield
B and B Accommodation in Minehead

Delightful family-run private guest house only a few minutes'
level walking distance from sea front
- Delicious home cooking • Full central heating
- 8 en suite bedrooms, all with courtesy tray, remote-control TV, hairdryer
- Totally non-smoking • Children and well behaved pets welcome

83 Summerland Avenue, Minehead TA24 5BW
Tel: 01643 703565 www.sunfieldminehead.co.uk

The Ship Inn Porlock TA24 8QD • 01643 862507

The thatched 13th century Ship Inn is within walking
distance of sea and moor. The genuine old bar with stone
floor and roaring log fire boasts six real ales and three
ciders, along with a range of home cooked food.

The pub also offers five bed and breakfast rooms,
all en suite, large terraced garden and
enclosed children's play area.

e-mail: enquiries@shipinnporlock.co.uk
www.shipinnporlock.co.uk

THE OLD CIDER HOUSE

4 ★ licensed guesthouse set in the picturesque and historic village of **Nether Stowey** at the
foot of the beautiful **Quantock Hills**. The ideal place for walking, sightseeing or just relaxing.
2008 Winner: Kennel Club's 'Somewhere to Sleep' Award.
01278 732228 • info@theoldciderhouse.co.uk
25 Castle Street, Nether Stowey, Somerset TA5 1LN • **www.theoldciderhouse.co.uk**

AA ★★★ ◉◉

Welcome to 'Farthings', an elegant Georgian hotel situated in the
heart of the Somerset countryside in the historic village of Hatch
Beauchamp. Set in three acres of peaceful gardens and overlooking the
village green, it enjoys an enviable reputation for hospitality, comfort,
pure relaxation and superb cuisine. All our bedrooms are individual,
spacious and en suite, tastefully decorated and furnished, with the usual
tea/coffee making facilities, including chilled fresh milk.

*The hotel is an ideal base for visiting the many attractions
just a short drive away. Within 30 minutes you can visit
Wells Cathedral, Bath, Cheddar Gorge, Wookey Hole, the
Mendips, Exmoor and both the North and South Devon
coasts. Many National Trust and other heritage sites
are also within easy reach.*

20% discount if you mention FHG when booking.

FARTHINGS HOTEL & RESTAURANT
Hatch Beauchamp, Taunton TA3 6SG
Tel: 01823 480664 • Fax: 01823 481118
www.farthingshotel.co.uk
e-mail: farthingshotel@yahoo.co.uk

Holly Bush Park

This two-acre site is hidden in Somerset's Blackdown
Hills, along a maze of narrow lanes. A genuine "away
from it all" site. Tents, campervans, caravans, dogs,
quiet families and couples welcome.

Culmhead, Taunton, Somerset TA3 7EA
Phone: 01823 421515
www.hollybushpark.com

AA ►►► ⚏⚏⚏

FARM & COTTAGE HOLIDAYS (01237 459897). An inspiring collection of holiday cottages throughout Cornwall, Devon, Somerset and Dorset in stunning rural and coastal locations. [Pets £20 per week] website: www.holidaycottages.co.uk

Bath

The best-preserved Georgian city in Britain, Bath has been famous since Roman times for its mineral springs. It is a noted centre for music and the arts, with a wide range of leisure facilities.

NEWTON MILL HOLIDAY PARK, NEWTON ROAD, BATH BA2 9JF (0844 272 9503). Tranquil caravan & camping park just 3 miles from the historic city of Bath. Convenience shop. Licensed bar and restaurant. Children's play area. Mains electricity and waste disposal points. Enjoy England ★★★★. e-mail: enquiries@newtonmillpark.co.uk   website: www.newtonmillpark.co.uk

DAVID & JACKIE BISHOP, TOGHILL HOUSE FARM, FREEZING HILL, WICK, NEAR BATH BS30 5RT (01225 891261; Fax: 01225 892128). Luxury barn conversions on working farm 3 miles north of Bath. Each equipped to very high standard, bed linen provided. Also en suite B&B accommodation in 17th century farmhouse. [pw! Pets £5 per night, £20 per week] website: www.toghillhousefarm.co.uk

Blue Anchor

Hamlet two miles west of Watchet. Beautiful beaches, and rocks and cliffs of geological interest.

PRIMROSE HILL HOLIDAYS, WOOD LANE, BLUE ANCHOR TA24 6LA (01643 821200). Award-winning, spacious, comfortable accommodation in a terrace of four bungalows. Private gardens with panoramic views. A dog-friendly beach is a 10-minute walk away, with other lovely walks from your doorstep. Fully wheelchair accessible. [Pets £15 per week]. e-mail: info@primrosehillholidays.co.uk   website: www.primrosehillholidays.co.uk

Brean

Coastal village with extensive sands. To north is the promontory of Brean Down. Weston-Super-Mare 9 miles.

WESTWARD RISE HOLIDAY PARK, SOUTH ROAD, BREAN, NEAR BURNHAM ON-SEA TA8 2RD (01278 751310). Highly Recommended Luxury 2/6 berth Chalet bungalows. 2 double bedrooms, shower, toilet, TV, fridge, cooker, duvets and linen. Open all year. Call for free brochure. [Pets £15 per week.] website: www.westwardrise.com

Bridgwater

An Area of Outstanding Natural Beauty at the foot of the Quantocks, a paradise for walkers.

THE HOOD ARMS, KILVE, BRIDGWATER TA5 1EA (01278 741210; Fax: 01278 741477). 17thC coaching inn on the A39 at the foot of the Quantock Hills. 12 en suite bedrooms, including four-posters. Beamed restaurant offering full à la carte menu; bar snacks and real ales available. Large garden. [Pets £5 per night] e-mail: info@thehoodarms.com   website: www.thehoodarms.com

Chard

At an altitude of 121 metres Chard is the highest town in Somerset. 15 miles south west of Yeovil.

LORDLEAZE HOTEL, HENDERSON DRIVE, FORTON ROAD, CHARD TA20 2HW (01460 61066). Once an 18th centry farmhouse, now a country hotel, close to the South Coast and minutes away from town centre. 25 en suite bedrooms, excellent restaurant and bar. AA ★★★ [pw! Pets £5 per night] e-mail: info@lordleazehotel.com   website: www.lordleazehotel.com

Cheddar

Picturesque little town in the Mendips, famous for its Gorge and unique caves. Cheese-making is a speciality. Good touring centre. Bath 24 miles, Burnham-on-sea 13, Weston-Super-Mare 11.

BROADWAY HOUSE HOLIDAY PARK, AXBRIDGE ROAD, CHEDDAR BS27 3DB (0844 272 9501). A fun-filled family holiday park in picturesque Somerset. Convenience shop. Licensed bar and restaurant. Swimming pool and cafe. Adventure playground. Mains electricity and waste disposal points. Enjoy England ★★★★.
e-mail: enquiries@broadwayhousepark.co.uk   website: www.broadwayhousepark.co.uk

SUNGATE HOLIDAY APARTMENTS, CHURCH STREET, CHEDDAR BS27 3RA. Ideally situated for walking, cycling and touring the Mendips and the West Country. Competitively priced for short or longer holidays. For full details contact MRS M. FIELDHOUSE (01934 842273/742264) ETC ★★ [Quote for Pets].
e-mail: enquiries@sungateholidayapartments.co.uk   web: www.sungateholidayapartments.co.uk

Clevedon

Small town on Bristol Channel with restored Victorian pier.

MRS JENNY HOPKINS, ROSE COTTAGE, 36 THACKERAY AVE, CLEVEDON BS21 7JJ (01275 879491). You are assured of a warm welcome at this pleasant semi-detached B&B. Private parking. Non smoking. Bristol 15 miles. Well behaved dogs by arrangement. [Pets £1 per night]
e-mail: jenny22hopkins@virginmedia.com   website: www.rosecottage-bandb.co.uk

Dunster

Pretty village with interesting features, including Yarn Market, imposing 14th century Castle. Priory Church and old houses and cottages. Minehead 3 miles.

DUDDINGS COUNTRY COTTAGES, TIMBERSCOMBE DUNSTER TA24 7TB (01643 841123) Thatched longhouse and 12 cottages for 2-16 persons, beautifully converted from old stone barns and stables. Two miles from the village of Dunster in the Exmoor National Park. Pets and families welcome. Open all year. Visit Britain ★★★★ Self Catering. [pw!, Pets £20 per week].
e-mail: richard@duddings.co.uk   website: www.duddings.co.uk

THE YARN MARKET HOTEL, HIGH STREET, DUNSTER TA24 6SF (01643 821425; Fax: 01643 821475). An ideal location for walking and exploring Exmoor. Family-run hotel with a friendly, relaxed atmosphere, home cooking, en suite rooms with colour TV and tea making facilities. Non-smoking. Mid-week breaks a speciality – Pets Welcome. ETC ★★★ Hotel [pw! ⛑]
e-mail: hotel@yarnmarkethotel.co.uk   website: www.yarnmarkethotel.co.uk

BURNELLS GARDENS, KNOWLE LANE, DUNSTER TA24 6TX (01643 822045; 07796 833183). Quality Exmoor farmhouse bed and breakfast. Pets very welcome, multiple pets no problem; superb breakfasts, wonderful walking. From £32 pppn, discounts available for stays of 3 nights or more. [pw! Pets £5 per stay]
e-mail: libbyportch@yahoo.co.uk   website: www.burnellsgardens.moonfruit.com

---

Classified Symbols

⛑   Pets are welcome free of charge.

£   A charge is made for pets: nightly or weekly.

pw!   Special provision for pets; exercise facility, feeding or accommodation arrangement.

⌂   Separate pets' accommodation.

Exford

Fine touring centre for Exmoor and North Devon, on River Exe. Dulverton 10 miles.

CHAPEL COTTAGE, EXFORD TA24 7PY (01788 810275). Enjoy walking or riding on the moors, by the rivers or the beach. Return to our cosy cottage, log fire and beams. Two bedrooms (sleeps 4+2), two bathrooms. Excellent inns within 100 yards. Open all year. ETC ★★★★. [🐕 Up to 2 dogs welcome, free of charge]
e-mail: stay@chapelcottage-exmoor.co.uk   website: www.chapelcottage-exmoor.co.uk

LEONE & BRIAN MARTIN, RISCOMBE FARM HOLIDAY COTTAGES, EXFORD, EXMOOR NATIONAL PARK TA24 7NH (01643 831480). Beside River Exe – centre of Exmoor National Park – close to coast. Four charming self-catering cottages. Dogs and horses welcome. Stabling available. VB ★★★★ [Pets £2.50 per night, £15 per week.]
website: www.riscombe.co.uk (with up-to-date vacancy info.)

EDGCOTT COTTAGE. A friendly welcome awaits you at our charming 18th century character cottage. A hearty breakfast served to set you up for the day. Superbly located on the outskirts of the delightful village of Exford, in the Exmoor National Park. Ideal base for walking, riding, cycling or touring Exmoor. For details tel 07891 437293/01643 831564. [Pets £3 per night]
e-mail: info@stilemoorexmoor.co.uk   website: www.stilemoorexmoor.co.uk

WESTERMILL, EXFORD, EXMOOR TA24 7NJ (01643 831238; Fax: 01643 831216). Idyllic Scandinavian cottages in grass paddocks by stream, with views across river valley. Heart of Exmoor. Woodburners. Four waymarked walks over 500 acre working farm. Disabled Category 2. Separate campsite by river. VisitBritain ★★★, David Bellamy Gold Award for Conservation. [Pets £2.50 per night, £15 per week.]
e-mail: pw@westermill.com   website: www.westermill.com

Exmoor

265 square miles of unspoiled heather moorland with deep wooded valleys and rivers, ideal for a walking, pony trekking or fishing holiday.

THE PACK HORSE, ALLERFORD, NEAR PORLOCK TA24 8HW (Tel & Fax: 01643 862475). Self-catering apartments and cottage within picturesque National Trust village. Immediate access to the beautiful surrounding countryside. Stabling available. Open all year. ETC ★★★★ [Pets £15 per week]
e-mail: holidays@thepackhorse-exmoor.co.uk   website: www.thepackhorse-exmoor.co.uk

JANE STYLES, WINTERSHEAD FARM, SIMONSBATH TA24 7LF (01643 831222). Five tastefully furnished and well-equipped cottages situated in the midst of beautiful Exmoor. Pets welcome, stabling and grazing, DIY livery. Colour brochure on request. ETC ★★★★ [Dogs £15 per week, Horses £20 per week.]
website: www.wintershead.co.uk

WESTERCLOSE HOUSE, WITHYPOOL, EXMOOR NATIONAL PARK TA24 7QR (01643 831302). Stunning views, complete peace, and wonderful moorland location. Five cosy cottages, including two bungalows, all with log fires and individual gardens. Pub/shop 300 metres. Dogs and horses welcome. ETC ★★★★ [pw! Dogs £15 per week]
website: www.westerclose.co.uk

IAN & LORENA MABBUTT, WEST WITHY FARM, UPTON, NEAR DULVERTON, TAUNTON TA4 2JH (01398 371322). Two local stone barns converted to spacious, comfortable self-catering cottages on a 23-acre smallholding. Sleep 4/5. Enclosed gardens. ETC ★★★★ [Pets £12 per week]
e-mail: westwithyfarm@exmoor-cottages.com   website: www.exmoor-cottages.com

WOODCOMBE LODGES, BRATTON, NEAR MINEHEAD TA24 8SQ (Tel & Fax: 01643 702789). Four self-catering lodges in a tranquil rural setting on the edge of Exmoor National Park, standing in a beautiful 2½ acre garden with wonderful views. VisitBritain ★★★★ [Pets £10 per week]
e-mail: nicola@woodcombelodge.co.uk   website: www.woodcombelodge.co.uk

NORTH DOWN FARM, PYNCOMBE LANE, WIVELISCOMBE, TAUNTON TA4 2BL (01984 623730). Traditional farm. All rooms en suite, furnished to high standard. Log fires. Central heating. B&B from £38pppn. BB&EM: 7 nights £310pp, 3-night B&B and evening meal £160pp. Dogs welcome. AA ★★★★ [🐕]
e-mail: jenniferblackshaw@btinternet.com   website: www.north-down-farm.co.uk

Minehead

Neat and stylish resort on Bristol Channel. Sandy bathing beach, attractive gardens, golf course and good facilities for tennis, bowls and horse riding. Within easy reach of the beauties of Exmoor.

SUNFIELD, 83 SUMMERLAND AVENUE, MINEHEAD TA24 5BW (01643 703565). Delightful family-run guest house only a few minutes' level walking distance from sea front. Delicious home cooking. 8 en suite bedrooms. Children and well behaved pets welcome. Totally non-smoking. ETC ★★★★ [🐾]
website: www.sunfieldminehead.co.uk

Porlock

Small resort near coast at foot of steep hill. Lynton 11 miles, Minehead 6.

THE SHIP INN, HIGH STREET, PORLOCK TA24 8QD (01643 862507). Thatched 13th century family-run inn within walking distance of sea and moor. Genuine old bar with stone floor and log fire. Home cooked food. Six real ales, three ciders. Five B&B bedrooms, all en suite. [🐾]
e-mail: enquiries@shipinnporlock.co.uk   website: www.shipinnporlock.co.uk

Quantock Hills

Granite and limestone ridge running north-west and south-east from Quantoxhead and Kingston.

THE OLD CIDER HOUSE, 25 CASTLE STREET, NETHER STOWEY TA5 1LN (01278 732228). In picturesque, historic village at the foot of the Quantocks. All en suite; licensed dining. Own car parking, walled garden. B&B from £30pppn. Wonderful dog-walking country; only 4 miles from coast. VisitBritain ★★★★ Guest Accommodation. [Pets £3 per night].
e-mail: info@theoldciderhouse.co.uk   website: www.theoldciderhouse.co.uk

Taunton

County capital in Vale of Taunton Deane. Museum, Civic Centre, remains of Norman castle.

FARTHINGS HOTEL & RESTAURANT, HATCH BEAUCHAMP, TAUNTON TA3 6SG (01823 480664; Fax: 01823 481118). Nestled in the midst of the wild and fertile countryside of Somerset, just 3 miles from the M5 and Taunton. An elegant Georgian Hotel with beautiful grounds and gardens, orchards, roses, and our own poultry for your breakfast eggs. AA ★★★ Two Rosettes. [Pets £6 per night, £30 per week]
e-mail: farthingshotel@yahoo.co.uk   website: www.farthingshotel.co.uk

HOLLY BUSH PARK, CULMHEAD, TAUNTON TA3 7EA (01823 421515). Hidden in Somerset's Blackdown Hills, along a maze of narrow lanes. A genuine "away from it all" site. Tents, campervans, caravans, dogs, quiet families and couples welcome. AA 3 Pennants.
website: www.hollybushpark.com

Watchet

Small port and resort with rocks and sands. Good centre for Exmoor and the Quantocks. Bathing, boating, fishing, rambling. Tiverton 24 miles, Bridgwater 19, Taunton 17, Dunster 6.

SUNNYBANK HOLIDAY PARK, DONIFORD, WATCHET TA23 0UD (0844 272 9505). Relax at this five star holiday park nestled in the Quantock Hills, Somerset. Well-appointed static caravans for hire. Convenience shop. Outdoor swimming pool. Children's play area. Laundry facilities.
e-mail: enquiries@sunnybankpark.co.uk   website: www.sunnybankpark.co.uk

MRS K. MUSGRAVE, CROFT HOLIDAY COTTAGES, THE CROFT, ANCHOR STREET, WATCHET TA23 0BY (01984 631121) Courtyard of six cottages/bungalows situated in a quiet backwater of the small harbour town of Watchet. Parking, central heating. TV, DVD, washing machine, fridge/freezer, microwave. Use of heated indoor pool. Sleeps 2-6 persons. £210-£795 per property per week. EnjoyEngland ★★★★ [Pets £15 per week]
e-mail: croftcottages@talk21.com   website: www.cottagessomerset.com

---

A useful index of towns/counties appears at the back of this book

Weston-Super-Mare

Popular resort on the Bristol Channel with a wide range of entertainments and leisure facilities. An ideal base for touring the West Country.

BRAESIDE HOTEL, 2 VICTORIA PARK, WESTON-SUPER-MARE BS23 2HZ (01934 626642). Delightful, family-run Hotel, close to shops, beach and park. Parking available. All rooms en suite, colour TV, tea/coffee making. Members of the Bed and Breakfast Association. [🛏]
e-mail: enquiries@braesidehotel.com   website: www.braesidehotel.com

SOMERSET COURT COTTAGES, WICK ST LAWRENCE, NEAR WESTON-SUPER-MARE BS22 7YR (01934 521383). Converted stone cottages in mediaeval village. 1, 2 or 3 beds. Some with four-posters, luxury whirlpool/spa baths. Superb centre for touring West Country. Short Breaks available. £198-£715 per week. [Pets £2 per night]
e-mail: pwhitehead99@yahoo.com   website: www.somersetcottages.com

LOWER FARM COTTAGES. Three luxury spacious cottages with enclosed gardens, sleep 3/6/7. Peaceful rural setting, lovely views. Three miles to sea. Families and dogs welcome. Off- Peak Short Breaks. EnjoyEngland ★★★★. CHRISTINE AND ROY BALL, LOWER FARM HOUSE, SOUTH ROAD, LYMPSHAM, WESTON-SUPER-MARE BS24 0DY (01934 750206) [Pets £20 per week]
e-mail: holidays@lowerfarmcottages.co.uk   website:www.lowerfarmcottages.co.uk

Williton

Village 2 miles South of Watchet.

THE WHITE HOUSE, 11 LONG STREET, WILLITON TA4 4QW (01984 632306). B & B from only £39pppn including a beautifully cooked Full English breakfast. Friendly and relaxed atmosphere. Families and pets welcome. AA ★★★★ [🛏]
e-mail: whitehouselive@btconnect.com   website: www.whitehousewilliton.co.uk

Yeovil

Vibrant market town situated at the southern boundary of Somerset 40 miles from Bristol and 30 miles from Taunton.

THE HALFWAY HOUSE INN COUNTRY LODGE, CHILTHORNE DOMER, NEAR YEOVIL BA22 8RE (01935 840350; Fax: 01935 849006) The very best in country hospitality and an ideal base from which to tour Somerset and Dorset. 20 en suite rooms including a disabled-friendly lodge and four-poster Bridal Suite. Well behaved pets by arrangement. AA ★★★ INN.
e-mail:paul@halfwayhouseinn.com   website:www.halfwayhouseinn.net

Grittleton, Westbury

Cricklade

Small town on banks of River Thames, 8 miles from Swindon and 9 miles from Cirencester.

THE RED LION INN, 74 HIGH STREET, CRICKLADE SN6 6DD (01793 750776). True Cotswold Free House with 10 Cask Ales. 5 en suite bedrooms. Dogs welcome. CAMRA Swindon and North Wiltshire Pub of the Year. County Dining Pub of the Year 2012.
e-mail: info@theredlioninncricklade.co.uk   website: www.theredlioninncricklade.co.uk

Grittleton

Village 6 miles north west of Chippenham.

THE NEELD ARMS INN, THE STREET, GRITTLETON SN14 6AP (01249 782470; Fax: 01249 782358). 17th century inn offering comfortable accommodation and home-cooked food; four-poster available. Children and pets welcome. Convenient for Bath, Stonehenge, Cotswolds. EnjoyEngland ★★★ Inn.
e-mail: info@neeldarms.co.uk   website: www.neeldarms.co.uk

Salisbury

13th century cathedral city, with England's highest spire at 404ft. Many fine buildings.

MR A. SHERING, SWAYNES FIRS FARM, GRIMSDYKE, COOMBE BISSETT, SALISBURY SP5 5RF (01725 519240). Small working farm with cattle, poultry, geese and duck ponds. Spacious rooms, all en suite with colour TV. Ideal for visiting the many historic sites in the area. ETC ★★★ [Pets £5 per night]
e-mail: swaynes.firs@virgin.net   website: www.swaynesfirs.co.uk

Westbury

Town at foot of Salisbury Plain, 4 miles south of Trowbridge.

SPINNEY FARMHOUSE, THOULSTONE, CHAPMANSLADE, WESTBURY BA13 4AQ (01373 832412). Enjoy farm fresh food in a warm, friendly, family atmosphere. Off A36, 16 miles from Bath. All rooms with washbasins, tea/coffee making. TV lounge. No smoking. Children and pets welcome. [🐾]
e-mail: isabelandbob@btinternet.com

The Christopher
110 High Street, Eton, Windsor SL4 6AN

A former Coaching Inn dating back to 1711, the hotel is situated in the heart of Eton, ideal for amenities and attractions. The rooms have a clean and simple design and are equipped with the latest technology and home comforts. Each room has internet access, laptop safe, and power shower and some have full air-conditioning. Many of our rooms are suitable for families and have either a sofa bed or space for extra beds. Christopher's Bar and Grill offers all day dining.

Tel: 01753 852359 • Fax: 01753 830914
e-mail: reservations@thechristopher.co.uk • www.thechristopher.co.uk

Hotel Boat GEANNA – as seen on *'Four in a Bed'* Channel 4 Stunning accommodation on the River Thames in a 4 Star luxury wide beam canal boat in Henley-on-Thames or Reading. Your party are the only guests, all driving done for you. 2 twin cabins/1 double, all en suite. Fully equipped kitchen and spacious saloon with 4 additional berths. (Sleeps 10). Dogs welcome.
Tel: 07780 887 172 • www.myrivercruising.com • janeasher@myrivercruising.com

Online booking available.

Eton

Town located 20 miles west of London on the west bank of the River Thames. opposite Windsor Castle.

THE CHRISTOPHER, 110 HIGH STREET, ETON, WINDSOR SL4 6AN (01753 852359; Fax: 01753 830914). Modernised hotel, centrally situated for amenities and attractions. Rooms are equipped with internet access, laptop safe, power shower. Family rooms available. Bar and Grill offers all day dining. AA ★★★. [Pets £10 per night]
e-mail: reservations@thechristopher.co.uk   website: www.thechristopher.co.uk

Reading

Large town in Thames Valley, 41 miles from Central London.

HOTEL BOAT GEANNA (07780 887 172). Stunning accommodation on the River Thames in luxury wide beam canal boat. Sleeps up to 10. All driving done for you. Dogs welcome. As seen on 'Four in a Bed' Channel 4. EnjoyEngland ★★★★.
e-mail: janeasher@myrivercruising.com   website: www.myrivercruising.com

Chesham, Milton Keynes

Chesham

Town on south side of Chiltern Hills. Ideal walking area.

GEORGE ORME, 49 LOWNDES AVENUE, CHESHAM HP5 2HH (01494 792647). B&B in detached house, 10 minutes from the Underground. Private bathroom, tea/coffee, TV. Good walking country - Chiltern Hills three minutes. ETC ★★★ [🐾]

Milton Keynes

Purpose-built new city, home to the Open University. Midway between London, Birmingham, Leicester, Oxford and Cambridge.

SWAN REVIVED HOTEL, HIGH STREET, NEWPORT PAGNELL, MILTON KEYNES MK16 8AR (01908 610565; Fax: 01908 210995). Delightful 16thC former coaching inn, extensively modernised to provide 40 comfortable guest rooms, two bars, à la carte restaurant, meeting rooms and banqueting facilities. Pets very welcome. [🐾]
e-mail: info@swanrevived.co.uk   website: www.swanrevived.co.uk

Fordingbridge, Lymington, Lyndhurst

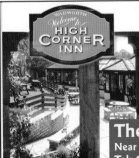

NEW FOREST COTTAGES (01590 679655). The finest selection of over 100 holiday cottages set in spectacular locations throughout the New Forest.
website: www.newforestcottages.co.uk

SHAMBA HOLIDAYS, RINGWOOD ROAD, ST LEONARDS BH24 2SB (01202 873302). Ideally situated to explore Hampshire and Dorset. Shamba offers touring and camping facilities with heated pool and clubhouse. Close to New Forest and Bournemouth with its fine beaches. Seasonal pitches available. ETC ★★★★ [pw! Pets £2.50 per night, £17.50 per week].
website: www.shambaholidays.co.uk

Ashurst

Residential location 3 miles NE of Lyndhurst.

WOODLANDS LODGE HOTEL, BARTLEY ROAD, ASHURST, WOODLANDS SO40 7GN ((023) 80 292257; Fax: (023) 80 293090). Luxury Hotel offering peace and tranquillity. 16 bedrooms, all en suite with whirlpool bath, TV, hairdryer, telephone etc. Award winning Restaurant. Direct access to Forest. ETC ★★★ [Pets £5 per night].
e-mail: reception@woodlands-lodge.co.uk   website: www.woodlands-lodge.co.uk

Fordingbridge

Town on River Avon 6 miles North of Ringwood.

THREE LIONS, STUCKTON, NEAR FORDINGBRIDGE SP6 2HF (01425 652489; Fax: 01425 656144) Relax in a beautiful setting and come and go as you please without the formality of a hotel. Hot tub and sauna. Three times Hampshire 'Restaurant of the Year', Good Food Guide. [pw! Pets £10 per stay]
website: www.thethreelionsrestaurant.co.uk

Lymington

Residential town and yachting centre 15 miles east of Bournemouth.

MRS P. J. ELLIS, EFFORD COTTAGE, EVERTON, LYMINGTON SO41 0JD (01590 642315). Outstanding B&B with old world charm in proprietor's own Georgian home. Excellent touring centre for New Forest and South Coast. All rooms en suite with luxury facilities. B&B from £25-£35pppn. No children. AA ★★★★, Michelin. [pw! Pets from £2 per night]
e-mail: pellis48@btinternet.com   website: www.effordcottage.co.uk

HONEYSUCKLE HOUSE, 24 CLINTON ROAD, LYMINGTON SO41 9EA (01590 676635). Ground floor double room/single, en suite, non-smoking. Woodland walks, park, quay and marinas nearby. B&B from £30.00 pppn. [🐾]
e-mail: derekfarrell317@btinternet.com   website: http://explorethenewforest.co.uk/honeysuckle.htm

Lyndhurst

Good base for enjoying the fascinating New Forest as well as the Hampshire coastal resorts. Bournemouth 20 miles, Southampton 9.

BEST WESTERN CROWN HOTEL, LYNDHURST, NEW FOREST S043 7NF (023 8028 2922; Fax: 023 8028 2751). An historic dwelling located in the centre of this lovely village, an ideal base for exploring the delights of the New Forest with your canine friend(s). Free parking, quiet garden, three star luxury and animal-loving staff. AA ★★★ [Pets £7 per night].
e-mail: reception@crownhotel-lyndhurst.co.uk   website: www.crownhotel-lyndhurst.co.uk

---

🐾   Pets are welcome free of charge.

£   A charge is made for pets: nightly or weekly.

pw! Special provision for pets; exercise facility, feeding or accommodation arrangement.

⌂   Separate pets' accommodation.

New Forest

Area of heath and woodland of nearly 150 square miles, formerly Royal hunting grounds.

MRS E.E. MATTHEWS, THE ACORNS, OGDENS, NEAR FORDINGBRIDGE SP6 2PY (01425 655552). Luxury two bedroom residential-type caravan. Sleeps 4/6. Maintained to high standard, dryer, use of washing machine, own garden. Lovely New Forest setting. Non-smoking, ample parking. Children over five years. Well-behaved dogs welcome (max. 2). Terms £205 - £385, Easter to mid-October. [pw! Pets £12 each per week].
e-mail: e_matthews@mypostoffice.co.uk   website: www.dogscome2.co.uk

MRS J. PEARCE, ST. URSULA, 30 HOBART ROAD, NEW MILTON BH25 6EG (01425 613515). Excellent facilities and warm welcome for well behaved pets and owners! Ground floor suite suitable for disabled guests, plus single and twin rooms. Bed & Breakfast from £28.50. [🐾]

LITTLE THATCH, 15 SOUTH STREET, PENNINGTON (01582 842831) Beautiful Grade II Listed thatched cob cottage, sleeps 4 in 2 bedrooms. Superbly renovated to offer traditional cottage features, tastefully combined with luxury modern comforts. Secluded secure garden. [Pets £10 per week].
e-mail: suzannah@littlethatchcottage.com   website: www.littlethatchcottage.com

GORSE COTTAGE, BALMER LAWN ROAD, BROCKENHURST. Cottage/bungalow on open forest road close to village in New Forest. Sleeps 4 in 2 bedrooms. Conservatory, luxury bathroom, log fire, TV/Freeview/DVD, secluded sunny garden. Pets welcome. Contact: MRS E. GILBERT (01582 872069). ETC ★★★★ [Pets £15 per week]
e-mail: info@gorsecottage.co.uk   website: www.gorsecottage.co.uk

THE WATERSPLASH HOTEL, THE RISE, BROCKENHURST SO42 7ZP (01590 622344). Prestigious New Forest family-run country house hotel set in large garden. Noted for fine personal service, accommodation and traditional English cuisine at its best. All rooms en suite. Luxury four-poster with double spa bath. Swimming pool. Short walk to open forest. AA ★★ Colour brochure available. [Pets from £5 per night.]
e-mail: bookings@watersplash.co.uk   website: www.watersplash.co.uk

Ringwood

Busy market town, centre for trout fishing, trekking and rambling. Bournemouth 13 miles.

DAVID SATCHELL, THE HIGH CORNER INN, LINWOOD, RINGWOOD, HANTS BH24 3QY (01425 473973, Fax: 01425 483052). Seven en suite bedrooms deep in the heart of The New Forest. Real ales, home-cooked food, Sunday carvery and log fires. Pets welcome. [🐾]
website: www.highcornerinn.com

Southsea

Residential and holiday district of Portsmouth 2km South of the city centre.

Quality Hotel accommodation with a superb sea front location. Good walking! All rooms en suite, etc. Passenger lift, licensed bar/restaurant, car park. Small charge for pets. Contact: MARK & JENNY BRUNNING, THE SEACREST HOTEL, 12 SOUTH PARADE, SOUTHSEA, PORTSMOUTH PO5 2JB (02392 733192; Fax: 02392 832523). AA ★★ 75%. [Pets £6 per night].
e-mail: office@seacresthotel.co.uk   website: www.seacresthotel.co.uk

Dog-Friendly Holiday Accommodation for Isle of Wight Holidays

Island View Holidays offer dog-friendly accommodation at our four and five star Isle of Wight holiday parks. At **Rookley Country Park** we offer accommodation in Standard two-and three-bedroom caravans, Luxury and Premier two-and three-bedroom caravans and some of our two-bedroom bungalows. The holiday park is set in acres of lush countryside for you and your dog to explore, and you are only a short journey away from the dog friendly beaches of Sandown, Shanklin and Ventnor.

Hillgrove and **Field Lane Holiday Parks** are especially convenient for the picturesque dog-friendly beaches of St. Helen's Duver and Ryde.
Perfect for couples and families who feel the secret to a good holiday lies in peaceful and beautiful surroundings.

Island View Bungalows at Colwell Bay and **Bay Close Court** at Freshwater (ground floor only) now also accept pets.

There is a charge of £30 per dog per short break or week and we allow a maximum of two dogs per party. There is a limited number of pet accommodation available so please enquire as soon as possible.

Call us now on 01983 721606 (9am to 9pm 7 days a week)
info@islandviewholidays.co.uk
www.islandviewholidays.co.uk

Cowes, Freshwater, Ryde, Totland Bay

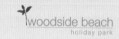

Ventnor, Whitwell, Yarmouth

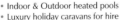

ISLAND VIEW HOLIDAYS, Great value holidays, the best facilities, and beautiful Isle of Wight locations. Island View Holidays offer something for dogs and dog-lovers alike. Booking: (01983 721606). [Pets £30 per week]
e-mail: info@islandviewholidays.co.uk   website: www.islandviewholidays.co.uk

ISLAND COTTAGE HOLIDAYS (01929 481555). Large range of pet and dog friendly cottages in beautiful rural and coastal locations. [Pets £29 per week]
website: www.islandcottageholidays.com

Bonchurch

One mile north-east of Ventnor.

MRS A. EVANS, "THE WATERFALL", SHORE ROAD, BONCHURCH, VENTNOR PO38 1RN (01983 852246). Spacious, self-contained Flat. Sleeps 3 adults. Colour TV. Sun verandah and garden. The beach, the sea and the downs. [🐾]
e-mail: benbrook.charioteer@virgin.net

MRS J. LINES, ASHCLIFF HOLIDAY APARTMENT, BONCHURCH PO38 1NT (01983 853919). Self-contained ground floor apartment (sleeps 2) adjoining Victorian house. Large south-facing gardens. Sea views from garden. Large private car park. Pets welcome to use garden. ETC ★★★ [🐾]
e-mail:judilines@hotmail.co.uk

THE LAKE, SHORE ROAD, LOWER BONCHURCH PO38 1RF (01983 852613). Lovely country house in a beautiful quiet two-acre garden. First class food and service, all in a relaxed and friendly atmosphere. All rooms en suite. Car ferry inclusive prices available. ETC ★★★★ [Pets £8 per night]
e-mail: fhg@lakehotel.co.uk   website: www.lakehotel.co.uk

WESTFIELD LODGES & APARTMENTS, BONCHURCH PO38 1RH (01983 852268; Fax: 01983 853992). Very well equipped lodges and apartments, only five minutes from beach. Sleep 2/6. Indoor pool, launderette, tennis court. Open all year. Pets welcome in selected properties. ETC ★★★/★★★★. [Pets £35 per week]
e-mail: mail@westfieldlodges.co.uk   website: www.westfieldlodges.co.uk

Cowes

Yachting centre with yearly regatta since 1814. Newport 4 miles.

SUNNYCOTT CARAVAN PARK, COWES PO31 8NN (01983 292859). Small, quiet, family-run park close to Cowes. All caravans have full cooker, microwave, fridge and colour TV. Shop and laundry room on site. We welcome pets. Short breaks arranged. ETC ★★★★ [Pets £20 per week]
e-mail: info@sunnycottcaravanpark.co.uk   website: www.sunnycottcaravanpark.co.uk

Freshwater

Two kilometres south of Totland. South-west of Farringford, formerly the home of Tennyson.

BRENDA & BORIS MOSCOFF, SEAHORSES, VICTORIA ROAD, FRESHWATER PO40 9PP (Tel & Fax: 01983 752574). Peaceful 19th century rectory set in two-and-a-half acres of lovely gardens. Good area for walking, golfing, sailing, paragliding and bird watching. Double, family and twin rooms, all en suite. TV lounge, log fires. B&B pppn: £33-£39 depending on season. Children half price. [🐾 pw!]
e-mail: seahorses-iow@tiscali.co.uk   website: www.seahorsesisleofwight.com

Ryde

Resort on north east coast of island, short ferry crossing from Portsmouth.

WOODSIDE BEACH, NEAR RYDE (0844 272 9506). Stunning Solent views at this peaceful caravan park. Private sandy beach. Excellent walking and cycling routes. Area of outstanding natural beauty. Short distance from ferry. Pets welcome.
e-mail: enquiries@woodsidebeachpark.co.uk   website: www.woodsidebeachpark.co.uk

Totland Bay

Small resort 3 miles south-west of Yarmouth Bay.

SENTRY MEAD HOTEL, MADEIRA ROAD, TOTLAND BAY PO39 0BJ (01983 753212; Fax: 01983 754710). This beautiful Victorian villa is set in its own spacious gardens in the tranquil surroundings of West Wight. Just 150 yards from the beach, and with scenic downland walks on the doorstep, this is the perfect place to relax and unwind. All bedrooms en suite. ETC ★★★★★ Silver Award, AA ★★★★★ [Pets £4 per day.]
e-mail: info@sentrymead.co.uk   website: www.sentrymead.co.uk

THE HERMITAGE BED & BREAKFAST, CLIFF ROAD, TOTLAND BAY PO39 0EW (01983 752518). Friendly, homely en suite accommodation in quiet setting. All rooms have TV and tea/coffee facilities. An ideal base from which to tour the island. Evening meals on request. Pets welcome.
e-mail: blake_david@btconnect.com   website: www.thehermitagebnb.co.uk

Ventnor

Well-known resort with good sands, downs, popular as a winter holiday resort. Nearby is St Boniface Down, the highest point on the island. Ryde 13 miles, Newport 12, Sandown 7, Shanklin 4.

MRS F. CORRY, LITTLE SPAN FARM, REW LANE, WROXALL, VENTNOR PO38 3AU (Tel & Fax: 01983 852419, Freephone 0800 2985819). Working farm in an Area of Outstanding Natural Beauty, close to footpaths and holiday attractions. Ideal for family holidays. B&B in farmhouse from £30 pppn or Self-Catering Cottages from £225-£725 per week. Dogs welcome. [pw! Pets £4 per night, £25 per week].
e-mail: info@spanfarm.co.uk   website: www.spanfarm.co.uk

VENTNOR HOLIDAY VILLAS, WHEELERS BAY ROAD, VENTNOR PO38 1HR (01983 852973). Apartments and Villas on south facing hillside leading down to a small rocky bay. Apartments open all year, villas April to October. Write or phone for a brochure. Pets welcome in villas. ETC ★★★ [Pets £20 per week]
e-mail: sales@ventnorholidayvillas.co.uk   website: www.ventnorholidayvillas.co.uk

Whitwell

Small village on south of island, 5km from Ventnor.

MRS JOSE MORRIS, NETTLECOMBE FARM, WHITWELL, NEAR VENTNOR PO38 2AF 01983 730783). Working farm offering luxurious, spacious self-catering holiday accommodation in three comfortably furnished apartments and four high quality cottages. Perfect for families. Sleep 3-10. Pets by arrangement. EnjoyEngland ★★★★.
e-mail: enquiries@nettlecombefarm.co.uk   website: www.nettlecombefarm.co.uk

Yarmouth

Coastal resort situated 9 miles west of Newport. Castle built by Henry VIII for coastal defence.

THE ORCHARDS HOLIDAY CARAVAN & CAMPING PARK, NEWBRIDGE, YARMOUTH PO41 0TS (01983 531331/531350). Luxury holiday caravans, most with central heating and double glazing. Well maintained touring pitches. Excellent facilities including indoor pool with licensed coffeeshop. Dog exercise area. Ideal walking and cycling. Open late February to New Year. Located in an Area of Outstanding Natural Beauty. Spectacular views. [First dog free, 2nd dog £2 per night].
e-mail: info@orchards-holiday-park.co.uk   website:www.orchards-holiday-park.co.uk

FREE or **REDUCED RATE** entry to Holiday Visits and Attractions –
see our **READERS' OFFER VOUCHERS** on pages 409-414

Ashford, Boughton Monchelsea, Broadstairs, Canterbury, Maidstone

Please mention PETS WELCOME!
when making enquiries about accommodation featured in this guide

GARDEN OF ENGLAND COTTAGES IN KENT & SUSSEX, CLAYFIELD HOUSE, 50 ST JOHNS ROAD, TUNBRIDGE WELLS, KENT TN4 9NY (01892 510117). Pets welcome in many of our holiday homes and go free. All properties VisitBritain quality assured. On-line booking and availability. [🐾]
e-mail: holidays@gardenofenglandcottages.co.uk   website: www.goec.co.uk

Ashford

Market town on Great Stour River, 13 miles south-west of Canterbury.

Luxury pine lodges, superior self-catering accommodation overlooking two lakes in beautiful Kent countryside. Rough shooting and coarse fishing on our farms. Weeks or short breaks. Contact: ASHBY FARMS LTD, PLACE FARM, KENARDINGTON, ASHFORD TN26 2LZ (01233 733332; Fax: 01233 733326). [Pets £10 per stay]
e-mail: info@ashbyfarms.com   website: www.ashbyfarms.com

Boughton Monchelsea

Village 3 miles south of Maidstone.

COCK INN, BOUGHTON MONCHELSEA, MAIDSTONE ME17 4JD (01622 743166) Glorious 16thC timbered black and white inn with inglenook fireplace and oak-beamed bar and restaurant. Patio and outside eating area.
e-mail: info@cockinnboughtonmonchelsea.com

Broadstairs

Quiet resort, once a favourite of Charles Dickens. Good sands and promenade.

THE HANSON, 41 BELVEDERE ROAD, BROADSTAIRS CT10 1PF (01843 868936). Small, friendly licensed Georgian Hotel. Home comforts; children and pets welcome. Attractive bar. SAE. EnjoyEngland ★★★ [pw! Pets £1 per night, £5 per week]
website: www.hansonhotel.co.uk

Canterbury

Cathedral City on River Great Stour, 54 miles east of London.

DOREEN ADY, HAWTHORN FARM COTTAGES, WARE, NEAR SANDWICH (01304 813560). Four converted two-bedroom cottages, sleeping 4-5. Ideally situated for relaxing or exploring the Kent coastline. Children's play field. Ample parking. Pets welcome by arrangement. ETC ★★★/★★★★. [pw! Pets £20 per week]
e-mail: hawthornfarmcottages@dsl.pipex.com   website: www.hawthornfarmcottages.co.uk

St Margaret's Bay

4 miles north-east of Dover

DEREK AND JACQUI MITCHELL, REACH COURT FARM COTTAGES, REACH COURT FARM, ST MARGARET'S BAY, DOVER CT15 6AQ (Tel & Fax: 01304 852159). Situated in the heart of the Mitchell family farm, surrounded by open countryside, these five luxury self-contained cottages are very special. The cottages are set around the old farmyard, which has been attractively set to lawns and shrubs, with open views of the rural valley both front and back. [🐕]
e-mail: enquiries@reachcourtfarmcottages.co.uk   website: www.reachcourtfarmcottages.co.uk

Maidstone

County town of Kent, 32 miles from London. Leeds Castle, "the loveliest castle in the world", is 7 miles away.

BLACK HORSE INN, PILGRIMS WAY, THURNHAM, MAIDSTONE ME14 3LD (01622 737185). Homely and welcoming inn with origins in the 18thC, The Black Horse is adorned with hops and beams, and has an open log fireplace. A separate annexe has 27 beautiful en suite bedrooms. [Pets £6 per night].
e-mail: info@wellieboot.net   website: www.wellieboot.net

Margate

Traditional seaside resort, with a vibrant cultural quarter and several historic buildings.

SMITHS COURT HOTEL, 21-27 EASTERN ESPLANADE, CLIFTONVILLE, MARGATE CT9 2HL (01843 222310). Elegant, Victorian family-run premier hotel. 43 individually decorated rooms and suites, many with superb sea views. Perfect for short breaks. Pets welcome. EnjoyEngland/AA ★★★. [Pets £10 per stay].
e-mail: info@smithscourt.co.uk   website: www.smithscourt.co.uk

Sevenoaks

Town on edge of North Downs 21 miles south east of London.

GOLDING HOP FARM COTTAGE, PLAXTOL, NEAR SEVENOAKS TN15 0PS (07771 520229). Three Star cottage on 13-acre cobnut farm in Bourne Valley. Sleeps 5 plus cot. Children and pets welcome. Open all year. £240-£460 pw. [Pets £12 per week each].
e-mail: info@goldinghopfarm.com   website: www.goldinghopfarm.com

Henley-on-Thames, Oxford, Standlake, Tackley/Kidlington

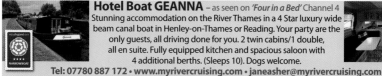

Abingdon

Market town and civil parish 5 miles south of Oxford in the Thames Valley.

KINGFISHER BARN HOLIDAY COTTAGES, ABINGDON OX14 3NN (Tel & Fax: 01235 537538). Self-
catering cottages, from one-bedroom loft apartments to four-bedroom lodges. Sleep 4/10. All fully
equipped, with TV with Freeview. Wi-Fi. Indoor swimming pool. Pets welcome. ETC ★★★★
e-mail: info@kingfisherbarn.com   website: www.kingfisherbarn.com

Bicester

Town 11 miles NE of Oxford.

TODDY AND CLIVE HAMILTON-GOULD, TOWER FIELDS, TUSMORE ROAD, NEAR SOULDERN,
BICESTER OX27 7HY (01869 346554). Ground floor en suite rooms, all with own entrance and ample
parking. Breakfast using local produce. Easy reach of Oxford, Stratford-upon-Avon, many National
Trust houses. Silverstone, Towcester. Dogs and horses welcome by arrangement. VisitBritain
★★★★ [🐾]
e-mail: toddyclive@towerfields.com   website: www.towerfields.com

Burford

Small Cotswold Town on River Windrush, 7 miles west of Witney.

THE INN FOR ALL SEASONS, THE BARRINGTONS, NEAR BURFORD OX18 4TN (01451 844324). Family-run and owned, an unspoilt former 16th century English Coaching Inn. Genuinely dog-friendly; ground floor rooms available with direct access to exercise area. AA ★★ and Rosette. [Pets £5.00 each per night]
email: sharp@innforallseasons.com　　　　website: www.innforallseasons.co.uk

Henley-on-Thames

Town on River Thames, 10 miles from Reading. World renowned centre for rowing, with annual Royal Regatta.

HOTEL BOAT GEANNA (07780 887 172). Stunning accommodation on the River Thames in luxury wide beam canal boat. Sleeps up to 10. All driving done for you. Dogs welcome. As seen on 'Four in a Bed' Channel 4. EnjoyEngland ★★★★.
e-mail: janeasher@myrivercruising.com　　　　website: www.myrivercruising.com

Oxford

City 52 miles from London. University dating from 13th century. Many notable buildings.

MR B. CRONIN, NANFORD GUEST HOUSE, 137 IFFLEY ROAD, OXFORD OX4 1EJ (01865 244743; Fax: 01865 249596). Period guest house located five minutes on foot from the University of Oxford. Wide range and number of rooms, all with private shower and toilet. [🐾]
e-mail: b.cronin@btinternet.com　　　　website: www.nanfordguesthouse.com

Standlake

Village approximately 5 miles south east of Witney and 7 miles west of Oxford.

LINCOLN FARM PARK, HIGH STREET, STANDLAKE OX29 7RH (01865 300 239). Small, quiet Family Park. Super and Hard standing pitches.Tenters' Kitchen. Games Room. Play-area. Indoor heated swimming pools, spas, saunas, children's pool & steam room, solarium, fitness suite. AA Best Campsite of the Year 2010. Best Regional Park 2007 Finalist 2008/2009. Practical Caravan. [pw! Pets £1.30 per night]
website: www.lincolnfarmpark.co.uk

Tackley/Kidlington

Village 3 miles north-east of Woodstock; approximately 5 miles north of Oxford.

JUNE AND GEORGE COLLIER, 55 NETHERCOTE ROAD, TACKLEY, KIDLINGTON, OXFORD OX5 3AT (01869 331255; mobile: 07790 338225). Bed and Breakfast in Tackley. An ideal base for touring, walking, cycling and riding. Central for Oxford, The Cotswolds, Stratford-on-Avon, Blenheim Palace. Woodstock four miles. There is a regular train and bus service with local Hostelries serving excellent food. [🐾 🏠]
e-mail: junecollier@btinternet.com　　　　website: www.colliersbnb.co.uk

Farnham, Kingston Upon Thames

Farnham

Bustling town at the western end of Surrey, bordering on Hampshire. Remains of Roman, Saxon and Stone Age dwellings have been found within the town boundaries.

TILFORD WOODS LODGES, TILFORD ROAD, FARNHAM GU10 2DD (0844 272 9507). A serene and relaxing retreat in the heart of beautiful rural Surrey. Well-appointed luxurious lodges for hire. Golf course opposite. Short stroll to local pub. Launderette. Saunas and outdoor hot tubs available.
e-mail: enquiries@tilfordwoods.co.uk   website: www.tilfordwoods.co.uk

Kingston Upon Thames

Market town, Royal borough and administrative centre of Surrey. Kingston is ideally placed for London and environs.

CHASE LODGE HOTEL, 10 PARK ROAD, HAMPTON WICK, KINGSTON UPON THAMES KT1 4AS (020 8943 1862; Fax: 020 8943 9363). Award-winning hotel offering quality en suite bedrooms. Easy access to town centre and major transport links. ★★★ [🐾]
e-mail: info@chaselodgehotel.com   website: www.chaselodgehotel.com

Pet-Friendly
Pubs, Inns & Hotels
on pages 403-404

These establishments may not feature in the main section of the book

Battle

Historic town, site of famous Battle of Hastings in 1066. Many fine Georgian buildings.

CRAZY LANE TOURIST PARK. Small secluded family park within easy reach of beaches and historic sites. 36 touring, 20 motor caravan, 36 electric hook-ups. First class toilet facilities, launderette. From £13 per night. Dogs welcome on lead. Contact WHYDOWN FARM, SEDLESCOMBE, BATTLE TN33 oQT. (01424 870147). EnjoyEngland ★★★.
e-mail: info@crazylane.co.uk   website: www.crazylane.co.uk

Chiddingly

Charming village, 4 miles north-west of Hailsham. Off the A22 London-Eastbourne road.

Unique self-catering accommodation in grounds of Tudor manor house. Large oast house (sleeps 7-11) and four period cottages (sleep 4-10). All very well equipped.Indoor heated swimming pool, sauna, jacuzzi, badminton, tennis. Children and dogs welcome. Open all year. Contact: EVA MORRIS, "PEKES", 124 ELM PARK MANSIONS, PARK WALK, LONDON SW10 0AR (020 7352 8088; Fax: 020 7352 8125). [pw! 2 dogs free, extra two £7 each].
e-mail: pekes.afa@virgin.net   website: www.pekesmanor.com

Fairlight

Village 3 miles east of Hastings

JANET & RAY ADAMS, FAIRLIGHT COTTAGE, WARREN ROAD, FAIRLIGHT TN35 4AG (01424 812545). Country house in idyllic location with clifftop walks. Tasteful en suite rooms, comfortable guest lounge. Delicious breakfasts. No smoking. Dogs stay with owners. VB ★★★★. Self catering bungalow in Fairlight village also available. [🐕]
e-mail: fairlightcottage@supanet.com   website: www.fairlightcottage.co.uk
                                                           www.littleoaksfairlight.co.uk

Polegate

Quiet position, 5 miles from the popular seaside resort of Eastbourne. London 58 miles, Lewes 12.

MRS P. FIELD, 20 ST JOHN'S ROAD, POLEGATE BN26 5BP (01323 482691). Homely private house. Quiet location; large enclosed garden. Parking space. Ideally situated for walking on South Downs and Forestry Commission land. All rooms, washbasins and tea/coffee making facilities. Bed and Breakfast. Pets very welcome. [pw! 🐕]

Rye

Picturesque hill town with steep cobbled streets. Many fine buildings of historic interest. Hastings 12 miles, Tunbridge Wells 28.

MRS JANE APPERLY, BRANDY'S COTTAGE, CADBOROUGH FARM, RYE TN31 6AA (01797 225426). Recently converted cottage provides luxurious and spacious accommodation for two people. Private courtyard. One small well-behaved dog and children over 12 welcome. ETC ★★★★ [🐕] Other properties also available.
e-mail: apperly@cadborough.co.uk   website: www.cadborough.co.uk

RYE LODGE HOTEL, HILDER'S CLIFF, RYE TN31 7LD (01797 223838; Fax: 01797 223585). Luxury, elegance and charm in a relaxed atmosphere. Luxurious rooms, full room service and an elegant Champagne Bar. Indoor swimming pool, spa and sauna. Ideal for exploring historic Rye. AA/VB ★★★ Gold Award. [Pets £8 per night, £50 per week]
website: www.ryelodge.co.uk

Seaford

On the coast midway between Newhaven and Beachy Head.

BEACH COTTAGE, CLAREMONT ROAD, SEAFORD BN25 2QQ. Well-equipped, three-bedroomed terraced cottage on seafront. CH, open fire and woodburner. South-facing patio overlooking sea. Downland walks (wonderful for dogs), fishing, golf, wind-surfing, etc. Details from JULIA LEWIS, 47 WANDLE BANK, LONDON SW19 1DW (020 8542 5073). [pw! 🐕]
e-mail: cottage@beachcottages.info   website: www.beachcottages.info

Arundel, Chichester, Eastergate, Henfield, Pulborough

Arundel

Arundel lies between Chichester and Brighton, 5 miles from Littlehampton on the south coast. Magnificent Arundel Castle with its impressive grounds overlooks the River Arun, and the town is also home to the Wildfowl and Wetlands Trust where thousands of rare and migratory birds can be seen.

MRS VICKI RICHARDS, WOODACRE, ARUNDEL ROAD, FONTWELL, ARUNDEL BN18 0QP (01243 814301). Bed & Breakfast in traditional family home. Ideal for Chichester, Goodwood and seaside. Clean, spacious rooms, two on ground floor. ETC ★★★★ [🐾].
e-mail: wacrebb@aol.com   website: www.woodacre.co.uk

Chichester

County town 9 miles east of Havant. Town has cathedral and 16th century market cross.

SPIRE COTTAGE, CHURCH LANE, HUNSTON, CHICHESTER PO20 1AJ (01243 778937). Stylish bed and breakfast accommodation in a friendly and relaxed atmosphere. Excellent facilities. Village pub and two golf courses. [Dogs £5 per night]
e-mail: jan@spirecottage.co.uk   website: www.spirecottage.co.uk

Eastergate

Village between the sea and South Downs. Fontwell Park nearby. Bognor Regis 5 miles south.

WANDLEYS CARAVAN PARK, EASTERGATE PO20 3SE (01243 543235 or 01243 543384). You will find peace, tranquillity and relaxation in one of our comfortable holiday caravans. All have internal WC and shower. Dogs welcome. Many historic and interesting places nearby. Telephone for brochure. [🐾]
e-mail: amandagent@btinternet.com   website: www.wandleyscaravanpark.com

Henfield

Large village in the Horsham District of West Sussex, 33 miles south of London, 12 miles north west of Brighton and 30 miles north east of Chichester.

GARDEN COTTAGE AND DAIRYMAID'S COTTAGE, NEW HALL, HENFIELD BN5 9YJ (01403 733982) Comfortable and well equipped cottages in owner's grounds offer a tranquil and pleasant retreat. Garden Cottage sleeps 2/4, Dairymaid's Cottage sleeps 5. Children and pets welcome. Open all year. ETC ★★★ [Pets £15 per week]
e-mail: norman.carreck@btinternet.com

Pulborough

Town on River Arun 12 miles NW of Worthing.

BEACON LODGE, LONDON ROAD, WATERSFIELD, PULBOROUGH RH20 1NH (01798 831026; 07941 884891). Charming self-contained annexe in centre of South Downs National Park. B&B accommodation, en suite, TV, coffee/tea making facilities. Wonderful countryside views. B&B from £35 per night (based on 2 people sharing). Excellent for country walks. No charge for your pets! [pw! 🐾]
e-mail: gbwingfield@yahoo.co.uk   website: www.beaconlodge.co.uk

Selsey

Seaside resort 8 miles south of Chichester. Selsey Bill is headland extending into the English Channel.

ST ANDREWS LODGE, CHICHESTER ROAD, SELSEY PO20 0LX (01243 606899; Fax: 01243 607826). 10 bedrooms, all en suite, with direct dial telephones and modem point, some on ground floor. Dining room overlooking garden; licensed bar for residents only. Wheelchair accessible room. Dogs welcome in rooms overlooking large garden. Apply for brochure and prices. ETC★★★★ [Pets £3 per stay (donation to local project)]
e-mail: info@standrewslodge.co.uk   website: www.standrewslodge.co.uk

Worthing

Residential town and seaside resort with 5-mile seafront. Situated 10 miles west of Brighton..

CAVENDISH HOTEL, 115/116 MARINE PARADE, WORTHING BN11 3QG (01903 236767). Recently refurbished sea front hotel with views over English Channel. All rooms en suite, with TV, tea/coffee making and telephone. A la carte and snack menus available. Ideal base for touring.
e-mail: reservations@cavendishworthing.co.uk   website: www.cavendishworthing.co.uk

Burwell

One of the largest villages in Cambridgeshire, with over 60 listed buildings of interest, and the 15th century Church of St Mary's. Ideal area for walkers, fishing enthusiasts and nature lovers.

THE MEADOW HOUSE, 2A HIGH STREET, BURWELL, CAMBRIDGE CB25 0HB (01638 741926; Fax: 01638 741861). Modern house in two acres of wooded grounds offering superior Bed and Breakfast. Variety of en suite accommodation. All rooms have TV, central heating and tea/coffee facilities. No smoking. Family rate on request. ETC ★★★★ [🐾]
e-mail: hilary@themeadowhouse.co.uk   website: www.themeadowhouse.co.uk
    www.hilaryscottage.co.uk

Ely

Magnificent Norman Cathedral dating from 1083. Ideal base for touring the fen country of East Anglia.

MRS C. H. BENNETT, STOCKYARD FARM, WISBECH ROAD, WELNEY PE14 9RQ (01354 610433; Fax: 01354 610422). Comfortable converted farmhouse, rurally situated between Ely and Wisbech. Conservatory breakfast room, guests' lounge. Free-range produce. Miles of riverside walks. Vegetarians welcome. B&B from £25. [🐾 pw!]

THE OLD SCHOOL B&B, THE OLD SCHOOL, SCHOOL LANE, COVENEY, ELY CB6 2DB (01353 777087; Mob: 07802 174541). Former village school set in an acre of gardens and horse paddocks, with splendid views across the Fens. All bedrooms on ground floor. Dogs very welcome. See reviews on TripAdvisor and eviivo. EnjoyEngland ★★★★. [pw! £3 per dog per night]
e-mail: info@TheOldSchoolBandB.co.uk   website: www.TheOldSchoolBandB.co.uk

Colchester, Mersea Island

Colchester

Britain's oldest recorded town. Many great visitor attractions, including the children's favourite, Colchester Zoo.

THE WHALEBONE, CHAPEL ROAD, FINGRINGHOE, COLCHESTER CO5 7BG (Tel/Fax: 01206 729307)
Only minutes from Colchester, offering a wide range of excellent food and real ales. Pets welcome
inside the pub and beer garden. Excellent dog-walking trails in and around Fingringhoe.
e-mail: vicki@thewhaleboneinn.co.uk   website: http://whaleboneinn.sm4.biz/

WALDEGRAVES HOLIDAY & LEISURE PARK, MERSEA ISLAND, COLCHESTER CO5 8SE (01206
382898; Fax: 01206 385359) Attractive serviced pitches, plenty of open space and hedges for
privacy. Toilet/showering facilities. Luxury self catering Holiday Homes. Modern laundry block.[pw!
🏠 Pets £2 per night (touring and camping); £15 per pet per stay (luxury holiday homes)]
e-mail: holidays@waldegraves.co.uk   website: www.waldegraves.co.uk

Mersea Island

Winding lanes cross open countryside, joined to mainland by Strood Causeway.

COSWAYS HOLIDAY PARK, MERSEA ISLAND CO5 8UA (01206 383252). Holiday homes for sale and
hire. Swimming pool, tennis court, clubhouse, play area, shop, launderette. Superb rural setting with
private beach. Safe and secure. [pw! 🏠 £15 per pet per stay]
e-mail: holidays@cosways.co.uk   website: www.cosways.co.uk

Pet-Friendly
Pubs, Inns & Hotels
on pages 403-404
These establishments may not feature in the main section of the book

Take a Blue Riband Holiday in beautiful Norfolk

Inexpensive Self Catering Holidays at
- **Caister** ● **Hemsby** ● **Scratby**
- **Winterton** ● **Great Yarmouth**

Detached Bungalows at Parklands
Hemsby Village, superb children's playground and playing field, miniature railway, Parkland's 'Fun Bus", mini-golf, weekly BBQ and fun nights. Launderette and shop.

Above: superb children's play area and Parklands "Fun Bus"
Below: one of our quality chalets, Beach Road, Hemsby

Sea-Dell & Belle Aire holiday homes close to beach.
In Hemsby: satellite TV, children's playground and "Club Belle" (Belle Aire) open to all. Pets are allowed on local beaches.

Seafront Bungalows, Caister-on-Sea
With enclosed gardens, close to the beach.

Open all year incl. Christmas and New Year.

Quality, Value and Service from a family business, since 1955

● *Popular low season breaks, bungalows from only £99*

● *Bargain Spring & Autumn breaks, excellent value chalets from £80*

Blue Riband Holidays

☎ **Direct Line for Bookings & Brochures**
01493 730445 – Call 8am to 9pm 7 days a week
www.blueribandholidays.co.uk
www.parklandshemsby.co.uk

Browse our full brochure on the above websites or write to:
Blue Riband Holidays, Parklands, Hemsby, Great Yarmouth, Norfolk NR29 4HA

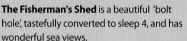
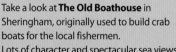

Caister-on-Sea, Cromer

Cromer, Dereham, Diss

A warm welcome for you and your pets. Inexpensive, 'live-as-you-please' self-catering holidays in beautiful Norfolk. Chalets, Bungalows, Caravans and Cottages near Great Yarmouth & Norfolk Broads.

SHORT BREAKS AVAILABLE ALL SEASON

PETS FREE APRIL/MAY/JUNE

Colour Brochure : Carefree Holidays, Chapel Briers, Yarmouth Road, Hemsby, Norfolk NR29 4NJ
Find us on the internet: www.carefree-holidays.co.uk

BOOKING HOTLINE 01493 732176

THE *Hill House*

Happisburgh NR12 0PW • Tel & Fax: 01692 650004

Excellent accommodation in spacious rooms in this attractive free house on the lonely Norfolk coast at Happisburgh. Bar and restaurant.

Ollands Farm Barn - Short Lane, Happisburgh NR12 0RR

Lovingly restored to a very high standard, this 18thC barn features a beamed cathedral ceiling, wood-burning stove, quaint paddle stairs, central heating, comfortable king-size bed in galleried bedroom, sofa-bed downstairs, fully fitted kitchen, shower room.
Well behaved dogs are welcome and receive a special treat when they come to stay. We are proud owners of two lurchers and two deerhounds, also two cats and small flock of chickens.
Tel: 01692 652280 • e-mail: mastuart@talk21.com • www.ollandsfarmbarn.co.uk

---

WEYBOURNE FOREST LODGES

Sandy Hill Lane, Weybourne, Holt, Norfolk NR25 7HW • Tel: 01263 588440

A PARADISE FOR DOGS AND THEIR OWNERS - Comfortable, well equipped lodges set in a tranquil forest glade with wonderful walks on the doorstep. Adjoining National Trust. 1½ miles from beach and cliffs, three miles from Holt and Sheringham.

e-mail: weybourneforestlodges@hotmail.com • www.weybourneforestlodges.co.uk

---

West Wing

Self Catering in Hunstanton, Norfolk

Glimpse sea from this 1st floor flatlet. Wonderful sunsets over the sea.
• Steps access the premises directly from the private car park.
• Spacious, centrally heated and well equipped. Sleeps 2 as a twin or super king, bedroom with balcony and garden views.

Tel: 01485 534036
e-mail: st.crispins@btinternet.com
PETS WELCOME

Contact: Ms L.D. Poore

Please mention PETS WELCOME!
when making enquiries about accommodation featured in this guide

Old Hunstanton, Sheringham, Stalham, Stiffkey

St Crispins
Self Catering in Old Hunstanton, Norfolk

Just for two, quiet, secluded and near the beach

- Quietly tucked away, near sandy beach, golf course and long distance coastal footpath/Peddars Way, and the village store.
- Situated a few miles from Norfolk Lavender, Royal Sandringham, and Titchwell/Snettisham RSPB. Near three pubs/restaurants.
- Short notice bargain breaks from £130 usually available early and late season • Linen provided • Easy parking.

Tel: 01485 534036   **e-mail: st.crispins@btinternet.com**

PETS WELCOME   *Contact: Ms L.D. Poore*

Six traditional self-catering properties, all within walking distance of a Blue Flag beach. All properties are comfortable and fully equipped, with TV and video or DVD. Parking. Some with Wi-Fi. Sleep 4/8. Sheringham has many attractions including the North Norfolk Steam Railway and Splash Leisure Centre. *Small/medium dogs welcome by prior arrangement.*

Sheringham Cottages   Tel: 01263 577560

Contact: Trevor Claydon, Camelot House, Holt Road, Gresham NR11 8AD
trevor.claydon@which.net • www.sheringhamcottages.com

20 & 69 Broadside Chalet Park

are situated near the Norfolk Broads at Stalham. The chalets have two bedrooms, shower, wc ,well equipped kitchen and lounge area with colour television. There is an on-site bar/restaurant and during the main season an open-air swimming pool is available. An ideal location for sightseeing coastal and inland attractions around Norfolk and the Broads. Dogs are very welcome. Open March to October, Christmas and New Year and most weekends during the winter

Kay & Tony Loveday, Mill View, Water Lane, Mundesley, Norfolk NR11 8BS
Telephone: 07785 517642 • e-mail northnorfolkchalets@yahoo.com
www.northnorfolkholidaychalets.co.uk

Stiffkey Red Lion Tel: 01328 830552
44 Wells Road, Stiffkey, Norfolk NR23 1AJ
e-mail: redlion@stiffkey.com • www.stiffkey.com
5 ground floor en suite bedrooms, 5 on first floor;
all with their own external door. *Pets warmly welcomed*

Thompson, Thorpe Market, Thurne, Weybourne

The Old Coach House

THORNHAM

www.oldcoachhousethornham.com

Charming and traditional, situated in the pretty village of Thornham on the North Norfolk Coast, The Old Coach House Bed and Breakfast is a lovely Norfolk Pub with superb accommodation. All of our bedrooms have been tastefully renovated enhancing the charm of this old building; family rooms available. Offering an extensive menu using fantastic seasonal produce. Our children's menu will tempt even the fussiest toddler, while an outside play area and mini-train will occupy them before their meal arrives! Many interesting places to visit including quaint fishing villages and historic houses. Dogs and muddy boots welcome!

The Old Coach House • Thornham • Norfolk PE36 6LY
Tel: 01485 512229 • Fax: 01485 512091 • E-mail: info@oldcoachhousethornham.com

The Lifeboat Inn

16th Century Smugglers' Ale House
Ship Lane • Thornham
Norfolk • PE36 6LT
Tel: 01485 512236 • Fax: 01485 512323
e-mail: reception@lifeboatinn.co.uk

THE LIFEBOAT INN has been a welcome sight for the weary traveller for centuries – roaring open fires, real ales and a hearty meal awaiting. The Summer brings its own charm – a cool beer, gazing over open meadows to the harbour, and rolling white horses gently breaking upon Thornham's sandy beach.

Dogs are welcome in all our bars and we provide the sort of breakfast that will enable you to keep up with your four-legged friend on the way to the beach!

Guests arriving at reception are greeted by our grand old fireplace in the lounge – ideal for toasting your feet after a day walking the coastal path – if you can coax your sleeping dog out of prime position!

Many travel miles for a pot of The Lifeboat's steaming mussels when in season - this is typically when there is an "r" in the month! - or for a huge traditional plate of locally caught fish and chips. These are just two of the delicious dishes from our extensive menu.

There are numerous and varied walks along miles of open beaches, across sweeping sand dunes, through pine woods or along chalk and sandstone cliff tops. It is truly a walker's paradise – especially if you're a dog.

We hope you will come and visit us. For our brochure and tariff which includes details of breaks please ring 01485 512236 **or visit our website**

www.lifeboatinnthornham.com

Winterton-on-Sea

Fishermans Return

This 300-year-old brick and flint pub is situated in the unspoilt village of Winterton-on-Sea, just a few minutes' stroll from sandy beaches and beautiful walks. The Inn is popular with locals and visitors alike, serving excellent food, from simple bar snacks to more substantial fare, with a good choice of local real ales and fine wines. Accommodation is available on a B&B basis, in three tastefully furnished en suite double bedrooms.

The Lane, Winterton-on-Sea NR29 4BN • Tel: 01493 393305
e-mail: enquiries@fishermansreturn.com • www.fishermansreturn.com

Go BLUE RIBAND for quality inexpensive self-catering holidays where your dog is welcome – choice of locations all in the borough of Great Yarmouth. Detached 3 bedroom bungalows, seafront bungalows, detached Sea-Dell chalets and modern sea front caravans. Free colour brochure: BLUE RIBAND HOLIDAYS, PARKLANDS, HEMSBY, GREAT YARMOUTH NR29 4HA (01493 730445).[Pets £10 per stay].
website: www.BlueRibandHolidays.co.uk   www.parklandhemsby.co.uk

NORFOLK COASTAL PROPERTIES. Quality self-catering holiday cottages in North Norfolk. Clean, comfortable and something a little bit different. Properties sleep up to 6. Late availability discounted prices. [Pets £15 per week]. Contact EMMA COOLING (01263 588926/01777 872618: Mob: 07989 567289).
e-mail: info@norfolkcoastalproperties.co.uk   website: www.norfolkcoastalproperties.co.uk

NORFOLK COUNTRY COTTAGES (01603 871872). We have more than 400 self-catering cottages to choose from, many accepting pets. Sweeping beaches, pretty countryside and many rural footpaths make Norfolk the perfect destination for you and your discerning pets.
e-mail: info@norfolk.cottages.co.uk   website: www.norfolkcottages.co.uk

Bacton-on-Sea

Village on coast. 5 miles from North Walsham.

CASTAWAYS HOLIDAY PARK, PASTON ROAD, BACTON-ON-SEA NR12 0JB (01692 650436 and 650418). In peaceful village with direct access to sandy beach. Modern caravans, Pine Lodges and Flats, with all amenities. Licensed club, entertainment, children's play area. Ideal for discovering Norfolk. ETC ★★★. [Pets £20 per week]
website: www.castawaysholidaypark.net

Burnham Market

Village 5 miles West of Wells.

THE HOSTE ARMS, THE GREEN, BURNHAM MARKET PE31 8HD (01328 738777; Fax: 01328 730103). Stylish hotel with relaxing friendly atmosphere and attentive service. Individually designed bedrooms. Cosy bar with log fire, terraced dining area, conservatory. Locally sourced food. Beauty spa. Midweek breaks. AA 2 Rosettes for food. [Pets £10 per stay]
e-mail: reception@hostearms.co.uk   website: www.hostearms.co.uk

Caister-on-Sea

Historic site with Roman ruins and 15th century Caister Castle with 100 foot tower.

Superior brick-built, tiled roof cottages with double glazing throughout. Adjacent golf course. Lovely walks on dunes and coast. 2-4 night breaks early/late season. Terms from £69 to £355. SAND DUNE COTTAGES, TAN LANE, CAISTER-ON-SEA, GREAT YARMOUTH NR30 5DT (01493 720352; mobile: 07785 561363). ETC ★★★ [Pets £15 per week]
e-mail: sanddunecottages@gmail.com
website: www.eastcoastlive.co.uk/sites/sanddunecottages.php

Cromer

Attractive resort built round old fishing village. Norwich 21 miles.

All-electric two and three bedroom Holiday Cottages sleeping 4/6 in beautiful surroundings, also detached bungalow. Sandy beaches, sports facilities, Cinema and Pier (live shows). Parking. Children and pets welcome. ETC ★★-★★★ Brochure: BROADGATES COTTAGES, NORTHREPPS, FOREST PARK CARAVAN SITE LTD, NORTHREPPS ROAD, CROMER, NORFOLK NR27 0JR (01263 513290; Fax: 01263 511992) [Pets £10 weekly].
e-mail: info@broadgates.co.uk   website: www.broadgates.co.uk

KINGS CHALET PARK, CROMER. Comfortable well-equipped chalets on quiet site; ideally placed for woodland and beach walks. 10 minutes' walk to town, shops nearby. Details from MRS I. SCOLTOCK, SHANGRI-LA, LITTLE CAMBRIDGE, DUTON HILL, DUNMOW, ESSEX (01371 870482; 07710 904048).[one pet free]

CLIFTONVILLE HOTEL, SEAFRONT, CROMER NR27 9AS (01263 512543; Fax: 01263 515700). Ideally situated on the Norfolk coast. Beautifully restored Edwardian Hotel. 30 en suite bedrooms all with sea view. Executive suites. Seafood Bistro, à la carte Restaurant. AA ★★★ [pw! pets £4 per night]
e-mail: reservations@cliftonvillehotel.co.uk   website: www.cliftonvillehotel.co.uk

KINGS CHALET PARK, CROMER. Self-catering holiday chalets set in an attractive landscaped park. Sleep 4-6 in two bedrooms and sofa bed. TV, cutlery, crockery, cooker and fridge provided. Dogs welcome. Contact: JACKIE ANDERSON, AMBLESIDE, PRIORY ROAD, BACTON NR12 0HQ (01692 650591; mobile: 07876 385609 OR 07747 517732).
website: www.chaletkings.co.uk

BRAMBLE PARK HOLIDAY CARAVANS, ROSELEA & BRAMBLE PARK, METTON ROAD, CROMER NR27 9JH (01263 511 870), Situated in the peaceful and pretty North Norfolk countryside, 1.5 miles from Cromer. Well equipped, comfortable, two bedroom caravans with their own secure gardens. Wonderful beach and country walks. Reasonable rates. Dogs very welcome at no extra charge.
email: deiraben@gmail.com   website: www.bramblepark.co.uk

Dereham

Situated 16 miles west of Norwich. St Nicholas Church has 16th century bell tower.

SCARNING DALE, SCARNING, EAST DEREHAM NR19 2QN (01362 687269). Self-catering cottages (not commercialised) in grounds of owner's house. On-site indoor heated swimming pool and full-size snooker table. Pets welcome by arrangement. [Pets £25 per week]. Grazing and Stables available.
website: www.scarningdale.co.uk

BARTLES LODGE, CHURCH STREET, ELSING, DEREHAM NR20 3EA (01362 637177). B&B in en suite rooms in converted dairy. Central heating, tea/coffee, freeview TV. Village inn 100 yards for evening meal [pw! Pets £2 per night, £10 per week]
e-mail: bartleslodge@yahoo.co.uk   website: www.bartleslodge.co.uk

Diss

Small market town on the River Waveney 19 miles SW of Norwich.

PAUL AND YOLANDA DAVEY, STRENNETH, AIRFIELD ROAD, FERSFIELD, DISS IP22 2BP (01379 688182; Fax 01379 688260). Family-run, fully renovated period property with two cottages. All rooms en suite, colour TVs, hospitality trays. Ground floor rooms. Non-smoking. Extensive breakfast menu. Licensed. Bed and Breakfast from £25. ETC ★★★★ Silver Award. [🐾]
e-mail: pdavey@strenneth.co.uk   website: www.strenneth.co.uk

WAVENEY VALLEY HOLIDAY PARK, AIRSTATION LANE, RUSHALL, DISS IP21 4QF (01379 741228/ 741690; Fax: 01379 741228). Touring Caravan and Camping Site. Licensed bar, electric hook-ups, restaurant, shop, laundry. Self-catering mobile homes. Outdoor swimming pool, horse riding on site; good fishing nearby. [Pets £4 per night.]
e-mail: waveneyvalleyhp@aol.com   website: www.caravanparksnorfolk.co.uk

East Ruston

Village 17 miles north east of Norwich.

EAST RUSTON COTTAGES. Four dog-friendly, self-catering holiday cottages near sandy beaches and woodland walks. Sleep 2-10 in welcoming, homely comfort. All very well equipped. Contact: MRS SUE ALLEN, GOTHIC COTTAGE, NEW BARN FARM, MILL LANE, EAST RUSTON NR12 9HS (01692 650083; Mobile: 07766 665684). [🐕]
e-mail: sue@eastrustoncottages.co.uk   website: www.eastrustoncottages.co.uk

Fakenham

Historic market town halfway between Norwich and King's Lynn.

ABBOTT FARM BED & BREAKFAST, WALSINGHAM ROAD, BINHAM, FAKENHAM NR21 0AW (01328 830519). Liz and Alan welcome you to their home which has two comfortable en suite bedrooms. Breakfast is served in the conversatory which overlooks the beautiful countryside. Near to the North Norfolk coastline. [pw! 🐕]
e-mail: enquiries@abbottfarm.co.uk   website: www.abbottfarm.co.uk

Foxley

Village 6 miles east of East Dereham.

Self-catering Cottages (2/3/4 bedrooms) on working farm. All fully equipped, with central heating. 20 miles from coast, 15 from Broads. Mature woodland nearby. Fishing in owners' lakes. Indoor heated swimming pool. ETC ★★★/★★★★. MOOR FARM STABLE COTTAGES, FOXLEY NR20 4QP (Tel & Fax: 01362 688523). [Pets £15 per week]
e-mail: mail@moorfarmstablecottages.co.uk   website: www.moorfarmstablecottages.co.uk

Great Yarmouth

Traditional lively seaside resort with a wide range of amusements, including the Marina Centre and Sealife Centre.

CAREFREE HOLIDAYS, CHAPEL BRIERS, YARMOUTH ROAD, HEMSBY, GREAT YARMOUTH NR29 4NJ (01493 732176). A wide selection of superior chalets for live-as-you-please holidays near Great Yarmouth and Norfolk Broads. All amenities on site. Parking. Children and pets welcome. [Pets £25 per week - Free of charge during April/May/June & early July.]
website: www.carefree-holidays.co.uk

Happisburgh

Coastal resort 6 miles East of North Walsham.

THE HILL HOUSE, HAPPISBURGH NR12 0PW (Tel & Fax: 01692 650004). Excellent accommodation in spacious rooms in this attractive free house on the lonely Norfolk coast at Happisburgh. Bar and restaurant.

OLLANDS FARM BARN, SHORT LANE, HAPPISBURGH NR12 0RR (01692 652280).18thC barn with beamed cathedral ceiling, wood-burning stove, quaint paddle stairs, central heating, comfortable king-size bed in galleried bedroom, sofa-bed downstairs, fully fitted kitchen, shower room. Well behaved dogs welcome.[Pets £10 per week].
e-mail: mastuart@talk21.com   website: www.ollandsfarmbarn.co.uk

Holt

Small town 10 miles west of Cromer.

WEYBOURNE FOREST LODGES, SANDY HILL LANE, WEYBOURNE, HOLT NR25 7HW (01263 588440). Comfortable, well equipped lodges set in a tranquil forest glade with wonderful walks on the doorstep. Adjoining National Trust. 1½ miles from beach and cliffs, three miles from Holt and Sheringham. [Pets £20 per week]
e-mail: weybourneforestlodges@hotmail.com   website: www.weybourneforestlodges.co.uk

Hunstanton

Coastal resort on the Wash 14 miles NE of King's Lynn.

WEST WING, HUNSTANTON (01485 534036). First-floor flatlet with direct access from private car park. Spacious, centrally heated and well equipped. Sleeps 2; bedroom with balcony and garden views. Contact Ms. L.D. Poore.
e-mail: st.crispins@btinternet.com

THE HAVEN, HUNSTANTON. Three-bedroom bungalow with large enclosed secluded garden. Sleeps 5. Minutes from town centre, cliff tops, the old lighthouse and beach. Convenient for Sandringham, Holkham, Peddars Way, RSPB Titchwell Reserve etc. Non-smoking. CONTACT: MRS SANDRA HOHOL, BIRDS NORFOLK HOLIDAY HOMES (01485 534267). (Please quote ref: SHF:HU61).
e-mail: shohol@birdsnorfolkholidayhomes.co.uk   www.norfolkholidayhomes-birds.co.uk

King's Lynn

Ancient market town and port on the Wash with many beautiful medieval and Georgian buildings.

MRS J. E. FORD, 129 LEZIATE DROVE, POTT ROW, KING'S LYNN PE32 1DE (01553 630356). Detached bungalow sleeps 4. In quiet village close to Sandringham and beaches. Facilities include colour TV, video, microwave, fridge/freezer, washing machine, off road parking, dog run. [🐾]
website: www.southsideholidayhome.co.uk

MRS G. DAVIDSON, HOLMDENE FARM, BEESTON, KING'S LYNN PE32 2NJ (01328 701284). 17th century farmhouse situated in central Norfolk within easy reach of the coast and Broads. Sporting activities available locally, village pub nearby. One double room, one twin and one single. Pets welcome. Bed and Breakfast from £25.00pp; Evening Meal from £15. Weekly terms available and child reductions. Two self-catering cottages. Sleeping 4/8. Terms on request. ETC ★★★ [🐾]
e-mail: holmdenefarm@farmersweekly.net   website: www.holmdenefarm.co.uk

Lowestoft

Resort town on the North Sea coast, 38 miles north east of Ipswich.

BROADLAND HOLIDAY VILLAGE, OULTON BROAD, LOWESTOFT NR33 9JY (01502 573033). Discover the delights of the forgotten Norfolk Broad with your faithful friend. Stay in cosy brick bungalows, some with outdoor hot tubs, or pine lodges. Indoor heated pool. The perfect holiday for the whole family! [Pets £30 per week].
website: www.broadlandvillage.co.uk

Mundesley-on-Sea

Small resort backed by low cliffs. Good sands and bathing. Norwich 20 miles, Cromer 7.

47 SEAWARD CREST, MUNDESLEY. West-facing brick built chalet on private site with lawns, flowers and parking. Large lounge/dining room, kitchenette, two bedrooms, bathroom. Beach and shops nearby. Pets most welcome. SAE please: MRS DOAR, 4 DENBURY ROAD, RAVENSHEAD, NOTTS. NG15 9FQ (01623 798032). [🐾]

KILN CLIFFS CARAVAN PARK, CROMER ROAD, MUNDESLEY NR11 8DF (01263 720449). Peaceful family-run site situated around an historic brick kiln. Six-berth caravans for hire, standing on ten acres of grassy cliff top. All caravans fully equipped (except linen) and price includes all gas and electricity. [🐾].

Norwich

Historic city with Cathedral, Castle, shops, restaurants and lots to see and do. Many medieval streets and lanes, with attractive timbered houses.

HALL FARM COTTAGES, HALL FARM, HORNING NR12 8NJ. Spacious Holiday Cottages, all with downstairs twin/double bedroom and en suite shower room with toilet facilities. Spacious lounge, fully fitted kitchen. One/two further bedrooms on first floor (twin or double). Contact Hannah or Alison (01692 630385 Mob: 07825 833920). [pw! Pets £25 per week]
e-mail: cottages@hallfarm.com   website: www.hallfarm.com

SOUTH NORFOLK GUEST HOUSE – OAKBROOK HOUSE, FRITH WAY, GREAT MOULTON, NORWICH NR15 2HE (01379 677359). This former village school, set in the heart of Norfolk's unspoilt countryside, is an ideal location from which to explore East Anglia. As a professionally run guest house, a comfortable stay is guaranteed, complemented by a delicious breakfast with locally sourced products. [Pets £5 per night]
e-mail: oakbrookhouse@btinternet.com   website: www.SouthNorfolkGuestHouse.co.uk

Old Hunstanton

Peaceful area to north of Hunstanton.

ST CRISPINS, OLD HUNSTANTON (01485 534036). Near sandy beach, golf course; shop, pubs. A few miles Royal Sandringham, Norfolk Lavender, RSPB reserves. Bargain breaks early/late from £130. Pets welcome. [One dog £15 per week]
e-mail: st.crispins@btinternet.com

Sheringham

Small, traditional resort with sandy beaches, which has grown around a flint-built fishing village.

SHERINGHAM COTTAGES. Six traditional self-catering properties within walking distance of the beach. Comfortable and fully equipped. Sleep 4/8. Dogs welcome by arrangement. ETC ★★★★. For details contact: TREVOR CLAYDON, CAMELOT HOUSE, HOLT ROAD, GRESHAM, NORWICH NR11 8AD (01263 577560).
e-mail: trevor.claydon@which.net   website: www.sheringhamcottages.com

Stalham

Village south east of North Walsham, ideal for exploring Norfolk Broads.

20 & 69 BROADSIDE CHALET PARK.The chalets have two bedrooms, shower, wc, well equipped kitchen and lounge area. On-site bar/restaurant. Ideal location for Norfolk and the Broads. Dogs are very welcome. Open March to October, Christmas and New Year and most weekends during the winter. KAY & TONY LOVEDAY, MILL VIEW, WATER LANE, MUNDESLEY NR11 8BS (07785 517642. [Pets £3 per night, £8 per week]
e-mail northnorfolkchalets@yahoo.com   website: www.northnorfolkholidaychalets.co.uk

Stiffkey

Village on the north coast of Norfolk. 25 miles north west of the city of Norwich.

STIFFKEY RED LION, 44 WELLS ROAD, STIFFKEY NR23 1AJ (01328 830552) Five ground floor en suite bedrooms, five on first floor; all with their own external door. Pets warmly welcomed. [Pets £5 per week]
e-mail: redlion@stiffkey.com   website: www.stiffkey.com

Thompson

Picturesque village with many thatched properties; mentioned in Domesday Book.

THE CHEQUERS INN, GRISTON ROAD, THOMPSON, THETFORD IP24 IPX (01953 483360). One of Norfolk's hidden gems tucked away in the picturesque village of Thompson. 3 purpose built en suite rooms with Wi-Fi and own private entrance. Patio for guests' use. Restaurant and bar.
website: www.thompsonchequers.co.uk

Thornham

Village 4 miles east of Hunstanton. Site of Roman signal station.

THE OLD COACH HOUSE, THORNHAM PE36 6LY (01485 512229; Fax: 01485 512091). Lovely, traditional Norfolk pub with superb family friendly B&B accommodation. Homemade food, friendly service, hearty breakfasts. Dogs and muddy boots welcome!
e-mail: info@oldcoachhousethornham.com   website: www.oldcoachhousethornham.com

THE LIFEBOAT INN, SHIP LANE, THORNHAM PE36 6LT (01485 512236; Fax: 01485 512323). A welcome sight for the weary traveller for centuries. Dogs welcome. Restaurant (one AA rosette). Bird watching and walking along miles of open beaches. Please ring for brochure and tariff. [Pets £10 per per dog per stay.]
e-mail: reception@lifeboatinn.co.uk   website: www.lifeboatinnthornham.com

Thorpe Market

Village 4 miles south of Cromer.

POPPYLAND TOURING PARK & HOLIDAY COTTAGE, THE GREEN, THORPE MARKET NR11 8AJ (01263 833219). Ideal for guests who want to relax or explore local area. Puddleduck Cottage (sleeps 2) has private enclosed garden. Touring park (adults only) in landscaped gardens surrounded by trees. Excellent food nearby. [Pets free on Touring Park; in Cottage £14 per week for 1st pet, £7 per week for 2nd pet.]
e-mail: enquiries@poppyland.com   website: www.poppyland.com

Thurne

Idyllic Broadland village. Great Yarmouth 10 miles.

HEDERA HOUSE AND PLANTATION BUNGALOWS, THURNE NR29 3BU (01692 670242 or 01493 844568). Adjacent river, seven bedroomed farmhouse, 10 competitively priced bungalows in peaceful gardens. Outdoor heated pool. Enjoy boating, fishing, walking, touring, nearby golf, sandy beaches and popular resorts. [Pets £20 per week]
website: www.hederahouse.co.uk

Weybourne

Located in an Area of Outstanding Natural Beauty and part of the Heritage Coastline. Sheringham and Holt 4 miles.

BOLDING WAY HOLIDAYS, THE BARN, BOLDING WAY, WEYBOURNE, HOLT NR25 7SW (01263 588666). The Stables (SC) sleeps 8, Biddles Cottage (SC) sleeps 2; Tack Room (room only) sleeps 2. In an Area of Outstanding Natural Beauty and on the Heritage Coast. Well behaved pets welcome. Fenced gardens. Shared use of hot tub and sauna. ETC ★★★★ Gold Award. [🐕]
e-mail: holidays@boldingway.co.uk   website: www.boldingway.co.uk

Winterton-on-Sea

Good sands and bathing. Great Yarmouth 8 miles.

WINTERTON HOLIDAYS, WINTERTON-ON-SEA. Privately owned one and two-bedroom chalets, furnished and equipped to a high standard, on picturesque park few minutes' walk from sea. Dogs allowed on beach all year. Ideal for quiet, relaxing break and for exploring Broads, coast, Norwich. Village has pub, restaurant and shops. MRS JUNE HUDSON, 15 LARK WAY, BRADWELL, GREAT YARMOUTH NR31 8SB (01493 444700). [Pets £20 per week or part week]
website: www.wintertonholidays.com

WINTERTON VALLEY HOLIDAYS. A selection of modern superior fully appointed holiday chalets in a choice of locations near Great Yarmouth. Enjoy panoramic views from WINTERTON, a quiet and picturesque 35-acre estate, while CALIFORNIA has all the usual amenities, with free entry to the pool and clubhouse. Pets are very welcome at both sites. For colour brochure: 15 KINGSTON AVENUE, CAISTER-ON-SEA NR30 5ET (01493 377175).
website: www.wintertonvalleyholidays.co.uk

FISHERMANS RETURN, THE LANE, WINTERTON-ON-SEA NR29 4BN (01493 393305). 300-year-old brick and flint pub, just a few minutes' stroll from sandy beaches and beautiful walks. Excellent food, simple bar snacks and good choice of real ales and fine wines. B&B available in 3 tastefully furnished en suite double bedrooms.
e-mail: enquiries@fishermansreturn.com   website: www.fishermansreturn.com

---

🐕   Pets are welcome free of charge.

£   A charge is made for pets: nightly or weekly.

pw! Special provision for pets; exercise facility, feeding or accommodation arrangement.

⌂   Separate pets' accommodation.

Aldeburgh

Coastal town 6 miles south-east of Saxmundham. Annual music festival at Snape Maltings.

WENTWORTH HOTEL, ALDEBURGH IP15 5BD (01728 452312). Overlooking the sea, with immediate access to the beach and walks. Two comfortable lounges with log fires and antique furniture. Refurbished bedrooms with all facilities and many with sea views. Restaurant specialises in fresh produce and sea food. AA ★★★ Two Rosettes. [Pets £2 per day]
e-mail: stay@wentworth-aldeburgh.co.uk   website: www.wentworth-aldeburgh.com

Bungay

Attractive town in the Waveney Valley, with a wealth of historic sites. Town centre has a Roman well, a Saxon church, and the remains of a Norman castle and Benedictine priory. 14 miles south east of Norwich.

EARSHAM PARK FARM, OLD RAILWAY ROAD, EARSHAM, BUNGAY NR35 2AQ (01986 892180). Superb Victorian property overlooking open countryside. Bedrooms attractively furnished; excellent breakfasts. All rooms en suite. ETC ★★★★ Gold Award. [Pets £5 per night]
website: www.earsham-parkfarm.co.uk

Bury St Edmunds

This prosperous market town on the River Lark lies 28 miles east of Cambridge.

RAVENWOOD HALL COUNTRY HOUSE HOTEL AND RESTAURANT, ROUGHAM, BURY ST EDMUNDS IP30 9JA (01359 270345; Fax: 01359 270788). 16th century beamed Tudor Hall set in seven acres of perfect dog walks. Individually furnished en suite bedrooms; 5 mews rooms with direct access to lawns; renowned restaurant; relaxing inglenook fires. AA ★★★, AA 2 Rosettes. [🐾 pw!]
e-mail: enquiries@ravenwoodhall.co.uk   website: www.ravenwoodhall.co.uk

REDE HALL FARM PARK, REDE, BURY ST EDMUNDS IP29 4UG (01284 850695; Fax: 01284 850345). Two well equipped cottages, ideal for touring East Anglia and the coast. Totally non-smoking. Hot Tub Spa available for exclusive use (inclusive). Well behaved dogs welcome. ETC ★★★★ [🐾 ⌂]
e-mail: chris@redehallfarmpark.co.uk   website: www.redehallfarmpark.co.uk

CULFORD FARM COTTAGES, BURY ST EDMUNDS IP28 6DS (Tel/Fax: 01284 728334). Three cottages set in 250 acres of peaceful farmland. Comfortable converted accommodation with all amenities. Sleep 4-6. Each with own hot tub and shared heated outdoor pool in summer. ETC ★★★★/★★★★★. [Pets £25 per week]
e-mail: enquiries@homefarmculford.co.uk   website: www.culfordfarmcottages.co.uk

Kessingland

Little seaside place with expansive beach, safe bathing, wildlife park, lake fishing. To the south is Benacre Broad, a beauty spot. Norwich 26 miles, Adleburgh 23, Lowestoft 5.

Quality seaside bungalows in lawned surrounds overlooking the sea. Open all year, fully eqipped. Sleep 1/6. Direct access to award-winning beach. Parking Pets very welcome. APPLY– KNIGHTS HOLIDAY HOMES, 195 LONG ROAD, LOWESTOFT, SUFFOLK NR33 9DE (FREEPHONE 0800 269067). [🐾]
e-mail: info@knightsholidays.co.uk   website: www.knightsholidays.co.uk

Laxfield

Village 6 miles North of Framlingham.

LODGE COTTAGE, LAXFIELD. Pretty 16C thatched cottage retaining some fine period features. Sleeps 4. Pets welcome. Fenced garden. One mile from village. 30 minutes to Southwold and coast. Rural, quiet and relaxing. ETC ★★★★. For brochure phone: MRS JANE BREWER, LODGE COTTAGE, LAXFIELD ROAD, CRATFIELD, HALESWORTH IP19 0QG (01986 798830 or 07788 853884). [🐾].
e-mail: janebrewer@live.co.uk   website: www.lodgeholidaycottages.co.uk

A useful index of towns/counties appears at the back of this book

Long Melford

Village in the beautiful countryside of Suffolk, in the River Stour valley, just north of Sudbury, beside the A314 road to Bury St Edmunds.

THE BLACK LION HOTEL & RESTAURANT, THE GREEN, LONG MELFORD CO10 9DN (01787 312356). The Georgian Black Lion Hotel overlooks the famous green, and the cosy bar and restaurant offer a range of innovative dishes. 10 en suite bedrooms refurbished to luxury status. Idyllic dog walks. [🐕]
e-mail: enquiries@blacklionhotel.net   website: www.blacklionhotel.net

Middleton

Village 3 miles from the coast.

MILL BARN COTTAGES, MILL HOUSE, MIDDLETON (01728 648377). Two fully equipped self-catering cottages with own private gardens. Sleeps 2. Sitting room/dining area, open plan kitchen, double bedroom with king-size bed, en suite bathroom. Pets welcome.
e-mail: rita.millhouse@btinternet.com

Orford

Village on River Ore, 9 miles east of Woodbridge.

THE CROWN AND CASTLE, ORFORD, WOODBRIDGE IP12 2LJ (01394 450205). Comfortable and very dog-friendly hotel situated close to 12th century castle in historic and unspoilt village of Orford. Honest good food served in award-winning Trinity Restaurant. [Pets £5.50 per night]
e-mail: info@crownandcastle.co.uk   website: www.crownandcastle.co.uk

Saxmundham

Small town 18 miles NE of Ipswich.

SWEFFLING HALL FARM, SWEFFLING, SAXMUNDHAM IP17 2BT (Tel & Fax: 01728 663644). In a quiet location. Two double and one family room with en suite/private bathrooms. Ideal for walking/cycling and Heritage Coast. Open all year. Always a warm welcome. [pw! 🐕 ⌂]
e-mail: stephen.mann@hotmail.co.uk   website: www.swefflinghallfarm.co.uk

Tattingstone

Small village 6 miles south of Ipswich.

BADGERS' BEND. Detached 18th century cottage ideally situated for touring Essex/Suffolk, visiting the seaside, or shopping in Ipswich and Woodbridge. Three bedrooms (one double, two twin). Children and dogs welcome. Please call Margaret and Howard for more information (01473 311309). [🐕]
e-mail: howardnuttallm@supanet.com   website:www.badgersbend.com

---

Classified Symbols

🐕   Pets are welcome free of charge.

£   A charge is made for pets: nightly or weekly.

pw!   Special provision for pets; exercise facility, feeding or accommodation arrangement.

⌂   Separate pets' accommodation.

Ashbourne

Bentley Brook Inn is a busy country inn in the beautiful Peak Park, providing quality accommodation, an award-winning restaurant and an all-day bar offering informal meals and snacks. The Inn has a large child and pet-friendly garden. Favourite centre for walking and for visiting Dovedale, the Manifold Valley, Chatsworth and Alton Towers. Eleven refurbished en suite rooms of great character. Free wireless broadband in the bar. Pets welcome by prior arrangement.

Bentley Brook Inn

Fenny Bentley, Ashbourne, Derbyshire DE6 1LF
Tel: 01335 350278 • Fax: 01335 350422
e-mail: all@bentleybrookinn.co.uk • www.bentleybrookinn.co.uk

Paddock House Farm Holiday Cottages
★★★★ *Luxury Holiday Cottage Accommodation*

Surrounded by 5 acres of delightful grounds and reached along its own long drive, Paddock House nestles peacefully in a secluded spot between the famous villages of Alstonefield and Hartington. Arranged around a courtyard, these charming cottages enjoy uninterrupted views. The area is a walker's paradise, and there are excellent cycle trails along Dovedale, Tissington and the Manifold Valley. Ideal base for families, many attractions closeby. Nearby Ashbourne offers shops, restaurants and other town amenities. Alton Towers 20 minutes.

Peak District National Park, Alstonefield, Ashbourne, Derbyshire DE6 2FT
Tel: 01335 310282 • Mobile: 07977 569618
e-mail: info@paddockhousefarm.co.uk • www.paddockhousefarm.co.uk

Church Farm Country Cottages • Edlaston, Ashbourne DE6 2DQ

Two characterful fully equipped two-bedroom cottages. Shared fully enclosed garden. Open fire/log burner for cosy nights in. Pets come for FREE!

01335 348776 • adeblake@aol.com • www.churchfarmcountrycottages.com

Holly Meadow Farm *Bed & Breakfast*

Award winning B&B in one of the most picturesque parts of Derbyshire. Spacious en suite rooms. Hearty farmhouse breakfasts. Well behaved dogs welcome.

 Mrs Lawton, Holly Meadow Farm, Bradley, Ashbourne, Derbyshire DE6 1PN
Tel: 01335 370261 • E-mail: info@hollymeadowfarm.co.uk
www.hollymeadowfarm.co.uk

Buxton, Dronfield, Hope Valley, Matlock

On alpaca breeding farm in the south west corner of the Peak District National Park.

GROUND FLOOR: Open-plan living area with fully equipped kitchen and log burning stove. Sky TV, BluRay DVD and music system. En suite bedroom with super-king bed.

UPSTAIRS: 3 twin/double bedrooms and bathroom. Oil-fired central heating • Free wireless broadband internet • Secure garden with barbeque area. Well behaved pets welcome and there's plenty of off-the-lead walking on the farm.

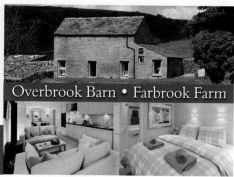

Overbrook Barn • Farbrook Farm

Gemma Toia • Farbrook Farm, Quarnford, Buxton SK17 0ST • Tel: 01298 213299
e-mail: gemma@farbrookcottages.com
www.farbrookcottages.com/?sender=pw

Mill Farm

Holiday Cottages and campsite

Mill Farm Holiday Cottages, Crowhole, Barlow, Dronfield, Derbyshire S18 7TJ
Tel 0114 289 0543
Fax: 0114 289 1473
e-mail:
cottages@barlowlakes.co.uk
www.millfarmcottages.com

All five cottages at Mill Farm are fully equipped with all the usual necessities such as bed linen, colour televisions, cutlery etc. Cots, folding beds and high chairs are available on request. Four-poster bed in Wood View. A launderette is on site; snack bar on site. Dogs are always welcome. A short walk from trout/coarse fishing lakes. Fishing included.

This handsome stone building which dates from the 19th century is popular with locals and visitors alike. It has won awards for its ale and carries a good selection of refreshments. This is just the place for a relaxing drink or meal after a day walking on the high moors. Home-cooked food is served in the bar, and there are two plasma screen TVs. Accommodation is available in six en suite rooms and three charming cottages
Owner Stephanie Bushell offers all guests a warm welcome.

THE **LITTLE JOHN** HOTEL
Station Road, Hathersage
Hope Valley
Derbyshire S32 1DD
Tel: 01433 650225

e-mail: littlejohnhotel@btconnect.com
www.littlejohnhotel.co.uk
www.hotelsinhathersage.co.uk

AA **ALISON HOUSE HOTEL** • Cromford, Derbyshire
Georgian-style house set in the Derwent Valley World Heritage site. Beautiful gardens in a peaceful setting. 16 en suite rooms. Bar, lounge and restaurant.
Alison House, Intake Lane, Cromford, Matlock, Derbyshire DE4 3RH
Tel: 01629 822211 • Fax: 01629 822316 • e-mail: info@alison-house-hotel.co.uk
• www.alison-house-hotel.co.uk • *Pets £5 per night.*

FREE or **REDUCED RATE** entry to Holiday Visits and Attractions –
see our **READERS' OFFER VOUCHERS** on pages 409-414

Wheeldon Trees Farm
HOLIDAY COTTAGES

Nine superbly equipped, award-winning and environmentally friendly cottages in the dramatic scenery of the Peak District National Park, near Buxton and Bakewell – a wonderful year-round destination where dogs and children are really welcome.

Earl Sterndale, Buxton SK17 0AA
Tel: 01298 83219

stay@wheeldontreesfarm.co.uk • www.wheeldontreesfarm.co.uk

BIGGIN HALL

Tranquilly set 1000ft up in the White Peak District National Park, 17th century Grade II* Listed Biggin Hall – a country house hotel of immense character and charm where guests experience the full benefits of the legendary Biggin Air – has been sympathetically restored, keeping its character while giving house room to contemporary comforts. Rooms are centrally heated with bathrooms en suite, colour television, tea-making facilities, silent fridge and telephone. Those in the main house have stone arched mullioned windows, others are in converted 18th century outbuildings. Centrally situated for stately homes and for exploring the natural beauty of the area. Return at the end of the day to enjoy your freshly cooked dinner alongside log fires and personally selected wines.

Well behaved pets are welcome by prior arrangement

Biggin-by-Hartington, Buxton,
Derbyshire SK17 0DH
Tel: 01298 84451
www.bigginhall.co.uk

The Wild Cherry Bed & Breakfast, Wirksworth, Peak District
A family-run B&B in a quiet location with panoramic views over the Ecclesbourne Valley. Two minute walk to town centre.
Two double bedrooms with tea/coffee facilities. Wi-Fi. Parking.
Excellent walks on the doorstep or ideal for touring the Peak District.
thewildcherry78@hotmail.co.uk • www.peakdistrictinformation.com • **01629 824712**

Visit www.holidayguides.com
for pet-friendly accommodation in Britain

PEAK COTTAGES (0844 686 1098). Quality self-catering farmhouses and cottages in the beautiful Peak District National Park and Derbyshire Dales. Many properties welcome pets, so discover the beauty of this delightful area with your "best friend". [Pets £12 per week.]
website: www.peakcottages.com

Ashbourne

Market town on River Henmore, close to its junction with River Dove. Several interesting old buildings. Birmingham 42 miles, Nottingham 29, Derby 13.

MR & MRS LENNARD, WINDLEHILL FARM, SUTTON ON THE HILL, ASHBOURNE DE6 5JH (Tel & Fax: 01283 732377). Converted beamed barns on small organic farm - the Chop House sleeps 6 and has a fenced garden, the Hayloft sleeps 2 and is a first floor apartment. Well behaved pets welcome. ETC ★★★★ [pw! Pets £10 per week minimum]
e-mail: windlehill@btinternet.com   website: www.windlehill.btinternet.co.uk

BENTLEY BROOK INN, FENNY BENTLEY, ASHBOURNE DE6 1LF(01335 350278; Fax: 01335 350422) Busy country inn in the beautiful Peak Park. Quality accommodation, award-winning restaurant and all day bar. Pet-friendly garden. Eleven refurbished en suite rooms of great character. Pets welcome by prior arrangement. Enjoy England/AA ★★★ Inn. [Pets £10 per night]
e-mail: all@bentleybrookinn.co.uk   website: www.bentleybrookinn.co.uk

PADDOCK HOUSE FARM HOLIDAY COTTAGES, PEAK DISTRICT NATIONAL PARK, ALSTONEFIELD, ASHBOURNE DE6 2FT (01335 310282; Mobile: 07977 569618). Surrounded by 5 acres of delightful grounds and arranged around a courtyard, these charming cottages enjoy uninterrupted views. Ideal base for families, many attractions close by; Alton Towers 20 minutes. ETC ★★★★ [pw! Pets £20 per break].
e-mail: info@paddockhousefarm.co.uk   website: www.paddockhousefarm.co.uk

CHURCH FARM COUNTRY COTTAGES, EDLASTON, ASHBOURNE, DE6 2DQ (01335 348776). Two modern fully equipped cottages. Comfortable living space, each with two bedrooms. Shared enclosed garden area. Up to 2 pets per cottage [🐾].
e-mail: adeblake@aol.com   website: www.churchfarmcountrycottages.com

HOLLY MEADOW FARM, BRADLEY, ASHBOURNE DE6 1PN (01335 370261). Award winning B&B in one of the most picturesque parts of Derbyshire. Spacious en suite rooms. Hearty farmhouse breakfasts. Well behaved dogs welcome. EnjoyEngland ★★★★ Silver [🐾].
e-mail: info@hollymeadowfarm.co.uk   website: www.hollymeadowfarm.co.uk

MRS M.M. STELFOX, DOG AND PARTRIDGE COUNTRY INN, SWINSCOE, ASHBOURNE DE6 2HS (01335 343183). 17thC Inn offering ideal holiday accommodation. Many leisure activities available. All bedrooms with washbasins, colour TV, telephone and private facilities. ETC/AA ★★ [🐾 pw!]
e-mail: info@dogandpartridge.co.uk   website: www.dogandpartridge.co.uk

MRS M.A. RICHARDSON, THROWLEY HALL FARM, ILAM, ASHBOURNE DE6 2BB (01538 308202/ 308243). Self-catering accommodation in farmhouse for up to 12 and cottages for five and seven people. Also Bed and Breakfast in farmhouse. Central heating, en suite rooms, TV, tea/coffee facilities in rooms. No smoking. Children and pets welcome. Near Alton Towers and stately homes. ETC ★★★★. [Pets £5 per week.]
e-mail: throwleyhall@btinternet.com   website: www.throwleyhallfarm.co.uk

Buxton

Well-known spa and centre for the Peak District. Beautiful scenery and good sporting amenities. Leeds 50 miles, Matlock 20, Macclesfield 12.

ALISON PARK HOTEL, 3 TEMPLE ROAD, BUXTON SK17 9BA (01298 22473; Fax: 01298 72709). Situated close to the Pavilion Gardens and Opera House. 17 bedrooms, all en suite or private bathroom. Lunches, bar meals and dinner available daily. Wheelchair ramp access; ground floor bedrooms. Licensed. ETC ★★ [🐾]
e-mail: reservations@alison-park-hotel.co.uk   website: www.alison-park-hotel.co.uk

PRIORY LEA HOLIDAY FLATS. Close to Poole's Cavern Country Park. Fully equipped. Full central heating. Sleep 2/6. Cleanliness assured. Terms from £125-£295. Open all year. Short Breaks available. ETC ★★/★★★. MRS GILL TAYLOR, 50 WHITE KNOWLE ROAD, BUXTON SK17 9NH (01298 23737). [pw! Pets £2 per night.]
e-mail: priorylea@hotmail.co.uk   website: www.priorylea.co.uk

GEMMA TOIA, OVERBROOK BARN, FARBROOK FARM, QUARNFORD, BUXTON SK17 0ST (01298 213299). Open-plan ground floor living space, fully equipped kitchen, log burning stove. Free Wi-Fi. Ground floor en suite bedroom and three upstairs twin/double bedrooms and bathroom. Secure garden. Well behaved pets welcome. [🐕]
e-mail: gemma@farbrookcottages.com   website: www.farbrookcottages.com/?sender=pw

Dronfield

Situated between Sheffield and Chesterfield on the River Drone in north east Derbyshire.

MILL FARM HOLIDAY COTTAGES, CROWHOLE, BARLOW, DRONFIELD S18 7TJ (0114 2890543: Fax: 0114 2891473) Five fully equipped cottages. Cots, folding beds and high chairs are available on request. Four-poster bed in Wood View. Launderette on site. Fishing included. Dogs always welcome. [Pets £10 per week]
e-mail: cottages@barlowlakes.co.uk   website: www.millfarmcottages.com

Hope Valley

Large valley in Peak District, 4 miles from Hathersage.

THE LITTLE JOHN HOTEL, STATION ROAD, HATHERSAGE, HOPE VALLEY S32 1DD (01433 650225). Ideal for a relaxing drink or meal after walking the high moors. Popular local pub with award-winning ales and good selection of refreshments. Home cooked food. Six en suite rooms and three charming cottages [🐕].
e-mail: littlejohnhotel@btconnect.com   website: www.littlejohnhotel.co.uk

Matlock

County town of Derbyshire, situated on a bend of the River Derwent.

ALISON HOUSE, INTAKE LANE, CROMFORD, MATLOCK DE4 3RH (01629 822211; Fax: 01629 822316). Georgian-style house set in the Derwent Valley World Heritage site. Beautiful gardens in a peaceful setting. 16 en suite rooms. Bar, lounge and restaurant. AA ★★★★ [pw! Pets £5 per night].
e-mail: info@alison-house-hotel.co.uk   website: www.alison-house-hotel.co.uk

Peak District National Park

A green and unspoilt area at the southern end of the Pennines, covering 555 square miles.

WHEELDON TREES FARM, EARL STERNDALE, BUXTON SK17 0AA (01298 83219). Nine superbly equipped, award-winning and environmentally friendly cottages in the dramatic scenery of the Peak District National Park, near Buxton and Bakewell – a wonderful year-round destination where dogs and children are really welcome. ETC ★★★★ [pw! 🐕]
e-mail: stay@wheeldontreesfarm.co.uk   website: www.wheeldontreesfarm.co.uk

BIGGIN HALL, PEAK PARK (01298 84451). Close Dove Dale. 17th century hall sympathetically restored. Bathrooms en suite, log fires, C/H comfort, warmth and quiet. Fresh home cooking. Beautiful uncrowded footpaths and cycle trails. ETC ★★[🐕]
website: www.bigginhall.co.uk

Wirksworth

An ancient Saxon town, once the principal lead mining centre of the Peak District, 4 miles south of Matlock.

THE WILD CHERRY BED & BREAKFAST, 78 GREENHILL, WIRKSWORTH DE4 4EN (01629 824712). A family run bed and breakfast in a quiet location with panoramic views over the Ecclesbourne Valley. Two double bedrooms with tea/coffee facilities. Wi-Fi. Parking. Pets welcome.
e-mail: thewildcherry78@hotmail.co.uk   website: www.peakdistrictinformation.com

---

🐕   Pets are welcome free of charge.

£   A charge is made for pets: nightly or weekly.

pw!   Special provision for pets; exercise facility, feeding or accommodation arrangement.

⌂   Separate pets' accommodation.

Classified Symbols

Sysonby Knoll

Melton Mowbray, Leicestershire LE13 0HP

Family-run hotel in rural setting on edge of market town. Grounds of five acres with river frontage. Superb food, individually styled rooms, and a genuine welcome for pets which is rarely found in a hotel of this standard. Prices from £42.50pppn.

Please see website for special offers and further details.

Tel: 01664 563563 • www.sysonby.com

Luxury Hotel & Restaurant in Melton Mowbray

Market Harborough

Town on River Welland 14 miles south-east of Leicester.

BROOK MEADOW HOLIDAYS. Three self-catering chalets, Carp fishing, camping and caravan site with electric hookups. Phone for brochure. ETC ★★★. VANESSA DUNN, WELFORD ROAD, SIBBERTOFT, MARKET HARBOROUGH LE16 9UJ (01858 880886). [pw! £12 per booking] e-mail: brookmeadow@farmline.com   website: www.brookmeadow.co.uk

Melton Mowbray

Old market town, centre of hunting country. Large cattle market. Church and Ann of Cleves' House are of interest. Kettering 29 miles, Market Harborough 22, Nottingham 18, Leicester 15.

SYSONBY KNOLL HOTEL, ASFORDBY ROAD, MELTON MOWBRAY LE13 0HP (01664 563563; Fax: 01664 410364). Family-run hotel on edge of market town. Grounds of five acres with river frontage. Superb food, individually styled rooms, and a genuine welcome for pets. Please see website for special offers and further details. ETC/AA ★★★ [🐕] website: www.sysonby.com

Rutland Water

Old market town, centre of hunting country. Large cattle market. Church and Ann of Cleves' House are of interest. Kettering 29 miles, Market Harborough 22, Nottingham 18, Leicester 15.

BARNSDALE LODGE, THE AVENUE, NEAR OAKHAM LE15 8AH (01572 724678). Delightful, friendly and welcoming country house hotel. 44 individually styled en suite rooms, freeview, broadband, coffee/tea making. Private gardens. Pets welcome. ETC/AA ★★★ e-mail: enquiries@barnsdalelodge.co.uk   website: www.barnsdalelodge.co.uk

Barnoldby-le-Beck, Barton-Upon-Humber, Boston, Gainsborough

Grantham, Horncastle, Langton-by-Wragby, Louth

Louth, Mablethorpe, North Somercotes, Skegness

Barnoldby-le-Beck

Village 4 miles SW of Grimsby.

GRANGE FARM COTTAGES & RIDING SCHOOL, WALTHAM ROAD, BARNOLDBY-LE-BECK DN37 0AR (01472 822216; Fax: 01472 233550; mobile: 07947 627663). Three well appointed cottages and riding school situated in the heart of the Lincolnshire Wolds. Sleep 4/6. ETC ★★★★. Equestrian Centre offers tuition, all-weather riding, stabling. [Pets £20 per week]
website: www.grangefarmcottages.com

Barton-Upon-Humber

Town on south bank of River Humber, 6 miles south west of Hull.

MRS PAM ATKIN, WEST WOLD FARMHOUSE, DEEPDALE, BARTON-UPON-HUMBER DN18 6ED (01652 633293). Friendly farmhouse. Rooms have en suite or private bathroom. We offer the 'Great British' breakfast, with fresh, locally sourced produce where possible; vegetarian and other diets as requested. Dogs and horses welcome by arrangement. ETC ★★★★
e-mail: pam@westwoldfarmhouse.co.uk   www.westwoldfarmhouse.co.uk

Boston

South east coast of Lincolnshire, 32 miles from Lincoln.

ELMS FARM COTTAGES, BOSTON PE20 3QP (01205 290840; mobile: 07887 652021). Fully equipped and furnished to a high standard with level access throughout. Walk to the village pub for good food. 2 miles from Boston, ideally located for Fens, Wolds and coast. ETC 4/5 Stars Gold Award. [Pets £20 per week]
e-mail carol@elmsfarmcottages.co.uk   website: www.elmsfarmcottages.co.uk

Gainsborough

Market town and River Port 15 miles NW of Lincoln.

THE BLACK SWAN GUEST HOUSE, 21 HIGH STREET, MARTON, GAINSBOROUGH DN21 5AH (01427 718878). Former 18th Century Coaching Inn, providing very comfortable accommodation. All rooms en suite, with digital TV and tea/coffee making facilities. Lincoln 12 miles away, many other attractions nearby. Non-smoking. AA ★★★★ [🐶]
e-mail: info@blackswanguesthouse.co.uk   website:www.blackswanguesthouse.co.uk

Grantham

Market town 24 miles south of Lincoln.

WOODLAND WATERS, WILLOUGHBY ROAD, ANCASTER, GRANTHAM NG32 3RT (Tel & Fax: 01400 230888). Set in 72 acres of beautiful woodland walks. Luxury holiday lodges, overlooking the lakes and excellently equipped. Dogs welcome in some lodges. Bar/restaurant on site. Fishing. Golf nearby. Short Breaks available. Open all year. [Pets £2 per night camping, £20 per week lodges.]
e-mail: info@woodlandwaters.co.uk   website: www.woodlandwaters.co.uk

Horncastle

Market town on banks of Rivers Waring and Bain noted for its many antique shops.

LITTLE LONDON COTTAGES, TETFORD, HORNCASTLE. Very well-equipped property standing in own garden, on our small estate. Lovely walks. Contact: MRS S.D. SUTCLIFFE, THE GARTH, LITTLE LONDON, TETFORD, HORNCASTLE LN9 6QL (01507 533697; mobile: 07767 321213). [🐶]
e-mail: debbiesutcliffe621@btinternet.com   website: www.littlelondoncottages.co.uk

POACHERS HIDEAWAY HOLIDAY COTTAGES, FLINTWOOD FARM, BELCHFORD, HORNCASTLE LN9 5QN (01507 533555; Susan: 0776 077 6594; Andrew: 0783 674 6865). Sleep 2-30. Gold award-winning self catering cottages set in 150 acres of wildflower meadows, fishing lakes and woodland. Quiet and relaxing with superb views. Linen and towels provided. Kennels available. ETC 4-5 Stars [Pets £20 per week]
website: www.poachershideaway.com

Langton-by-Wragby

Village located south-east of Wragby.

MISS JESSIE SKELLERN, LEA HOLME, LANGTON-BY-WRAGBY, LINCOLN LN8 5PZ (01673 858339). Ground floor accommodation in chalet-type house. Central for Wolds, coast, fens, historic Lincoln. Market towns, Louth, Horncastle, Boston, Spilsby, Alford, Woodhall Spa. Two double bedrooms. Washbasin, TV; bathroom, toilet adjoining; lounge with colour TV, separate dining room. Drinks provided. Children welcome reduced rates. Car almost essential, parking. Numerous eating places nearby. B&B from £30pp (double/single let). Open all year. Pets welcome free. Tourist Board Listed [🐶]

www.holidayguides.com

Louth

Quaint market town with old fashioned architecture. Knwn as the 'Capital of the Lincolnshire Wolds'. 26 miles from Lincoln.

GRASSWELLS FARM HOLIDAY COTTAGES, SOUTH COCKERINGTON, LOUTH. Two single barn conversions - spacious, comfortable and well equipped. Set in three acres of grounds with private fishing lake. Pets welcome. Sleep 2-5. ETC ★★★★ Contact: MS J. FOSTER, GRASSWELLS HOLIDAY COTTAGES (SADDLEBACK LEISURE LTD), SADDLEBACK ROAD, HOWDALES, SOUTH COCKERINGTON, LOUTH LN11 7DJ (01507 338508). [🐾]
website: www.grasswells.co.uk

WESTFIELD FARM SELF-CATERING HOLIDAY COTTAGES, STEWTON, LOUTH LN11 8SD(01507 354892 or 07885 280787). One, two and three bedroom converted cottages, sleeping 2, 4 or 6 people. Set in open countryside, just 2 miles from Louth. Open all year, short breaks available. ETC ★★★/★★★★.
website: www.westfieldfarmcottages.co.uk

BRACKENBOROUGH HALL COACH HOUSE HOLIDAYS. Winner: Best Self-Catering Holiday in England 2009/10, Silver Award. Three self-catering apartments in a listed 18thC Coach House in the beautiful county of Lincolnshire. Accommodates 1-24. Short Breaks available. PAUL & FLORA BENNETT, BRACKENBOROUGH HALL, LOUTH LN11 0NS (01507 603193; 07974 687779). ★★★★/
★★★★★ [Pets £10 per dog per week]
e-mail: PaulandFlora@BrackenboroughHall.com   website: www.BrackenboroughHall.com

Mablethorpe

Coastal resort 11 miles from Louth.

MRS GRAVES, GRANGE FARM, MALTBY-LE-MARSH, ALFORD LN13 0JP (01507 450267). Farmhouse B&B and self-catering country cottages set in15 idyllic acres of Lincolnshire countryside. 2 miles from beach. Peaceful base for leisure, walking and sightseeing. Two private fishing lakes. Many farm animals. Brochure available. [Pets £5 per night B&B, £30 per week in cottages, ⌂]
website: www.grange-farmhouse.co.uk

North Somercotes

Large coastal village in the Marshes area.

FOUR LUXURY 4-STAR COTTAGES, LINCOLNSHIRE COAST. On a quiet lane leading to the sea, an ideal holiday home for people who want the best modern comforts, the calm of the Lincolnshire coast,and plenty to see and do nearby. Each has 1 or 2 double bedrooms, sleep up to 5. (01507 358256/07724 76434) . EnjoyEngland ★★★★ [Pets £20 per week].
e-mail: nurserycottage@hotmail.co.uk   website: www.mealsfarm.com

Skegness

Coastal resort 19 miles north east of Boston.

THE CHESTNUTS, WAINFLEET ROAD, BURGH LE MARSH PE24 5AH (Tel & Fax: 01754 810904). Farm Cottages with private fishing on a real farm, only 5 miles from Skegness. Children's play area, farm animals. Brochure available. [Pets £30 per week].
e-mail: chestnutsfarmbreaks@gmail.com   website: www.chestnutsfarmbreaks.com

---

Classified Symbols

🐾   Pets are welcome free of charge.

£   A charge is made for pets: nightly or weekly.

pw! Special provision for pets; exercise facility, feeding or accommodation arrangement.

⌂   Separate pets' accommodation.

Daventry

Murcott Mill Farmhouse

Murcott, Long Buckby, Northampton NN6 7QR

• Tel: 01327 842236 •

- Fabulous location for pets • Off-road, quiet, plenty of walks • Beautiful Georgian mill house
- All rooms well appointed • En suite bathrooms newly refurbished • Friendly, animal-loving hosts
- Delicious farmhouse breakfast • Separate lounge and dining room. • £65-£70 double, £35-£40 single.

Credit cards accepted

e-mail: carrie.murcottmill@virgin.net • www.murcottmill.com

Daventry

Long Buckby is a village 5 miles north east of Daventry.

MURCOTT MILL FARMHOUSE, MURCOTT, LONG BUCKBY NN6 7QR (01327 842236). Beautiful Georgian mill house, all rooms well appointed. Friendly, animal-loving hosts. Delicious farmhouse breakfast. Off road, quiet, plenty of walks. ETC ★★★★ [🐾]
e-mail: carrie.murcottmill@virgin.net   website: www.murcottmill.co.uk

Nottinghamshire

Burton Joyce

Residential area 4 miles north-east of Nottingham.

MRS V. BAKER, WILLOW HOUSE, BURTON JOYCE, NOTTINGHAMSHIRE NG14 5FD (0115 931 2070 or 07816 347706). Victorian house, authentically furnished, in quiet village near beautiful stretch of River Trent. Four miles city. Close to station/bus stop. Bright, clean rooms. TV. En suite. Parking. From £26pppn. Good local eating. Please phone first for directions. [🐾]
website: www.willowhousebedandbreakfast.co.uk

Bromyard, Hereford, Ledbury, Ross-on-Wye

LEA HOUSE BED & BREAKFAST
by the Forest of Dean and the Wye Valley

Our 16th Century home is beautifully refurbished with antiques, an inglenook fireplace and loads of beams. Spacious bedrooms with kingsize or twin beds and en suite bathrooms with fluffy towels. AA award-winning breakfasts with all home-made and local produce. The area is a doggy paradise – walks galore. Footpath and fields 20yds away for all your dog's needs. Free Wi-Fi. Flat screen digital TV.

See guests' comments on www.tripadvisor.com
From £34pppn. Dogs welcome @ £7.50 per stay

Lea, Ross-on-Wye HR9 7JZ
Tel: 01989 750652
e-mail: enquiries@leahouse.co.uk
www.leahouse.co.uk

The Rock B&B
Coleford

Located at 600ft on the ridge between the Wye and Ruardean Valleys, The Rock B&B offers friendly family-run Bed and Breakfast accommodation in the Forest of Dean. Quiet, well behaved dogs are welcome and can enjoy miles of ideal dog walking - forest tracks starting just 30 paces away. All the three dog-friendly rooms have direct access from the outside, meaning you and your dog can come and go as you please.

**The Rock, Hillersland,
Near Symonds Yat Rock GL16 7NY
Tel: 01594 837893
www.stayattherock.com**

Allt yr Ynys Country House   WTB ★★★
Walterstone, Near Abergavenny HR2 0DU • Tel: 01873 890307
Beautifully preserved 16thC manor house set in the foothills of the Black Mountains on the fringes of the Brecon Beacons National Park. 22 luxury en suite bedrooms • Award-winning restaurant and Cider Mill bar Indoor heated swimming pool, sauna and spa pool   **www.allthotel.co.uk**

Bromyard

Medieval market town 12 miles west of Worcester; the streets are lined with half-timbered buildings.

ELCOCKS COTTAGE, NEAR BROMYARD. A beautiful 17th century detached cottage set in 3 acres bordering Badley Wood Common. Features include exposed beams, wood-burning stove, period-style furnishings. Enclosed garden and cottage face south. Pets welcome. ETC ★★★ Contact: MIKE HOGG (0121 427 1395). [Pets £19 per week]
e-mail: Mike@elcocks.net   website: www.elcocks.net

Hereford

Cathedral town on River Wye 45 miles SW of Birmingham.

SINK GREEN FARM, ROTHERWAS, HEREFORD HR2 6LE (01432 870223). 16th century farmhouse overlooking picturesque Wye Valley. En suite rooms, one four-poster. Extensive garden with summer house and hot tub. Prices from £35pp. Children welcome. Pets by arrangement. [🐕]
e-mail: enquiries@sinkgreenfarm.co.uk   website: www.sinkgreenfarm.co.uk

Terms quoted in this publication may be subject to increase if rises in costs necessitate

Ledbury

Town 12 miles east of Hereford with many timbered houses.

CHURCH FARM, CODDINGTON, LEDBURY HR8 IJJ (01531 640271). Black and white 16th-century Farmhouse on a working farm close to the Malvern Hills — ideal for touring and walking. Two double and one twin bedrooms. Excellent home cooking. Warm welcome assured. Open all year. From £38. Single supplement. AA ★★★★ [Small charge for pets]
website: www.dexta.co.uk

Leominster

Known as "The Town in the Marches", this historic market town is located in the heart of the beautiful border countryside and possesses some fine examples of architecture throughout the ages, such as The Priory Church and Grange Court. Ludlow 9 ½ miles, Hereford 12 miles.

CLIVE & CYNTHIA PRIOR, MOCKTREE BARNS, LEINTWARDINE, LUDLOW SY7 0LY (01547 540441). Gold Award winning cottages around a sunny courtyard. Sleep 2-6. Comfortable, well-equipped. Friendly owners. Dogs and children welcome. Non-Smoking. Lovely country walks. Ludlow, seven miles. Brochure. NAS Level 1 Accessibility. VB ★★★ [🐾] See also colour advertisement page 228
e-mail: mocktreebarns@care4free.net   website: www.mocktreeholidays.co.uk

Ross-on-Wye

An attractive town standing on a hill rising from the left bank on the Wye. Cardiff 47 miles, Gloucester 17.

THE HOSTELRIE AT GOODRICH, GOODRICH, ROSS-ON-WYE HR9 6HX (01600 890241). Enjoy comfort and good food at this fully centrally heated 17th Century Inn. We have a reputation for quality food at a reasonable price. Dogs welcome in bedrooms, main bar and garden. ETC/AA ★★ [🐾]
e-mail: info@thehostelrieatgoodrich.com   website: www.thehostelrieatgoodrich.com

GAME LARDERS & OLD BAKEHOUSE, WYTHALL ESTATE, ROSS-ON-WYE HR9 5SD (01989 562688). Enjoy peace and quiet in the secluded setting of Wythall Estate. The self contained cottages sleep 2/4, each with sitting room, dining area, fully fitted kitchen, bedroom(s) and family bathroom.
e-mail: bookings@wythallestate.co.uk   website: www.wythallestate.co.uk

LEA HOUSE BED & BREAKFAST, LEA, ROSS-ON-WYE HR9 7JZ (01989 750652). Spacious bedrooms with kingsize or twin beds and en suite bathrooms; all individually styled, with flat screen digital TV and beverage tray. Free Wi-Fi. Secluded garden. Dogs very welcome. AA ★★★★ [Dogs £7.50 per stay]. See Display Advert
e-mail: enquiries@leahouse.co.uk   website: www.leahouse.co.uk

Symonds Yat

Well known beauty spot on River Wye, 4 miles from Monmouth.

THE ROCK B&B, HILLERSLAND, NEAR SYMONDS YAT GL16 7NY (01594 837893). Located on the ridge between the Wye and Ruardean Valleys. Quiet well behaved dogs welcome. All three dog-friendly bedrooms have direct access from the outside, meaning you and your dog can come and go as you please.AA ★★★★. [Pets £10 per stay]
website: www.stayattherock.com

Walterstone

Set at the base of the Black Mountains on the edge of the Brecon Beacons National Park.

ALLT YR YNYS COUNTRY HOUSE, WALTERSTONE, NEAR ABERGAVENNY HR2 0DU (01873 890307). Beautifully preserved 16thC manor house set in the foothills of the Black Mountains on the fringes of the Brecon Beacons National Park. 22 luxury en suite bedrooms. Award-winning restaurant and Cider Mill bar. Indoor heated swimming pool, sauna and spa pool. WTB ★★★
website: www.allthotel.co.uk

FHG Guides publish a range of well-known accommodation guides. We will be happy to send you details or you can use the order form at the back of this book.

Bridgnorth, Burford, Church Stretton

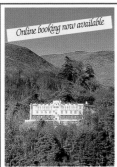

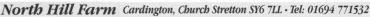

Clun, Craven Arms, Ludlow

Bridgnorth

Town on cliff above River Severn.

THE GRANARY, THE OLD VICARAGE, DITTON PRIORS, BRIDGNORTH WV16 6SP (01746 712272; Fax: 01746 712288) Early 19th century Granary in hill country. Sleeps two/four with view over farmland. Antique furniture complements surroundings. Excellent walking, cycling. Pets welcome. Contact MRS S. ALLEN. VisitBritain ★★★. [🐾]
 e-mail: allens@oldvicditton.freeserve.co.uk   website: www.stmem.com/thegranary

Burford

Small village to the north of the River Teme. Many NT properties in the area.

MARGARET ANDERSON, OLD HARPFIELDS, BURFORD, TENBURY WELLS WR15 8HP (01584 810099 or 01584 811298). Unusual converted Victorian building in unspoilt countryside. Perfect for a rural self-catering holiday in a traditional farmyard setting. Sleeps 4. EnjoyEngland ★★★★ Gold Award. [🐾]
e-mail: janderson117@btinternet.com   website: www.harpfields-hopkiln.co.uk

Church Stretton

Delightful little town in lee of Shropshire Hills. Walking and riding country. Knighton 22 miles, Bridgnorth 19, Ludlow 15, Shrewsbury 12.

BOTVYLE FARM, ALL STRETTON, CHURCH STRETTON SY6 7JN (01694 722869). A warm welcome awaits at our family-run cottages, maintained and equipped to a high standard. Beautiful location at Church Stretton, easy access to Ludlow, Shrewsbury, Ironbridge. Ideal for all the family. [Pets £15 per week] website: www.botvylefarm.co.uk

THE LONGMYND HOTEL, CHURCH STRETTON SY6 6AG (01694 722244). In 10 acre grounds, with sweeping views over Welsh border country. Outdoor pool, pitch-and-putt, sauna. Excellent and varied cuisine. Self-catering lodges in grounds. AA ★★★ [Pets £6 per night].
e-mail: info@longmynd.co.uk   website: www.longmynd.co.uk

MRS C.F. BRANDON-LODGE, NORTH HILL FARM, CARDINGTON, CHURCH STRETTON SY6 7LL (01694 771532). Rooms with a view! B&B in beautiful Shropshire hills. TV in rooms, tea etc. Ideal walking country. From £28 per person; en suite available. AA ★★★★ [pw! Pets £3 per night, ⬠]
e-mail: cbrandon@btinternet.com   website: www.virtual-shropshire.co.uk/northhill/

Clun

Small town in Area of Outstanding Natural Beauty, convenient for exploring Welsh Borders.

THE WHITE HORSE INN, THE SQUARE, CLUN SY7 8JA (01588 640305). Characterful, friendly and comfortable Inn. Ideal for walkers, cyclists and those wanting a relaxing break. All rooms en suite; dogs welcome. Real ales; lunch and dinner available daily. [🐕].
e-mail: room@whi-clun.co.uk   website: www.whi-clun.co.uk

Craven Arms

Beautiful Stokesey Castle lies just outside the town. Ludlow 6½ miles, Shrewsbury 19 miles.

Two modern static caravans, each sleeps 6. Pets and children welcome; horses also accommodated. Open Easter to October. Also campsite for all types of unit. THE ANCHORAGE, ANCHOR, NEWCASTLE ON CLUN, CRAVEN ARMS SY7 8PR (01686 670737). [🐕].
e-mail: nancynewcwm@btinternet.com   website: www.adamsanchor.co.uk

Ludlow

Lovely and historic town on Rivers Teme and Corve with numerous old half-timbered houses and inns. Worcester 29 miles, Shrewsbury 27.

THE MOOR HALL, NEAR LUDLOW SY8 3EG (01584 823209). Built in 1789, a splendid example of the Georgian Palladian style. Breathtaking views, 5-acre garden. B&B from £35pppn. AA ★★★★ [🐕]
e-mail: info@moorhall.co.uk   website: www.moorhall.co.uk

SALLY AND TIM LOFT, GOOSEFOOT BARN, PINSTONES, DIDDLEBURY, CRAVEN ARMS, SHROPSHIRE SY7 9LB (01584 861326). Four delightful cottages thoughtfully converted and equipped to the highest standard. All with en suite facilities and garden or seating area. One cottage with disabled access. Situated in a secluded valley and ideally located to explore the beautiful South Shropshire countryside. Sleep 2-6. ETC ★★★★ [🐕]
e-mail: info@goosefootbarn.co.uk   website: www.goosefootbarn.co.uk

CLIVE & CYNTHIA PRIOR, MOCKTREE BARNS, LEINTWARDINE, LUDLOW SY7 0LY (01547 540441). Gold Award winning self-catering cottages around a sunny courtyard. Sleep 2-6. Comfortable, well-equipped. Friendly owners. Dogs and children welcome. Non-smoking. Lovely country walks. Ludlow, seven miles. Brochure. NAS Level 1 Accessibility. VB ★★★ [pw! 🐕] See also colour advertisement page 228
e-mail: mocktreebarns@care4free.net   website: www.mocktreeholidays.co.uk

SIR HENRY SIDNEY APARTMENT, LUDLOW CASTLE. Superbly renovated apartment, full of charm and character. Sitting/dining room, two twin bedrooms with en suite bathrooms. Parking space in the heart of Ludlow. A unique opportunity to reside within the walls of Ludlow Castle. Open all year. 01584 874465 for full colour brochure. EnjoyEngland★★★★★ GOLD AWARD. [Pets £3 per night]
e-mail: info@ludlowcastle.com   website: www.castle-accommodation.com

Oswestry

Borderland market town. Many old castles and fortifications. Shrewsbury 16, Vyrnwy 18.

PEN-Y-DYFFRYN COUNTRY HOTEL, NEAR RHYDYCROESAU, OSWESTRY SY10 7JD (01691 653700). Picturesque Georgian Rectory quietly set in Shropshire/ Welsh Hills. 12 en suite bedrooms, four with private patios. 5-acre grounds. No passing traffic. Johansens recommended. Dinner, Bed and Breakfast from £92 per person per day. AA ★★★. [🐕 pw!]
e-mail: stay@peny.co.uk   website: www.peny.co.uk

Leek

Busy market town in Staffordshire Moorlands on edge of Peak District.

EDITH & ALWYN MYCOCK, ROSEWOOD COTTAGE, LOWER BERKHAMSYTCH FARM, BOTTOM HOUSE, NEAR LEEK ST13 7QP (Tel & Fax: 01538 308213). Cosy three bedroomed cottage with four-poster, sleeps six. Fully equipped and carpeted. Electricity and linen inclusive, laundry room. Ideal base for Alton Towers, Potteries and Peak District. Terms £230 to £375. [Pets £7.50 per week] website: www.rosewoodcottage.co.uk

Stafford

Town on River Sow, 14 miles south of Stoke-on-Trent.

MRS N. ROBINSON, WYNDALE GUEST HOUSE, 199 CORPORATION STREET, STAFFORD ST16 3LQ (01785 223069). Comfortable Victorian Guest House situated quarter mile from Stafford town centre and 3 miles from County Showground. Small nature reserve across the road ideal for dog walking. ETC ★★★ [🐕]
e-mail: wyndale@aol.com   website: www.wyndaleguesthouse.co.uk

Tutbury

Village 4 miles north west of Burton-Upon-Trent. Ruins of 14c castle.

LITTLE PARK HOLIDAY HOMES, PARK LANE, TUTBURY, NEAR BURTON-ON-TRENT DE13 9JQ (Tel: 01283 812654; Mobile: 07557 119666). Barn Conversion Units. Full self-catering. Facilities situated near to medieval castle and tourist village. Spectacular views. Near Alton Towers and other theme parks. Ample parking. Please phone for brochure. [🐕]

Leamington Spa, Stratford-Upon-Avon, Warwick

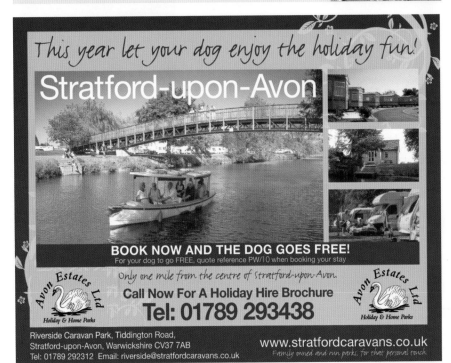

Leamington Spa

Spa town on River Leam, 8 miles South of Coventry.

WENDY HARRISON, BUBBENHALL HOUSE, PAGET'S LANE, BUBBENHALL CV8 3BJ. (Tel/Fax: 02476 302409). A charming country house offering superior bed and breakfast accommodation, located in the heart of Warwickshire, between Royal Leamington Spa and Coventry. Pet friendly. AA ★★★★ [🐕]
e-mail: wharrison@bubbenhallhouse.freeserve.co.uk   website: www.bubbenhallhouse.com

Stratford-Upon-Avon

Historic town famous as Shakespeare's birthplace and home. Birmingham 24, Warwick 8 miles.

RIVERSIDE CARAVAN PARK, TIDDINGTON ROAD, STRATFORD-UPON-AVON CV37 7BE (01789 292312). Luxury Caravans, sleep 6. Fully equipped kitchens, bathroom/ shower/WC. Also two riverside Cottages, all modern facilities to first-class standards. Private fishing. On banks of River Avon. [Pets £15 weekly.]
e-mail: riverside@stratfordcaravans.co.uk   website: www.stratfordcaravans.co.uk

MRS JULIA DOWNIE, HOLLY TREE COTTAGE, BIRMINGHAM RD, STRATFORD-UPON-AVON CV37 0ES (Tel/Fax: 01789 204461). Tastefully decorated period cottage with friendly atmosphere. Many local attractions. Children welcome. Pets by arrangement. [pw! 🐕]
e-mail: john@hollytree-cottage.co.uk   website: www.hollytree-cottage.co.uk

Warwick

Town on the River Avon, 9 miles south-west of Coventry, with medieval castle and many fine old buildings.

DAVID & PATRICIA CLAPP, CROFT GUESTHOUSE, HASELEY KNOB, WARWICK CV35 7NL (Tel & Fax: 01926 484 447). All bedrooms en suite or with private bathroom, some ground floor. Non-smoking. Picturesque rural setting. Central for NEC, Warwick, Stratford, Stoneleigh and Coventry. B&B single £40, double/twin £60. ETC ★★★★ [Dogs £4 per night]
e-mail: david@croftguesthouse.co.uk   website: www.croftguesthouse.co.uk

Bishop's Frome, Droitwich, Tenbury Wells

Pirton, Worcester

Bishop's Frome

Village 4 miles south of Bromyard.

FIVE BRIDGES COTTAGES, NEAR BISHOP'S FROME, WORCESTER WR6 5BX (01531 640340). Nestled in the heart of the Herefordshire cider apple and hop growing regions, the cottages are set within the owner's 4-acre garden and smallholding. ETC ★★★★. [Pets £10 per week. pw!]
e-mail: info@fivebridgescottages.co.uk   website: www.fivebridgescottages.co.uk

Droitwich

Town 6 miles north east of Worcester. Former spa status due to saline springs.

MRS SALLI HARRISON, MIDDLETON GRANGE, SALWARPE, DROITWICH SPA WR9 0AH (01905 451678). Traditional 18th century country house surrounded by picturesque gardens. Children welcome. Well behaved pets welcome; dog sitting available. All rooms en suite. M5 motorway six minutes. Worcester 10 minutes. [🐾].
e-mail: salli@middletongrange.com   website: www.middletongrange.com

Pirton

Midway between Worcester and Pershore.

PIRTON HOUSE FARM, PIRTON, WORCESTER WR8 9EJ (01905 820728 / 07780 510610). Set in tranquil countryside, this 19th century farmhouse offers an away from it all break. Two double en suite rooms. Children, dogs and horses welcome. Lots of footpaths. Close to Malvern Showground. 15 minutes from M5, Junctions 7/8. Free Wi-Fi. [pw!🐾]
e-mail: info@pirtonhousefarm.com   website: www.pirtonhousefarm.com

Tenbury Wells

Market town on the south bank of the River Teme which forms the border between Shropshire and Worcestershire.

LONG COVER COTTAGE & THE COACH HOUSE. Two properties with a home-from-home feel. Long Cover Cottage has three double rooms and sleeps 6. Coach House is open plan and sleeps 2. Acres of outdoor space. ETC ★★★★. For details contact: FISHPOOL COTTAGE, KYRE, TENBURY WELLS WR15 8RL (01885 410208; Mobile: 07725 972486).
e-mail: ellie_vanstraaten@yahoo.co.uk   website: www.a-country-break.co.uk

Worcester

Cathedral city on River Severn, 24 miles south-west of Birmingham.

MOSELEY FARM BED & BREAKFAST, MOSELEY ROAD, HALLOW, WORCESTER WR2 6NL (01905 641343).17th Century former farmhouse with large enclosed garden. Rural location, 4 miles from Worcester. Full English Breakfast or Room only. Three family (two en suite) and one twin room, all with Freeview TV, radio alarm clock, tea/coffee making facilities and free Wi-Fi access. Off-road parking. 20 minutes drive from M5, J5 or J7. From £25pppn. [pw! 🐾]
e-mail: moseleyfarmbandb@aol.com   website: www.moseleyfarmbandb.co.uk

DALES & VALES COTTAGE HOLIDAYS. Carefully selected self-catering accommodation at affordable prices from basic to luxury. Many are pet friendly and most welcome pets free. Locations across Yorkshire's Dales, Moors and Coast, Cumbria, Northumberland and the Scottish Borders. Call 01756 792498.[🐾].
website: www.dales-vales-cottages.com

East Yorkshire

Beverley, Bridlington

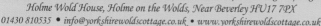

Driffield, Hornsea, Howden, Kilnwick Percy

Beverley

Popular medieval market and county town in the East Riding of Yorkshire, 8 miles from Kingston upon Hull, 10 miles from Market Weighton and 12 from Hornsea.

HOLME WOLD COTTAGE, HOLME ON THE WOLDS, NEAR BEVERLEY HU17 7PX (01430 810535). A two/three bedroom holiday cottage on working arable farm. Views over the Yorkshire Wolds. Large garden with patio area. Within easy reach of the coast, towns and cities; close to the Wolds Way for walking or cycling holidays. ETC ★★★★ Gold Award. [Pets £3 per night]
e-mail: info@yorkshirewoldscottage.co.uk   website: www.yorkshirewoldscottage.co.uk

ROBEANNE HOUSE, DRIFFIELD LANE, SHIPTONTHORPE, YORK YO43 3PW (01430 873312). Family B&B, country location, 18 miles from historic York. Ideal for coast, Moors, racing, Beverley, Cycle Route 66 and Wolds Way. Beautiful country house and gardens. All rooms en suite. Contact: JEANNE WILSON. AA ★★★ [pw! Pets £5 per night]
e-mail: enquiries@robeannehouse.co.uk   website: www.robeannehouse.co.uk

Bridlington

Traditional family resort with picturesque harbour and a wide range of entertainments and leisure facilities. Ideal for exploring the Heritage coastline and the Wolds.

THE TENNYSON, 19 TENNYSON AVENUE, BRIDLINGTON YO15 2EU (01262 604382). Friendly, good quality guest house offering spacious en suite rooms. Ground floor room available. Non-smoking. Evening meals by arrangement. An easy walk to town centre, North Beach and cliff walks. B&B from £25pppn. AA ★★★ [Pets £5 per stay].
website: www.thetennyson-brid.co.uk

Driffield

Town 11 miles south west of Bridlington.

OLD COBBLER'S COTTAGE, NORTH DALTON. Pretty cottage with garden looking over village mere with ducks and fish. Good walking area and easy access to York and coast. Open fire. Local pub serving real ale and good food within 20 yards. Short breaks available. For details contact (01377 219901/217523 or 07801 124264). ETC ★★★ [🐾]
e-mail: chris.wade@adastra-music.co.uk   website: www.waterfrontcottages.co.uk

Hornsea

Coastal resort 14 miles NE of Hull.

CHERRY TREE, HORNSEA. Cosy well appointed holiday bungalow in quiet cul-de-sac off town centre. Fully equipped. Large conservatory. Open all year. Contact: MRS RITA LEONARD, COWDEN PARVA FARM, MAIN ROAD, COWDEN, ALDBROUGH HU11 4UG (01964 527245; Fax: 01964 527521). Visit Britain ★★★. [Pets £10 per week]
e-mail: leonardritaruth@yahoo.co.uk   website: www.cherrytreeyorkshire.co.uk

Howden

Small town 3 miles North of Goole.

VIVIENNE & JOHN SWEETING, APPLE TREE COTTAGES, THE DAIRY FARM, SALTMARSHE, HOWDEN DN14 7RX. (01430 430 677; Mobile: 07960 300 337). Two self-catering Cottages or Farmhouse B&B on a Yorkshire family farm. A wonderful stay in friendly, well appointed comfortable surroundings. [Pets £5 per night]
e-mail: vivienne.sweeting@btinternet.com   website: www.appletree-cottages.co.uk

Kilnwick Percy

Located 2 miles east of Pocklington

PAWS-A-WHILE, KILNWICK PERCY, POCKLINGTON YO42 1UF (01759 301168; Mobile: 07711 866869). Small family B & B set in forty acres of parkland twixt York and Beverley. Golf, walking, riding. Pets and horses most welcome. Brochure available. ETC ★★★★ [pw! 🐾]
e-mail: paws.a.while@lineone.net   website: www.pawsawhile.net
www.dickyphotos.com

Bentham, Carperby, Clapham, Coverdale

Hawes, Helmsley

Valley View Farm Cottages

Old Byland, Helmsley YO62 5LG
Tel: 01439 798221
Fax: 01439 798477

HOLIDAY COTTAGES

Our six cottages, sleeping 2-10 are situated on a working farm within the scenic countryside of the North Yorkshire Moors National Park, close to Rievaulx Abbey and five miles from the delightful market town of Helmsley. Enjoy rural peace and tranquillity in an ideal location for exploring Yorkshire.

- Private parking.
- Good walking area.
- Choice of cottages for 2.
- Short breaks are offered, subject to availability.
- Dogs welcome by arrangement.
- Optional on-line booking.
- Wi-Fi.

e-mail: sally@valleyviewfarm.com
www.valleyviewfarm.com

Helmsley, Ingleton, Kirkbymoorside, Knaresborough

Scalby Nabs (Scarborough), Scarborough, Skipton

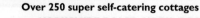

Stainforth (Settle), Staithes, Thirsk

Thirsk, Whitby

York

Bentham

Quiet village amidst the fells. Good centre for rambling and fishing. Ingleton 5 miles north-east.

MRS L. J. STORY, HOLMES FARM, LOW BENTHAM, LANCASTER LA2 7DE (015242 61198). Cottage conversion in easy reach of Dales, Lake District and coast. Central heating, fridge, TV, washer, games room. ETC ★★★★. [🐾]
e-mail: lucy@holmesfarmcottage.co.uk   website: www.holmesfarmcottage.co.uk

Carperby

Village one mile North of Aysgarth.

THE WHEATSHEAF, CARPERBY, NEAR LEYBURN DL8 4DF (01969 663216; Fax: 01969 663019) Excellent en suite accommodation in 12 bedrooms (including four posters), at this comfortable family-owned hotel offering the best of local cuisine and comfort. [Pets £5 per week].
e-mail: info@wheatsheafinwensleydale.co.uk   website: www.wheatsheafinwensleydale.co.uk

Clapham

Village 6 miles NW of Settle.

NEW INN, CLAPHAM, NEAR INGLETON LA2 8HH (015242 51203; Fax: 015242 51824). 'As relaxed as you like'. A comfortable hotel in the Yorkshire Dales National Park. The ideal holiday destination for your pet, be assured of a warm and friendly reception, sit back, close your eyes and soak up the history and atmosphere. ETC ★★ [Pets £5 per night]
e-mail: info@newinn-clapham.co.uk   website: www.newinn-clapham.co.uk

Coverdale

Located in the Yorkshire Dales National Park, famous for Middleham Castle, Richard III and the Forbidden Corner.

MRS JULIE CLARKE, MIDDLE FARM, WOODALE, COVERDALE, LEYBURN DL8 4TY (01969 640271). Peacefully situated farmhouse away from the madding crowd. B&B with optional Evening Meal. Home cooking. Pets sleep where you prefer. Ideally positioned for exploring the beautiful Yorkshire Dales. [🐾 pw!]
e-mail: j-a-clarke@hotmail.co.uk

Danby

Village on River Esk 12 miles west of Whitby.

THE FOX & HOUNDS INN, AINTHORPE, DANBY YO21 2LD (01287 660218). Residential country pub and restaurant. All rooms en suite. Enjoy our real ales or quality selected wines. Freshly prepared food served every day. Open all year. ETC ★★★★ Inn [Pets £3 per night.]
e-mail: info@foxandhounds-ainthorpe.com   website: www.foxandhounds-ainthorpe.com

Goathland

Small village high on the North York Moors, famous as the village of Aidensfield in the TV series "Heartbeat".

EMMA BRICE, ROSE COTTAGE B&B, GOATHLAND YO22 5AN (01947 896253; Mobile: 07920 474321). One of the most beautiful cottages in the North Yorkshire Moors. Good location for walks and local amenities. Sky TV in all double bedrooms. Wi-Fi. Pets allowed. Non smoking. Private parking. [🐾]
e-mail: emmabrice@rosecottage-heartbeat.com   website: www.rosecottage-heartbeat.com

Grassington

Wharfedale village in attractive moorland setting. Ripon 22 miles, Skipton 9.

FORESTERS ARMS, MAIN STREET, GRASSINGTON, SKIPTON BD23 5AA (01756 752349). The Foresters Arms is situated in the heart of the Yorkshire Dales and provides an ideal centre for walking or touring. Within easy reach of York and Harrogate. ETC ★★★ [🐾]
e-mail: theforesters@totalise.co.uk   website: www.forestersarmsgrassington.co.uk

Harrogate

Charming and elegant spa town set amid some of Britain's most scenic countryside. Ideal for exploring Herriot Country and the moors and dales. York 22 miles, Bradford 19, Leeds 16.

ROSEMARY HELME, HELME PASTURE LODGES & COTTAGES, OLD SPRING WOOD, HARTWITH BANK, SUMMERBRIDGE, HARROGATE HG3 4DR (01423 780279). Country accommodation for owners and dogs and numerous walks in unspoilt Nidderdale. Central for Harrogate, York, Herriot and Bronte country. National Trust area. ETC ★★★★, ETC Category 1 for Disabled Access. [pw! Pets £5 per night, £25 per week; some free.] Please see page 240 for Colour Advertisement.
e-mail: info@helmepasture.co.uk   website: www.helmepasture.co.uk

THE COURTYARD AT DUKE'S PLACE, BISHOP THORNTON, NEAR HARROGATE HG3 3JY (01765 620229 or 07979 521960). In glorious Nidderdale, group of well maintained and equipped holiday cottages. Sleep 2/6; linen, fully equipped kitchens. Riding stables on site. B&B now available. Pets, horses and children most welcome. ETC ★★★/★★★★★ [🐾]
e-mail: enquiries@dukesplace-courtyard.co.uk   website: www.dukesplace-courtyard.co.uk

RUDDING HOLIDAY PARK, FOLLIFOOT, HARROGATE HG3 1JH (01423 870439; Fax: 01423 870859). ★★★ cottages and lodges sleeping two to seven people. All equipped to a high standard. Pool, family pub and licensed bar, golf and children's playground in the Parkland. Brochure tariff available. [Pets £3 per dog]
e-mail: stay@ruddingpark.com   website: www.ruddingholidaypark.co.uk

SOUTHFIELD FARM HOLIDAY COTTAGES, DARLEY, HARROGATE HG3 2PR (01423 780258). Two well equipped holiday cottages between Harrogate and Pateley Bridge. Ideal for touring the Dales, with York within easy driving distance. Ample parking. Well behaved pets welcome. [🐾]
e-mail: info@southfieldcottages.co.uk   website: www.southfieldcottages.co.uk

Hawes

Small town in Wensleydale, 14 miles south east of Kirkby Stephen.

STONE HOUSE HOTEL, SEDBUSK, HAWES DL8 3PT (01969 667571). This fine Edwardian country house has spectacular views and serves delicious Yorkshire cooking with fine wines. Comfortable en suite bedrooms, some ground floor. Phone for details. [🐾]
website: www.stonehousehotel.co.uk

SIMONSTONE HALL, HAWES, WENSLEYDALE DL8 3LY (01969 667255; Fax: 01969 667741). Facing south across picturesque Wensleydale. All rooms en suite with colour TV. Fine cuisine. Extensive wine list. Friendly personal attention. A relaxing break away from it all. AA ★★ [Pets £10 per stay]
e-mail: enquiries@simonstonehall.com   website: www.simonstonehall.com

COUNTRY COTTAGE HOLIDAYS, DRYDEN HOUSE, MARKET PLACE, HAWES DL8 3RA (01969 667654). 80 cottages in the lovely Yorkshire Dales. Colour TV, central heating, open fires. Gardens, private parking. Many allow pets. Rents from £200 per week. Sleep 1-10. [Pets from £16 per week]
website: www.countrycottageholidays.co.uk

Helmsley

A delightful stone-built town on River Rye with a large cobbled square. Thirsk 12 miles.

THE BLACK SWAN HOTEL, MARKET PLACE, HELMSLEY YO62 5BJ (01439 770466). Luxury Yorkshire hotel in Helmsley market square. Romantic interludes, great food, boutique shopping, walking on the North Yorkshire Moors, weddings and business meetings. AA ★★★. [Pets £10 per stay]
e-mail: enquiries@blackswan-helmsley.co.uk   website: www.blackswan-helmsley.co.uk

SALLY ROBINSON'S VALLEY VIEW FARM, OLD BYLAND, HELMSLEY, YORK YO62 5LG (01439 798221). Fully equipped self-catering cottages on working farm in North York Moors. Ideal for touring Yorkshire, or just walking the hills and lanes around. Rural peace and tranquillity. Dogs free. Kennel and run available. ETC ★★★★ [🐾]
e-mail: sally@valleyviewfarm.com   website: www.valleyviewfarm.com

SUE SMITH, LASKILL GRANGE, HAWNBY, NEAR HELMSLEY YO62 5NB (01439 798268). Delightful country house set in one-acre gardens; all rooms en suite. Generous cuisine of a high standard using fresh local produce, vegetarians catered for. Newly installed hot tubs. Open all year. Also 7 luxury self-catering cottages. ETC ★★★★ Silver Award, AA ★★★★ Highly Commended.[🐾]
e-mail: laskillgrange@tiscali.co.uk   website: www.laskillgrange.co.uk

Ingleton

Small village in the heart of Three Peaks Country in the Yorkshire Dales.

JILL HOWARTH, GALE GREEN COTTAGE, INGLETON LA6 3NJ (015242 41245) A warm welcome, great food and superb scenery at our friendly B&B ideally located for all types of hill and mountain walking in one of England's natural beauty spots. Two double and one twin rooms, all en suite. Guest lounge. AA ★★★★. [🐾]
e-mail: jill@galegreen.com   website: www.galegreen.com

Kirkbymoorside

Small market town midway between Pickering and Helmsley. York 25 miles.

MRS F. WILES, SINNINGTON COMMON FARM, KIRKBYMOORSIDE, YORK YO62 6NX (01751 431719). One and two bedroomed cottages (all en suite) situated in beautiful countryside. Many farmyard and rescue animals, horses and abundant wildlife. Pets welcome. [🐾]
e-mail: felicity@scfarm.demon.co.uk   website: www.sinningtoncommonfarm.co.uk

Knaresborough

Town on escarpment above the River Nidd, 3 miles NE of Harrogate..

NEWTON HOUSE, 5-7 YORK PLACE, KNARESBOROUGH HG5 0AD (01423 863539). Dogs have been welcomed at Newton House for hundreds of years. We have two spacious dog-friendly en suite ground floor rooms with direct access from our private car park. We serve award winning breakfasts for owners, and home-made biscuits for dogs. Contact: Denise Carter. AA ★★★★ Highly Commended, AA Breakfast Award. [pw! Pets £10 per stay]
e-mail: info@newtonhousehotel.com   website: www.newtonhouseyorkshire.com

Leyburn

Small market town, 8 miles south-west of Richmond, standing above the River Ure in Wensleydale.

BARBARA & BARRIE MARTIN, THE OLD STAR, WEST WITTON, LEYBURN DL8 4LU (01969 622949). Former 17th century Coaching Inn now run as a guest house. Oak beams, log fire, home cooking. En suite B&B from £29 pppn. ETC ★★★ [🐾]
e-mail: enquiries@theoldstar.com   website: www.theoldstar.com

FREE or REDUCED RATE entry to Holiday Visits and Attractions –
see our **READERS' OFFER VOUCHERS** on pages 409-414

Malham

Village in upper Airedale, 5 miles east of Settle, across the moors.

MR C. SHARP, MIRESFIELD FARM, MALHAM, SKIPTON BD23 4DA (01729 830414). In beautiful gardens bordering village green and stream. Excellent food. 11 bedrooms, all with private facilities. Full central heating. Two well-furnished lounges and conservatory. B&B from £24pppn. ETC ★★★ [🐾 pw!]

Northallerton

Town 14 miles South of Darlington.

JULIE & JIM GRIFFITH, HILL HOUSE FARM, LITTLE LANGTON, NORTHALLERTON DL7 0PZ (01609 770643). Sleep 2/4. Four well-equipped cottages, cosily heated for year round appeal. Centrally located between Dales and Moors. Weekly rates from £210 incl. Short breaks available. Golf 2 miles, shops 3 miles, pub food 1.5 miles. Pets welcome. VisitBritain ★★★★ [pw! 🐾]
e-mail: info@hillhousefarmcottages.com   website: www.hillhousefarmcottages.com

Nunthorpe

Between Middlesbrough and Stokesley, on edge of North York Moors National Park

BLACKTHORN GATE, EASTFIELDS FARM, NUNTHORPE TS7 0PB (01642 324496). Four luxury lodges, each with living room/dining room, fully equipped kitchen and two bedrooms; each also has own sauna. Sleep 4-6. On edge of North Yorks Moors National Park. Pets welcome in two lodges. ETC ★★★★
e-mail: info@blackthorngate.co.uk   website: www.blackthorngate.co.uk

Pickering

Pleasant market town on southern fringe of North York Moors National Park with moated Norman Castle. Bridlington 31 miles, Whitby 20, Scarborough 16, Helmsley 13, Malton 3.

THE WHITE SWAN INN AT PICKERING (01751 472288). 16th century inn with a buzz. Dog friendly with excellent: service, rooms, food and wine. "...consistently brilliant.." Please phone or visit our website for a brochure. ETC ★★★, AA Rosette [Pets £12.50 per stay].
e-mail: welcome@white-swan.co.uk   website: www.white-swan.co.uk

Port Mulgrave

Located 1km north of Hinderwell.

NORTH YORK MOORS NATIONAL PARK. Stone Cottage (sleeps) 4 in North York Moors National Park. Sea view, near Cleveland coastal footpath. Log fire, non-smoking. Whitby 9 miles. Brochure available (01642 613888). [🐾]
e-mail: judy.sylvale@virginmedia.com

Scalby Nabs (Scarborough)

Small town and suburb 2 miles north west of Scarborough.

EAST FARM COUNTRY COTTAGES, SCALBY NABS, SCALBY, SCARBOROUGH (01723 353635). Three single-storey two-bedroom stone cottages (no steps/stairs) in national Park; only 5 minutes from Scarborough. All completely non-smoking. Ideal base for walking or touring. VisitBritain ★★★ [Pets from £10 per week.]
e-mail: joeastfarmcottages@hotmail.co.uk   website: www.eastfarmcountrycottages.co.uk

Classified Symbols

🐾   Pets are welcome free of charge.

£   A charge is made for pets: nightly or week

pw! Special provision for pets; exercise facility, feeding or accommodation arrangement.

⌂   Separate pets' accommodation.

Scarborough

Very popular family resort with good sands. York 41 miles, Whitby 20, Bridlington 17, Filey 7.

SUE AND TONY HEWITT, HARMONY COUNTRY LODGE, LIMESTONE ROAD, BURNISTON, SCARBOROUGH YO13 0DG (0800 2985840 or 01723 870276). A peaceful retreat set in two acres of private grounds with 360° panoramic views of the National Park and sea. An ideal centre for walking or touring. En suite centrally heated rooms with superb views. Non-smoking, licensed, private parking facilities. B&B from £28 to £40.75. ETC ★★★★ [Pets £4 per night, £15 per week]
e-mail: mail@harmonylodge.net   website: www.harmonycountrylodge.co.uk

CAYTON VILLAGE CARAVAN PARK LTD, MILL LANE, CAYTON BAY, SCARBOROUGH YO11 3NN (01723 583171). Luxurious facilities, playground, shop, 4-acre floodlit dog walk. Seasonal pitches available, winter storage and caravan sales. Open 1st March - 31st October. Half-a-mile to beach adjoining village. ETC ★★★★★, David Bellamy Gold Award. [Pets £1 per night].
e-mail: info@caytontouring.co.uk   website: www.caytontouring.co.uk

Skipton

Airedale market town, centre for picturesque Craven district. Fine Castle (14th cent). York 43 miles, Manchester 42, Leeds 26, Harrogate 22, Settle 16.

THE CONISTON HOTEL, CONISTON COLD, SKIPTON BD23 4EA (01756 748080). Set in a stunning 1400-acre estate, an ideal base for guests wishing to explore the Yorkshire Dales. 71 en suite bedrooms with full facilities. Special rates for leisure breaks and family rooms. ETC ★★★ Silver Award, AA ★★★. [pw! Pets £10 per stay]
e-mail: info@theconistonhotel.com   website: www.theconistonhotel.com

BECK HALL, MALHAM BD23 4DJ (01729 830332). 18th century B&B on the Pennine Way, log fires and huge breakfasts. Midweek and 4-night specials. Ideal for exploring the Yorkshire Dales. AA ★★★, WELCOME HOST [🐾]
e-mail: alice@beckhallmalham.com   website: www.beckhallmalham.com

Over 250 super self-catering Cottages in the Yorkshire Dales, York, Coast, Moors, Lancashire, Peak and Lake District. For our fully illustrated brochure apply: HOLIDAY COTTAGES YORKSHIRE LTD (INCORPORATING RED ROSE COTTAGES), WATER STREET, SKIPTON BD23 1PB (01756 700872). [🐾]
website: www.holidaycotts.co.uk

CRAVEN HOUSE, 56 KEIGHLEY ROAD, SKIPTON BD23 2NB (01756 794657/07960 864916). Large terraced house with 7 bedrooms, sleeps up to 14. Suitable for large groups, extended families or just for the luxury of plenty of space! Dogs welcome by arrangement. Well equipped kitchen, dining room, lounge and cosy basement TV room. ETC ★★★★ [🐾]
e-mail: info@craven-house.co.uk   website: www.craven-house.co.uk

Stainforth (Settle)

Picturesque village in the Yorkshire Dales, 2½ miles from Settle.

2 HOLLIES COTTAGES. Traditional Dales 2-bedroom cottage situated in the Yorkshire Dales National Park. Sleeps 4. Open coal fire. Linen provided. Pets welcome. Contact: BRIDGE COTTAGE, STAINFORTH, NEAR SETTLE BD24 9PG (01729 822649). [🐾]
e-mail: vivmills30@hotmail.com   website: www.stainforth-holiday-cottage-settle.co.uk

Staithes

Fishing village on North Sea coast 9 miles NW of Whitby.

MS M.J. HEALD, BROOKLYN B&B, BROWN'S TERRACE, STAITHES TS13 5BG (01947 841396). Situated in the old part of picturesque and historic Staithes. Two double and one twin bedrooms available, generous breakfasts, vegetarians catered for. Pets and children most welcome. ETC ★★★ [🐾]
e-mail: margaret@heald.org.uk   website: www.brooklynuk.co.uk

PENNYSTEEL COTTAGE. Beamed and wood-panelled old fisherman's cottage located in the beautiful fishing village of Staithes. Breathtaking views from every room and from its sun terrace. One double, twin and single bedroom. CONTACT: CHRIS WADE, 2 STAR ROW, NORTH DALTON, DRIFFIELD YO25 9UX (01377 219901 day; 01377 217523 eve; 07801 124264). EnjoyEngland ★★★ [🐾]
e-mail:chris.wade@adastra-music.co.uk   website: www.waterfrontcottages.co.uk

Thirsk

Market town with attractive square. Excellent touring area. Northallerton 3 miles.

POPLARS HOLIDAY COTTAGES AND BED & BREAKFAST, THIRSK. The Poplars stands in two acres of lovely gardens with a field for dog walking. We have brick cottages as well as log cabins, with bed and breakfast in the main house. Contact AMANDA RICHARDS, THE POPLARS, CARLTON MINIOTT, THIRSK YO7 4LX (01845 522712). ETC ★★★★, Silver Award. [Pets £5 per night B&B, £10 per week SC]
website: www.thepoplarsthirsk.com

GOLDEN FLEECE HOTEL, MARKET PLACE, THIRSK YO7 1LL (01845 523108; Fax: 01845 523996). Characterful Coaching Inn offering good food and up to date facilities. All rooms are en suite, with TV, phone, trouser press, hairdryer. ETC ★★★ [🐾]
e-mail: reservations@goldenfleecehotel.com   website: www.goldenfleecehotel.com

ROSE COTTAGE FARM HOLIDAY COTTAGES, SUTTON-UNDER-WHITESTONECLIFFE, THIRSK YO7 2QA (01845 597309). Self-catering holiday cottages with superb scenery and wonderful walking. Each sleeps two. All linen, towels, welcome pack and heating included. Shared patio area. Well behaved pets accepted by arrangement. ETC ★★★
e-mail: jim.dickinson@btinternet.com   website: www.rose-cottage-farm.co.uk

FOXHILLS HIDEAWAYS, FELIXKIRK, THIRSK YO7 2DS (01845 537575). 4 Scandinavian log cabins, heated throughout, linen provided. A supremely relaxed atmosphere on the edge of the North York Moors National Park. Open all year. Village pub round the corner. [🐾]

Whitby

Charming resort with harbour and sands. Of note is the 13th century ruined Abbey. Stockton-on-Tees 34 miles, Scarborough 20, Saltburn-by-the-Sea 19.

THE SEACLIFFE HOTEL, 12 NORTH PROMENADE, WHITBY YO21 3JX (Freephone 0808 1682118). Magnificent seafront position overlooking beach and harbour entrance. Lovely scenic walks. Fully refurbished en suite bedrooms. Restaurant; extensive menus. Licensed bar. Lounge, patio-garden. Private car park (8). Dogs welcome by arrangement. Please visit website for photos, menus and special offers. [🐾]
e-mail: stay@seacliffehotelwhitby.co.uk   website: www.seacliffehotelwhitby.co.uk

SWALLOW HOLIDAY COTTAGES. Discover historic Whitby, pretty fishing villages, way-marked walks. Four cottages, one or two bedrooms. Private parking. Children and dogs welcome. Weekly rates from £195 to £500. Please phone or write for a brochure. KARL HEYES, MANOR RIDGE, MANOR ROAD, ROBIN HOOD'S BAY, WHITBY YO22 4RP (07545 641943). [Pets: first free, second pet £20 per week].
e-mail: karl@swallowcottages.co.uk   website: www.swallowcottages.co.uk

MRS CATHERINE HARLAND, CLITHERBECKS FARM, DANBY, WHITBY YO21 2NT (01287 660321). Self catering accommodation for up to seven people in this traditional hill farmhouse. Near Danby and the National Parks Moors Centre. Own entrance. Open all year. VisitBritain ★★★.[🐾]
e-mail: enquiries@clitherbecks.co.uk   website: www.clitherbecks.co.uk

BOLTHOLE COTTAGE, WALKERS YARD, CLIFF STREET, WHITBY. Secluded cottage offering lounge, modern kitchen, double bedroom. Gas and electricity incl. Central location for restaurants, museum, art gallery etc. An ideal location for touring the Whitby area. Pets welcome. Contact: MRS K.E. NOBLE, STORMVILLE, ROBIN HOOD'S BAY, WHITBY YO22 4RA (01947 880063; mobile: 07881 523141). [🐾]
e-mail: kaaren@noble47.freeserve.co.uk   website: www.boltholecottage.co.uk

WHITE ROSE HOLIDAY COTTAGES, NEAR WHITBY. Quality cottages and bungalows offering a warm and friendly welcome. Sleep 1-9. Private parking, gardens. Ideal for coast and country. APPLY: MRS J. ROBERTS (PW), 5 BROOK PARK, SLEIGHTS, NEAR WHITBY YO21 1RT (01947 810763) ETC ★★★-★★★★. [Pets £5 per week, pw!]
website: www.whiterosecottages.co.uk

A useful index of towns/counties appears at the back of this book

York

Historic cathedral city and former Roman Station on River Ouse. Magnificent Minster and 3 miles of ancient walls. Facilities for a wide range of sports and entertainments. Horse-racing on Knavesmire. Bridlington 41 miles, Filey 41, Leeds 24, Harrogate 22.

ASCOT HOUSE, 80 EAST PARADE, YORK YO31 7YH (01904 426826; Fax: 01904 431077). Attractive Victorian house with easy access to city centre. Family and double rooms en suite. Comfortable residents' lounge, dining room. Single room £60-£70, double room £70-£90. Free private enclosed car park. ETC/AA ★★★★ Silver Award. [🐾]
e-mail: admin@ascothouseyork.com   website: www.ascothouseyork.com

HIGH BELTHORPE, BISHOP WILTON, YORK YO42 1SB (01759 368238; Mobile: 07786 923330). Set on an ancient moated site at the foot of the Yorkshire Wolds, this comfortable Victorian farmhouse offers huge breakfasts, private fishing and fabulous walks. Dogs and owners will love it! Open all year except Christmas. Prices from £29. ETC ★★★ [pw! 🐾]
e-mail: meg@highbelthorpe.co.uk

YORK LAKESIDE LODGES, MOOR LANE, YORK YO24 2QU (01904 702346). Self-catering pine lodges. Mature parkland setting. Large fishing lake. Nearby superstore with coach to centre every 10 mins. ETC ★★★★/★★★★★★ [pw! Pets £25 per week]
e-mail: neil@yorklakesidelodges.co.uk   website: www.lakesidelodges.co.uk

ST GEORGE'S, 6 ST GEORGE'S PLACE, YORK YO24 1DR (01904 625056). Family-run guest house in quiet cul-de-sac near racecourse. All rooms en suite with large screen colour TV, tea/coffee making facilities. Breakfast in bed at no extra charge. Private parking. Pets welcome by arrangement. £68 double or twin room. ETC/AA ★★★ [🐾]
e-mail: breakfastinyork@aol.com   website: www.stgeorgesyork.com

THE NEW INN MOTEL, MAIN STEEET, HUBY, YORK YO61 1HQ (01347 810219) Modern, motel-style accommodation in quiet location 9 miles north of York. Comfortable en suite bedrooms. Breakfast from locally sourced produce served in dining room. Pets by arrangement. AA ★★★ [Pets £5 per night]
e-mail: enquiries@newinnmotel.freeserve.co.uk   website: www.newinnmotel.co.uk

Bingley, Haworth, Ossett

Bingley

Town on River Aire 5 miles north-west of Bradford.

THE FIVE RISE LOCKS HOTEL & RESTAURANT, BECK LANE, BINGLEY BD16 4DD (01274 565296).
Large Victorian house in tranquil area, but close main roads, tourist sites. Good views, individual
decor, informal style. Historic canal locks and excellent walking (dogs and humans) close by. AA/
VisitBritain ★★★★ [Pets £5 per night]
e-mail: info@five-rise-locks.co.uk   website: www.five-rise-locks.co.uk

Haworth

Rural village in Pennines in heart of Bronte Country.

WESTFIELD LODGE (BRONTELAND) LIMITED, NEW WESTFIELD FARM, UPPER MARSH,
OXENHOPE, KEIGHLEY BD22 9RH (07780 602524) Twenty high quality self-catering apartments
facing out onto the moors above Haworth. All fully furnished, with bedding, linen, towels, power,
water services, free satellite TV and Wi-Fi included in the price. Enjoy England ★★★ [pw! 🐴]
email: enquiry@westfield-lodge.co.uk   website:www.westfield-lodge.co.uk

Ossett

Market town situated halfway between Dewsbury and Wakefield.

HEATH HOUSE, CHANCERY ROAD, OSSETT WF5 9RZ (01924 260654). An elegant Victorian house
set in 4 acres; all rooms comfortably furnished with TV, tea/coffee tray. Breakfast freshly cooked to
order. Open all year. Easy drive to Leeds, Bradford and Dewsbury. AA ★★★★
e-mail: bookings@heath-house.co.uk   website: www.heath-house.co.uk

Barnard Castle

Named after the castle it was built around, 34 miles south of Newcastle Upon Tyne. The Bowes museum is a popular attraction.

LAVEROCK MULTI-DOG COTTAGES, BARNARD CASTLE (01833 650695). Two cottages each sleeping up to 5 people. Fantastic views on sheep farm, enclosed gardens, doggy shower room, 5-acre stock free field. 120 foot indoor Agility Building and sheepdog lessons on site. [pw! 1st 4 dogs free!! £25 per week for 5th].
e-mail: comebyanaway@hotmail.com   website: www.multidogcottages.co.uk

Bishop Auckland

Town on right bank of River Wear, 9 miles south-west of Durham Castle, of varying dates, residence of the Bishop of Durham.

ALISON & KEITH TALLENTIRE, LOW LANDS FARM, LOW LANDS, COCKFIELD, BISHOP AUCKLAND DL13 5AW (01388 718251; mobile: 07745 067754). Two self-catering cottages on a working livestock farm. Each sleeps up to 4, plus cot. Prices from £160-£360. Call for a brochure. Pets and children most welcome. ETC ★★★★ ETC CATEGORY 3 DISABLED ACCESSIBILITY (one cottage). [Pets £10 per week]
e-mail: info@farmholidaysuk.com   website: www.farmholidaysuk.com

Darlington

Market town in Tees Valley, ideal for exploring Yorkshire dales and moors.

HEADLAM HALL, HEADLAM, NEAR GAINFORD, DARLINGTON DL2 3HA (01325 730238). 17th Century country mansion offering luxurious accommodation, spa and 9-hole golf course. Pets welcome in Mews bedrooms with direct outside access . ETC/AA★★★★. [🐾]
website: www.headlamhall.co.uk

Allendale, Alnmouth, Alnwick, Bamburgh

Corbridge, Eals, Guyzance, Haltwhistle, Hexham

Allendale

Pretty stone-built village in the North Pennines Area of Outstanding Natural Beauty.

FELL VIEW COTTAGE, ALLENDALE. Detached traditional self-catering cottage in a designated
area of outstanding beauty. Highest possible standard unrestricted views and wonderful walks.
Sleeps 1-6. Pets welcome. Contact: MR C. VERNE-JONES, 69 BUCKINGHAMSHIRE ROAD,
BELMONT, DURHAM DH1 2BE (0191 386 9045). EnjoyEngland ★★★★.
e-mail: info@fellviewcottage.co.uk   website: www.fellviewcottage.co.uk

Alnmouth

Seaside village situated at the mouth of the River Aln.

SADDLE B&B, 24/25 NORTHUMBERLAND STREET, ALNMOUTH NE66 2RA (01665 830476). Friendly, family-run B&B on the Northumberland coast. Car park. All bedrooms en suite. Children and pets most welcome. ETC ★★★ [🐾]
e-mail: thesaddlebedandbreakfast@hotmail.com   website: www.thesaddlebedandbreakfast.co.uk

Alnwick

Town situated 32 miles south of Berwick-Upon-Tweed and the Scottish Border.

ALNWICK LODGE WEST CAWLEDGE PARK, ALNWICK NE66 2HJ (01665 604363/603377). In a picturesque setting close to the A1, with 15 well equipped en suite bedrooms, decorated and furnished to the highest standards. Locally sourced produce features in the splendid breakfast; evening meals available if ordered in advance. Children and dogs welcome. ETC ★★★ [Pets £8 per night]
e-mail: bookings@alnwicklodge.com   website: www.alnwicklodge.com

Bamburgh

Village on North Sea coast with magnificent castle. Grace Darling buried in churchyard.

WAREN HOUSE HOTEL, WAREN MILL, BAMBURGH NE70 7EE (01668 214581). Luxurious Country House Hotel. Excellent accommodation, superb food, moderately priced wine list. Rural setting. No children under 14 please. ETC ★★★ Silver Award, AA ★★★ One Rosette.[🐾]
e-mail: enquiries@warenhousehotel.co.uk   website: www.warenhousehotel.co.uk

Belford

Village 14 miles SE of Berwick-Upon-Tweed.

ETIVE COTTAGE, WARENFORD, NEAR BELFORD NE70 7HZ. Well-equipped two-bedroomed cottage with double glazing, central heating. Open views to coast. Fenced garden; secure parking. Pet and owners welcome pack. Pets welcome to bring along well behaved owners. Regional Winner, Winalot 'Best Place to Stay'. VisitBritain ★★★★★ Self-catering. Brochure: JAN THOMPSON (01668 213233). [🐾]
e-mail: janet.thompson1@homecall.co.uk   website: www.etivecottage.co.uk

Berwick-upon-Tweed

Border town at mouth of River Tweed 58 miles north west of Newcastle and 47 miles south east of Edinburgh. Medieval town walls, remains of a Norman Castle.

FRIENDLY HOUND COTTAGE, FORD COMMON, BERWICK-UPON-TWEED TD15 2QD (01289 388554) Set in a quiet rural location, convienient for Holy Island, Berwick, Bamburgh and the Heritage coastline. Come and enjoy our top quality accommodation, excellent breakfasts, and warm welcome. Arrive as our guests and leave as our friends. EnjoyEngland ★★★★ [🐾]
website: www.friendlyhoundcottage.co.uk

2, THE COURTYARD, BERWICK-UPON-TWEED. Secluded Self catering Townhouse in heart of old Berwick. Planted courtyard garden and sunny verandah. Historic ramparts 400 yards. Choice of walks. Ideal for exercising pets. Contact: J. MORTON, 1, THE COURTYARD, CHURCH STREET, BERWICK -UPON-TWEED, TD15 1EE (01289 308737). [🐾]
e-mail: patmosphere@yahoo.co.uk   website: www.berwickselfcatering.co.uk

FREE or **REDUCED RATE** entry to Holiday Visits and Attractions –
see our **READERS' OFFER VOUCHERS** on pages 409-414

Chathill

Hamlet 4 miles SW of Seahouses.

SARAH SHELL, DOXFORD FARM COTTAGES, CHATHILL, ALNWICK NE67 5DY (01665 579348; mobile: 07734 247277). Comfortable self-catering family accommodation on working farm situated amidst unspoilt wooded countryside, five miles from the coast. 8 stone built terrace cottages. VisitBritain ★★★/★★★★ [Pets £20 per week].
e-mail: sarah@doxfordfarmcottages.com   website: www.doxfordfarmcottages.com

Corbridge

Small town on the north bank of the River Tyne, 3 miles west of Hexham. Nearby are remains of Roman military town of Corstopitum.

MRS T. BROWN, FELLCROFT BED & BREAKFAST, STATION ROAD, CORBRIDGE NE45 5AY (01434 632384; Fax: 01434 633918). Delightful family-run B&B in a large Edwardian house close to the centre of Corbridge. Special facilities for walkers, cyclists and tourists. Families, children and dogs welcome. EnjoyEngland ★★★★.
e-mail: tove.brown@ukonline.co.uk   website: www.fellcroftbandb.com

MR & MRS MATTHEWS, THE HAYES GUEST HOUSE, NEWCASTLE ROAD, CORBRIDGE NE45 5LP (01434 632010). Stone-built stables in grounds of large country house converted into two self-catering cottages, each accommodating 4/5. WiFi available. ETC ★★★ [Pets £15 per week]
e-mail: camon@onebillinternet.co.uk   website: www.hayes-corbridge.co.uk

Eals

Village 7 miles from Haltwhistle, 8 miles from Alston.

STONECROP. A delightful white-washed cottage with its own orchard and large garden in a beautiful valley; recently renovated, with modern comforts - 3 bedrooms. Well behaved pets welcome. Close to Hadrian's Wall. Contact: RICHARD PARKER, EASTGATE, MILBURN, PENRITH, CUMBRIA CA10 1TN (01768 361509) [🐾]
website: www.stonecrop.co.uk

Guyzance

Hamlet located south east of Alnwick on the River Coquet.

LINDA TAYLOR, BANK HOUSE HOLIDAY COTTAGES, GUYZANCE NE65 9AP (07957 100615). One, two, three and four-bedroom luxuriously converted stone buildings and farmhouse, set in natural woodland close to the beautiful Northumberland coastline. VisitBritain ★★★★ Self Catering. [🐾]
e-mail: info@bankhouseholidaycottages.co.uk   website: www.bankhouseholidaycottages.co.uk

Haltwhistle

Small market town about one mile South of Hadrian's Wall.

KATH AND BRAD DOWLE, SAUGHY RIGG FARM, TWICE BREWED, HALTWHISTLE NE49 9PT (01434 344120). Close to the best parts of Hadrian's Wall. A warm welcome and good food. All rooms en suite. Parking. TV. Central heating. Children and pets welcome. Open all year. Prices from £35 pppn. ETC ★★★★ [Pets £5 per stay]
e-mail: info@saughyrigg.co.uk   website: www.saughyrigg.co.uk

🐾   Pets are welcome free of charge.

£   A charge is made for pets: nightly or weekly.

pw! Special provision for pets; exercise facility, feeding or accommodation arrangement.

⌂   Separate pets' accommodation.

Classified Symbols

Hexham

Market town on south bank of the River Tyne, 20 miles west of Newcastle-upon-Tyne.

MRS RUBY KEENLEYSIDE, STRUTHERS FARM, CATTON, ALLENDALE, HEXHAM NE47 9LP (01434 683580). Panoramic views, splendid walks. Double/twin rooms, en suite bathrooms, central heating. Good farmhouse cooking. Ample safe parking. Children welcome. Pets by prior arrangement. Open all year. ETC ★★★★.
website: www.struthersfarmbandb.com

BATTLESTEADS HOTEL & RESTAURANT, WARK, HEXHAM NE48 3LS (01434 230209). Friendly family-run hotel with 17 en suite bedrooms including ground floor with disabled access. Excellent bar meals and à la carte menus; good choice wines and beers. Pets by prior arrangement. [Pets £5 per night].
e-mail: info@battlesteads.com   website: www.battlesteads.com

Otterburn

Site of the Battle of Otterburn in 1388, part of the continuing skirmishes between the Scottish and English.

THE BORDER FOREST HOLIDAY PARK, COTTONSHOPEBURNFOOT, NEAR OTTERBURN NE19 1TF (01830 520259). Small secluded family run park, ideal for touring, and with many outdoor pursuits and historic sites within easy reach. A paradise for dogs and nature lovers. [Pets £15 per stay]
e-mail: info@borderforest.com   website: www.borderforest.com

Wooler

Small town on Harthope Burn 15 miles NW of Alnwick.

LYNNEY HOLDEN, CROOKHOUSE, KIRKNEWTON, WOOLER NE71 6TN (01668 216113). Superior self catering accommodation in a traditional Northumbrian steading, Secluded and tranquil. Sleeps 2-12. Horses and dogs welcome. VisitBritain ★★★★. [🐾 pw!]
e-mail: stay@crookhousecottages.co.uk   website: www.crookhousecottages.co.uk

Balterley Green Farm

Deans Lane, Balterley, Near Crewe CW2 5QJ
Tel: 01270 820214

Jo and Pete Hollins offer guests a friendly welcome to their home on a 145-acre working farm in quiet and peaceful surroundings. Situated on the Cheshire/Staffordshire border within easy reach of Junction 16 on the M6. Convenient for Chester, Alton Towers and the Potteries. Two family rooms en suite; two double and two twin en suite in converted cottage, also available for self catering. Bed and Breakfast from £25pp. Caravans and tents welcome. Pets £2 per night.

Newton Hall — Tattenhall, Chester CH3 9NE

Enjoy a quiet, relaxing holiday on our family-run farm. Newton Hall is a part 16thC timbered country house wih lovely gardens and views of Beeston and Peckforton Castles. We are close to the Canal and Sandstone Trail for enjoyable walks. Chester is only 15 minutes by car; also on good bus route. Breakfast consists of fresh, locally sourced produce, served in our elegant dining room overlooking the gardens. Ample secure parking. B&B £35-£50pppn.

Tel: 01829 770153 • Mobile: 07974 745676
e-mail: saarden@btinternet.com • www.newtonhallfarm.co.uk

THE EATON HOTEL
CITY ROAD, CHESTER CH1 3AE
Tel: 01244 320840 • Fax: 0870 6221691

Ideally located for you and your dog, in the heart of Chester, with parking, and bordering the Shropshire Union Canal towpath.

www.eatonhotelchester.co.uk

Astle Farm East · Chelford, Macclesfield SK10 4TA

A warm and friendly welcome awaits on this picturesque arable farm surrounded by a large garden. We offer you a quiet stay in an idyllic setting. All bedrooms en suite, open all year. Pets & children welcome.

Tel & Fax: 01625 861270 • e-mail: stubg@aol.com
www.astlefarmeast.co.uk

Tucked in a peaceful corner of rural Cheshire, with the most magnificent panoramic views of the Cheshire plains. Whether you come to drink, dine or unwind for a few days in one of our 12 en suite bedrooms, this atmospheric location will quickly have you under its spell. Freshly cooked wholesome food using local produce is on the menu, rewarded for its quality with a listing in the Michelin Good Pub Guide and Egon Ronay Guide. Delightful old sandstone buildings, open log fires, and the friendly, cosy atmosphere all add to the magic!

THE PHEASANT INN

The Pheasant Inn

Higher Burwardsley, Tattenhall, Cheshire CH3 9PF
Tel: 01829 770434 • Fax: 01829 771097
e-mail: info@thepheasantinn.co.uk • www.thepheasantinn.co.uk

FHG
K·U·P·E·R·A·R·D

Bestselling holiday accommodation guides for 65 years

Balterley

Small village two miles west of Audley.

MR & MRS HOLLINS, BALTERLEY GREEN FARM, DEANS LANE, BALTERLEY, NEAR CREWE CW2 5QJ (01270 820214). 145-acre farm in quiet and peaceful surroundings. Within easy reach of Junction 16 on the M6. Bed and Breakfast from £25pp. Also cottage for self-catering. Caravans and tents welcome. [pw! Pets £2 per night]

Chester

Former Roman city on the River Dee, with well-preserved walls and beautiful 14th century Cathedral. Liverpool 25 miles

MRS ANNE ARDEN, NEWTON HALL, TATTENHALL, CHESTER CH3 9NE (01829 770153; Mobile: 07974 745676). Part 16thC country house on a family-run farm, surrounded by beautiful scenery, with views of Beeston and Peckforton Castles. Ideal for a quiet, relaxing holiday. Chester 15 minutes' drive. ETC ★★★★ Silver Award & Breakfast Award [Pets £5 per stay]
e-mail: saarden@btinternet.com   website: www.newtonhallfarm.co.uk

THE EATON HOTEL, CITY ROAD, CHESTER CH1 3AE (01244 320840; Fax: 0870 6221691). Ideally located for you and your dog, in the heart of Chester, with parking, and bordering the Shropshire Union Canal towpath. [🐾]
website: www.eatonhotelchester.co.uk

Macclesfield

Town 10 miles south of Stockport.

MRS STUBBS, ASTLE FARM EAST, CHELFORD, MACCLESFIELD SK10 4TA (Tel & Fax: 01625 861270). A warm and friendly welcome awaits on this picturesque arable farm surrounded by a large garden. We offer you a quiet stay in an idyllic setting. All bedrooms en suite, open all year. ETC ★★. [⌂ 🐾]
e-mail: stubg@aol.com   website: www.astlefarmeast.co.uk

Tattenhall

Village 8 miles south east of Chester.

THE PHEASANT INN, HIGHER BURWARDSLEY, TATTENHALL CH3 9PF (01829 770434; Fax: 01829 771097). With panoramic views of Cheshire plains. Twelve en suite bedrooms. Freshly cooked food using local produce. Listed in the Michelin Good Pub Guide and Egon Ronay Guide. AA ★★★★★ [🐾]
e-mail: info@thepheasantinn.co.uk   website: www.thepheasantinn.co.uk

Skiddaw View Holiday Park

Bothel, near Bassenthwaite, Cumbria, CA7 2JN

Skiddaw View is an award winning holiday home park, situated in a secluded and delightful setting on the outskirts of Bassenthwaite in the Northern Lake District. The twenty acre park is nestled into the hillside with panoramic views of Skiddaw and the Northern Fells. We can offer a range of pet friendly self catering holiday properties including holiday static caravans, timber lodges as well as a number of holiday cottages in the surrounding towns and villages.

Timber Lodges

Holiday Static Caravans

Breathtaking views....

Fantastic for all the Family

Modern Contemporary Homes

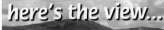

Children's Play Area & Recreational Field

Luxurious Homes

We both enjoyed our stay!

here's the view...

Tel: 016973 20919
Or for more information and online booking visit:
www.SkiddawView.co.uk

Ambleside

Ambleside, Appleby-in-Westmorland

015394 32330
www.smallwoodhotel.co.uk

Smallwood House
Compston Road, Ambleside,
Cumbria LA22 9DH
...where quality and the customer come first
En suite rooms • Car parking • Leisure Club Membership

Use promo code
"Pets" on
online booking to get
special pricing.

THE
BRITANNIA
INN

Elterwater, Langdale, Cumbria LA22 9HP
Tel: 015394 37210 • www.britinn.co.uk

A 500 year-old quintessential Lakeland Inn nestled in
the centre of the picturesque village of Elterwater
amidst the imposing fells of the Langdale Valley.
Comfortable, quality en suite double and twin-bedded rooms.
Dogs welcome. Enquire about our Mid-Week Special Offers.
Relax in the oak-beamed Bars or Dining Room whilst sampling
local real ales and dishes from our extensive menu of fresh,
home-cooked food using lots of Cumbrian produce.
See website for special offers
e-mail: info@britinn.co.uk

Brathay Lodge   Guest accommodation
in bright contemporary style

Spacious en suite bedrooms, spa baths with shower over. Some ground floor rooms
with own entrance. Double, twin and family rooms. Private off road parking.
From £30 pppn. Pets welcome. Short walk to park/lake.
Brathay Lodge, Rothay Road, Ambleside LA22 0EE • Tel: 015394 32000
e-mail: enquiries@amblesideholidays.co.uk • www.amblesideholidays.co.uk

---

015394 36611   **Betty Fold, Hawkshead Hill, Ambleside LA22 0PS**
e-mail: claire@bettyfold.co.uk • www.bettyfold.co.uk

Situated near Hawkshead and Tarn Hows, large country house in spacious grounds in the
heart of Lake District National Park. Betty Fold offers self-catering accommodation in
ground floor apartment with private entrance, sleeps 4. One double en suite and one small
twin with bathroom and colour TV. Open-plan kitchen/livingroom with electric cooker,
fridge, microwave, dishwasher. Terms inclusive of heat, light, power, bed linen and towels.

HALL CROFT Dufton

Large, detached, beautifully restored Victorian house in the
Westmorland village of Dufton, offering high quality facilities
in an idyllic setting. Three large guest rooms (two en suite,
adjacent bathroom in third). Substantial breakfasts; packed
lunches available. Ideal for peaceful break or stopover.
B&B from £31 pppn.

Ray & Frei Walker, Hall Croft, Dufton,
Appleby in Westmorland, Cumbria CA16 6DB
Tel: 017683 52902 • e-mail: hallcroft@phonecoop.coop

Our beautiful cottages and snug apartment are the delight of families, couples, walkers, and those seeking me-time in a stunning rural location. With two National Parks on the doorstep, just open the front door of the 1,2 & 3 bedroom cottages for stress-free days in fresh, hillside air and old fashioned family fun. Dogs very welcome and open all year.

Milburn Grange Holiday Cottages

Knock, Appleby, Cumbria CA16 6DR • Tel: 017683 61867
e-mail: petswelcome@milburngrange.co.uk • www.milburngrange.co.uk

Oakfold House www.oakfoldhouse.co.uk

Beresford Road, Bowness-on-Windermere, Cumbria LA23 2JG

Award winning Victorian guesthouse. Free WiFi. Close to Lake Windermere, shops, restaurants and Beatrix Potter attraction. Car Park. Gardens.

Tel: 015394 43239 • e-mail: oakfoldhouse@fsmail.net

Windermere Lake Holidays

Holiday houseboats on the lake shore with stunning views.
Sleep 4. Pets welcome. Open all year round.

For brochure: Tel: 015394 43415
e-mail: email@lakewindermere.net   www.lakewindermere.net

Langdale View

SELF CATERING HOLIDAY APARTMENTS

Bowness-on-Windermere, The Lake District

Langdale View Self Catering Apartments, a large semi-detached Lakeland house situated close to the village of Bowness. 2 minute walk to village, shops, pubs and restaurants. Four apartments, (sleep 2/6), personally managed by the owners to ensure high standards.
• Fully equipped fitted kitchen area • TV/DVD with Freeview channels • Free wireless internet access
• Central heating • Bed linen • Car Park • Pets welcome in some apartments at £20 per week
• Open all year. • Short breaks usually available.

Langdale View Holiday Apartments • 112 Craig Walk • Bowness-on-Windermere • Cumbria LA23 3AX
• Tel: 015394 46655 • Mobile: 077302 53422
email: enquiries@langdale-view.co.uk • www.langdale-view.co.uk

Farlam Hall Hotel Brampton, Cumbria CA8 2NG
Tel: 016977 46234 • Fax: 016977 46683

Standing in four acres of gardens, with its own lake, Farlam Hall has that indefinable quality that makes a stay here something really special. Fine quality cuisine, individually decorated and well-equipped guest rooms. Ideal touring centre for the Lakes, Borders & Hadrian's Wall.

AA ★★★
Inspectors' Choice
Relais & Chateaux

e-mail: farlam@relaischateaux.com • www.farlamhall.co.uk

Walk your dog straight from the cottages up the hill and on to the fells. 7 cottages on North Pennines farm, sleeping 2-8; excellent base for Hadrian's Wall, Scottish Borders and the Lake District. Local food cooked by Harriet and delivered to your cottage.

Tel: 016977 3435 • e-mail: stay@longbyres.co.uk
www.longbyres.co.uk

Long Byres at Talkin Head

www.lakedistrictcottages.co.uk

Two well-equipped cottages and two caravans in excellent walking area. Wildlife/birdwatchers paradise. Private fishing lake. Ancient woodlands, quiet, relaxing, warm welcome. Established 1968. ETC ★★★★ Gold Award

J. JACKSON, THORNTHWAITE FARM, WOODLAND HALL, WOODLAND, BROUGHTON-IN-FURNESS LA20 6DF
Tel & Fax: 01229 716340 • e-mail: info@lakedistrictcottages.co.uk

Broughton-in-Furness, Carlisle, Cockermouth

Keswick, Kirkby-in-Furness, Kirkby Lonsdale

Kirkby Stephen, Lake District, Lamplugh (near Loweswater), Langdale

Little Langdale, Millom, Newby Bridge, Penrith

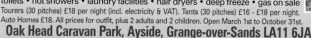

Ravenstonedale, Silloth-on-Solway, Skelwith Bridge, Ullswater

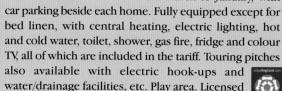

Wasdale, Wigton, Windermere

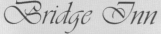

Windermere

STAY LAKELAND. A range of high quality self-catering holiday accommodation in the most popular northern Lake District destinations, including traditional cottages, houses, timber lodges and holiday static caravans. Sleep 2/24. (01900 821973) [🐾]
website: www.staylakeland.co.uk

Alston

Small market town 16 miles NE of Penrith.

PAUL & CAROL HUISH, ROCK HOUSE ESTATE, VALLEY VIEW, NENTHEAD, ALSTON CA9 3NA (01434 382 684). Five luxury cottages sleeping 2, 4, 7, 7, or 14. Undiscovered Cumbria, accessible to the Lakes, Dales and Borders. 100 acre estate is surrounded by spectacular views. Short breaks available. Open all year. VisitBritain ★★★/★★★★. [Pets £20 each].
e-mail: Info@RockHouseEstate.co.uk   website: www.RockHouseEstate.co.uk

CUMBERLAND INN, TOWNFOOT, ALSTON CA9 3HX (01434 381875). A comfy retreat in the secluded North Pennines. Home-made hearty fare available all day. All 5 bedrooms are en suite. Muddy dogs and boots welcome. Pets welcome in bedrooms and bar. No charge for pets.
e-mail: stay@cumberlandinnalston.com   website: www.cumberlandinnalston.com.

ISAAC'S BYRE, LOANING HEAD, GARRIGILL, ALSTON CA9 3EY (01434 381013). A lovely old barn conversion, sleeping 6. Open-plan living room with wood-burning stove, kitchen with range cooker, three bedrooms and three bath/shower rooms. Ideal for touring the Lake District, Northumberland and Scottish Borders. [pw! 🐾]
e-mail: judith-annwardlaw@hotmail.com   website: www.isaacsbyre.co.uk

Ambleside

Popular centre for exploring Lake District at northern end of Lake Windermere. Picturesque Stock Ghyll waterfall nearby, lovely walks. Associations with Wordsworth. Penrith 30 miles, Keswick 17, Windermere 5.

**THE OLD VICARAGE, VICARAGE ROAD, AMBLESIDE LA22 9DH (015394 33364). 'Rest a while in style'. Quality B&B set in tranquil wooded grounds in the heart of the village. Car park. All rooms en suite. Kettle, clock/radio, TV. Heated indoor pool, sauna, hot tub, sun lounge and rooftop terrace. Special breaks. Friendly service where your pets are welcome. Telephone Ian or Helen Burt. [🐾]
website: www.oldvicarageambleside.co.uk**

2 LOWFIELD, OLD LAKE ROAD, AMBLESIDE. Ground floor garden flat half a mile from town centre; sleeps 4. Lounge/diningroom, kitchen, bathroom/WC, two bedrooms, one with en suite shower. Linen supplied. Children and pets welcome. Parking. Terms from £160 to £300 per week. Contact: MR P. F. QUARMBY, 3 LOWFIELD, OLD LAKE ROAD, AMBLESIDE LA22 0DH (015394 32326) [🐾]
e-mail: paul.quarmby@zen.co.uk

KIRKSTONE FOOT, KIRKSTONE PASS ROAD, AMBLESIDE LA22 9EH (015394 32232; Fax: 015394 32805). Superior cottage and apartment complex, set in peaceful gardens, adjoining the Lakeland fells and village centre. Open all year. ETC ★★★★ and ETC ★★★★ GOLD AWARD [pw! Pets £5.00 per night.]
e-mail: enquiries@kirkstonefoot.co.uk   website: www.kirkstonefoot.co.uk

GRIZEDALE LODGE, HAWKSHEAD, AMBLESIDE LA22 0QL (015394 36532). In the heart of Grizedale Forest National Park, within easy reach of Windermere, Coniston, Ambleside and other attractions. All rooms en suite, some with four-posters. Open all year. [Pets £10 per night]
e-mail: enquiries@grizedale-lodge.com   website: www.grizedale-lodge.com

LYNDALE GUEST HOUSE LAKE ROAD, AMBLESIDE LA22 0DN (015394 34244) Nestled midway between Lake Windermere and Ambleside village, with superb views of Loughrigg Fell and the Langdales beyond. Excellent base for walking, touring, or just relaxing. [🐾]
e-mail: alison@lyndale-guesthouse.co.uk   website: www.lyndale-guesthouse.co.uk

GREENHOWE CARAVAN PARK, GREAT LANGDALE, AMBLESIDE LA22 9JU (015394 37231; Fax: 015394 37464). Permanent Caravan Park with Self Contained Holiday Accommodation. An ideal centre for Climbing, Fell Walking, Riding, Swimming, or just a lazy holiday. [Pets £6 per night, £30 per week]
website: www.greenhowe.com

SMALLWOOD HOUSE, COMPSTON ROAD, AMBLESIDE LA22 9DJ (015394 32330). Where quality and the customer come first. En suite rooms, car parking, leisure club membership. ETC ★★★★
[Pets £3 per night]
website: www.smallwoodhotel.co.uk

THE BRITANNIA INN, ELTERWATER, AMBLESIDE LA22 9HP (015394 37210; Fax: 015396 78075). 500-year-old traditional Lakeland inn. Extensive, home-cooked menu, real ales, cosy bars, log fires. Comfortable, high quality en suite accommodation. Well-behaved pets welcome. ETC ★★★.[🐾]
Use Promo code 'Pets' on our online booking system.
e-mail: info@britinn.co.uk   website: www.britinn.co.uk

BRATHAY LODGE, ROTHAY ROAD, AMBLESIDE LA22 0EE (015394 32000) Spacious en suite bedrooms, spa baths with shower over. Ground floor rooms with own entrance. Double, twin and family rooms, rates from £30 pppn. Pets welcome. Private off-road parking. EnjoyEngland ★★★★.
[Pets £7 per pet per night]
e-mail: info@amblesideholidays.co.uk   website: www.amblesideholidays.co.uk

BETTY FOLD, HAWKSHEAD HILL, AMBLESIDE LA22 0PS (015394 36611). Ground floor apartment sleeping four. Private entrance. Set in peaceful and spacious grounds, ideal for walkers and families with pets. Open all year. [pw! Pets £2 per night.]
e-mail: claire@bettyfold.co.uk   website: www.bettyfold.co.uk

Appleby-in-Westmorland

Located in the Eden Valley, ideal for walking, riding, fishing and cycling. Annual events include The Gypsy Horse Fair and the Jazz Festival.

RAY & FREI WALKER, HALL CROFT, DUFTON, APPLEBY-IN-WESTMORLAND CA16 6DB (017683 52902). Large, detached, beautifully restored Victorian house in peaceful village, offering high quality facilities in an idyllic setting. Three large guest rooms. Ideal for peaceful break, or centre for activity holiday. B&B from £31 pppn. AA ★★★★. [🐾]
e-mail: hallcroft@phonecoop.coop

MILBURN GRANGE HOLIDAY COTTAGES, KNOCK, APPLEBY CA16 6DR (017683 61867) 1,2 & 3 bedroom cottages and a snug apartment in a stunning rural location. Two National Parks on the doorstep. Dogs very welcome and open all year. VisitBritain ★★★ Self Catering. [Pets £20 per week]
e-mail: petswelcome@milburngrange.co.uk   website: www.milburngrange.co.uk

Bassenthwaite

Village on Bassenthwaite Lake with traces of Norse and Roman settlements.

SKIDDAW VIEW HOLIDAY PARK, BOTHEL, NEAR BASSENTHWAITE CA7 2JN (016973 20919). Award-winning 20-acre holiday home park situated in a secluded and delightful setting in the Northern Lake District. Range of self catering properties including static caravans, timber lodges as well as holiday cottages in the surrounding towns and villages. David Bellamy Gold Award. ETC ★★★★ Holiday Park. [Pets £5 per week].
website: www.skiddawview.co.uk

🐾   Pets are welcome free of charge.   **Classified Symbols**

£   A charge is made for pets: nightly or week

pw! Special provision for pets; exercise facility, feeding or accommodation arrangement.

⌂   Separate pets' accommodation.

Bowness-on-Windermere

Location on East shore of Lake Windermere adjoining Windermere town.

OAKFOLD HOUSE, BERESFORD ROAD, BOWNESS-ON-WINDERMERE LA23 2JG (015394 43239) Award-winning Victorian Guesthouse. Free WiFi. Close to Lake, steamers, shops, restaurants and Beatrix Potter attraction. Car park. Gardens. VisitBritain ★★★★ Gold Award. [🐾]
e-mail: oakfoldhouse@fsmail.net   website: www.oakfoldhouse.co.uk

WINDERMERE LAKE HOLIDAYS. Holiday houseboats on the lake shore with stunning views. Sleep 4. Open all year round. Pets welcome. For brochure: 015394 43415. [Pets £10 per week]
e-mail: email@lakewindermere.net   website: www.lakewindermere.net

LANGDALE VIEW HOLIDAY APARTMENTS, 112 CRAIG WALK, BOWNESS-ON-WINDERMERE LA23 3AX (015394 46655; Mobile: 077302 53422). Four self catering apartments in large Lakeland house. 2 minutes to village. Fully equipped. Sleep from 2 to 6; pets welcome by arrangement. EnjoyEngland ★★★★.[Pets £20 per week]
email: enquiries@langdale-view.co.uk   website: www.langdale-view.co.uk

Brampton

Market town with cobbled streets. Octagonal Moat Hall with exterior staircases and iron stocks.

FARLAM HALL HOTEL, BRAMPTON CA8 2NG (016977 46234; Fax: 016977 46683). Standing in four acres of gardens, with its own lake, Farlam Hall offers fine quality cuisine and individually decorated guest rooms. Ideal touring centre for the Lakes, Borders and Hadrian's Wall. AA Three Stars Inspectors' Choice and Two Rosettes, Relais & Chateaux. [🐾]
e-mail: farlam@relaischateaux.com   website: www.farlamhall.co.uk

LONG BYRES AT TALKIN HEAD (016977 3435). Walk your dog straight from the cottages up the hill and on to the fells. 7 cottages on North Pennines farm, sleeping 2-8; excellent base for Hadrian's Wall, Scottish Borders and the Lake District. Local food cooked by Harriet and delivered to your cottage. [🐾]
e-mail: stay@longbyres.co.uk   website: www.longbyres.co.uk

Broughton-in-Furness

Village 8 miles NW of Ulverston.

J. JACKSON, THORNTHWAITE FARM, WOODLAND HALL, WOODLAND, BROUGHTON-IN-FURNESS LA20 6DF (Tel & Fax: 01229 716340). Two well-equipped cottages and two caravans in excellent walking area. Wildlife/birdwatchers paradise. Private fishing lake. Ancient woodlands, quiet, relaxing, warm welcome. Established 1968. ETC ★★★★ GOLD AWARD [Pets £15 per week]
e-mail: info@lakedistrictcottages.co.uk   website: www.lakedistrictcottages.co.uk

PAUL SANDFORD, WOODEND COTTAGES, WOODEND, ULPHA, BROUGHTON-IN-FURNESS LA20 6DY (019467 23277). Woodend is remote and surrounded by hills and fells, with views towards Scafell Pike. The cottages offer cosy accommodation for two to six people. Short breaks available out of season. [🐾]
website: www.woodendhouse.co.uk

LAKELAND PACK PONY HOLIDAYS AT MOSS SIDE FARM. Enjoy walking holidays in Lakeland with a Lakeland Fell Pony carrying all you need. Stay in spacious Bell tents. Dogs welcome at some campsites. Also holiday cottage (sleeps 6), campsite, converted railway carriages. Stabling for horses. MOSS SIDE FARM, WOODLAND, BROUGHTON-IN-FURNESS LA20 6DJ (01229 716947).
e-mail: info@lakelandpackponies.co.uk   website: www.lakelandpackponies.co.uk

Carlisle

Important Border city and former Roman station on River Eden. Castle is of historic interest, also Tullie House Museum and Art Gallery. Good sports facilities inc. football and racecourse. Kendal 45 miles, Dumfries 33, Penrith 18.

GRAHAM ARMS HOTEL, ENGLISH STREET, LONGTOWN, CARLISLE CA6 5SE (01228 791213; Fax: 01228 794110). 16 bedrooms en suite, including four-poster and family rooms, all with tea/coffee facilities, TV and radio. Secure courtyard locked overnight. Pets welcome with well-behaved owners. ETC ★★ [🐾]
e-mail: office@grahamarms.com   website: www.grahamarms.com

GEORGINA & JOHN ELWEN, NEW PALLYARDS, HETHERSGILL, CARLISLE CA6 6HZ (01228 577308). Relax and see beautiful North Cumbria and the Borders. Self-catering cottages; Bed and Breakfast also available in en suite rooms. Dogs/pets by arrangement. See website specials.[Pets from £10 per week] e-mail: newpallyards@btinternet.com   website: www.4starsc.co.uk

Cockermouth

Market town and popular touring centre for Lake District and quiet Cumbrian coast. On Rivers Derwent and Cocker. Penrith 30 miles, Carlisle 26, Whitehaven 14, Keswick 12.

THE MANOR HOUSE, OUGHTERSIDE, ASPATRIA CA7 2PT (016973 22420). 18th century manor farmhouse retaining many original features and several acres of land. Spacious en suite rooms, tea/coffee making facilities, TV and lots of little extras. All pets welcome. Inspection Commended. [🐾] e-mail: richardandjudy@themanorhouse.net   website: www.themanorhouse.net

THE PHEASANT, BASSENTHWAITE LAKE, NEAR COCKERMOUTH CA13 9YE (017687 76234; Fax: 017687 76002). Traditional Cumbrian hostelry with tastefully renovated accommodation, fine dining and outstanding hospitality. ETC ★★★ Silver Award, AA ★★★ and Rosette e-mail: info@the-pheasant.co.uk   website: www.the-pheasant.co.uk

Coniston

Village 8 miles south-west of Ambleside, dominated by Old Man of Coniston (2635ft).

THE COPPERMINES AND CONISTON LAKES COTTAGES (015394 41765). Unique Lakeland cottages for 2 – 30 of quality and character in stunning mountain scenery. Log fires, exposed beams. Pets welcome! ★★★ - ★★★★ Book online. [Pets £25 per stay] website: www.coppermines.co.uk

BLUEBIRD LODGE, WATERHEAD, CONISTON LA21 8AJ (Tel/Fax: 01539 441442) In a quiet corner of the English Lakes, with comfortable rooms, a warm welcome and some of the best views in the area. An ideal location for fell walkers, dog owners and cyclists. All bedrooms are of a high standard.[🐾] website: www.bluebirdlodge.co.uk

THE YEWDALE HOTEL, YEWDALE ROAD, CONISTON LA21 8DU (015394 41280). Central for activities such as fishing, boating, canoeing, walking and pony trekking. 8 en suite bedrooms with TV and tea-making. Bar and dining room offer varied menus featuring fresh local produce. Excellent Cumbrian breakfasts. ETC ★★★ [Pets £6 per night] e-mail: info@yewdalehotel.com   website: www.yewdalehotel.com

THE SUN, CONISTON LA21 8HQ (015394 41248; Fax 015394 41219). Unique mix of great bar, diner and Four Star inn in extremely comfortable and informal atmosphere. Locally sourced food. Eight refurbished bedrooms with superb views. ETC ★★★★ [Pets £10 per night] e-mail: info@thesunconiston.com   website: www.thesunconiston.com

WATERHEAD HOTEL, CONISTON LA21 8AJ (015394 41244; Fax: 015394 41193). Situated alongside Coniston Water, The Waterhead Hotel makes a perfect retreat. 24 en suite bedrooms, two junior suites. Mountain View Restaurant, lounge bar with views across the Lake. Non-smoking. Ideal base for outdoor activities, also lake cruises and historic houses. ETC ★★★ [Pets £10 per night]. website: www.waterhead-hotel.co.uk

Crosthwaite

Hamlet 5 miles west of Kendal.

SAM AND TIREE DAWSON, CROSTHWAITE HOUSE, CROSTHWAITE, NEAR KENDAL LA8 8BP (015395 68264). Comfortable, relaxing B&B in area of real natural beauty, with pleasant fell and woodland walks. Relax, unwind and enjoy the easy-going atmosphere. AA ★★★★.[🐾] e-mail: bookings@crosthwaitehouse.co.uk   website: www.crosthwaitehouse.co.uk

DAMSON DENE HOTEL, CROSTHWAITE LA8 8JE (015395 68676). Tranquil location only 10 minutes from Lake Windermere. Best Lakes Breaks from £99 per person for 2 nights. [Pets £5 per night]. e-mail: info@damsondene.co.uk   website: www.bestlakesbreaks.co.uk

Duddon Valley

Majestic valley running between Cockley Beck and Duddon Bridge.

COCKLEY BECK FARM COTTAGE, SEATHWAITE, BROUGHTON-IN-FURNESS LA20 6EQ (01229 716480). In the heart of the Lake District National Park, just 4 miles from the summit of Scafell Pike. Self-contained holiday cottage (sleeps 4). Large open-plan kitchen. Well behaved dogs free of charge. Available all year. Private enclosed garden with patio and parking. [🐾 pw!]
e-mail: Sandra@cockleybeck.co.uk   website: www.cockleybeck.co.uk

Eskdale

Lakeless valley, noted for waterfalls and ascended by a light-gauge railway. Tremendous views. Roman fort. Keswick 35 miles, Broughton-in-Furness 10 miles.

THE BOOT INN (FORMERLY THE BURNMOOR INN), BOOT, ESKDALE CA19 1TG (019467 23224). Nine en suite bedrooms. Dogs and their owners made very welcome. Special breaks available all year on our web site. [🐾]
e-mail: enquiries@bootinn.co.uk   website: www.bootinn.co.uk

WOOLPACK INN, ESKDALE CA19 1TH (019467 23230). Historic inn in spectacular scenery. Comfortable bedrooms, most en suite. Selection of real ales, delicious food served all day. Pets welcome by arangement.
e-mail: enquiries@woolpack.co.uk   website: www.woolpack.co.uk

STANLEY HOUSE, ESKDALE CA19 1TF (019467 23327). Relaxed self-catering available in spacious house; can be booked for as many nights as required. Breakfast is served, but guests then have free use of kitchen and dining room. B&B also available.
website: www.stanleyghyll-eskdale.co.uk

FISHERGROUND LODGES, ESKDALE. Traditional hill farm, with three pine lodges sharing an acre of orchard. Ideal for walkers, nature lovers, dogs and children. Games room, raft pool and a station on the miniature railway! Good pubs nearby. PETER & KATHRYN KETCHEN, BETWEEN GUARDS, GOSFORTH CA20 1EN (01946 720810) [Pets £15 per week]
e-mail: holidays@fisherground.co.uk   website: www.fisherground.co.uk

Grange-in-Borrowdale

Hamlet in Borrowdale at the end of Derwent Water.

THE BORROWDALE GATES HOTEL, GRANGE-IN-BORROWDALE, KESWICK CA12 5UQ (017687 77204). Superbly situated amidst breathtaking scenery. Comfortable lounges, log fires and antiques will welcome you. 26 comfortable bedrooms and award-winning food. VisitBritain/AA ★★★, VisitBritain SILVER AWARD.
e-mail: hotel@borrowdale-gates.com   website: www.borrowdale-gates.com

Grasmere

Village famous for Wordsworth associations; the poet lived in Dove Cottage (preserved as it was), and is buried in the churchyard. Museum has manuscripts and relics.

DALE LODGE HOTEL AND TWEEDIES BAR, GRASMERE LA22 9SW (015394 35300). Beautiful Georgian house right in the heart of Grasmere. Stylish, modern bedrooms retaining the character of the house, exquisite food; Tweedies Bar for quality local ales, fine wines and the best pub food around. Enjoy England ★★★. Silver Award. [Pets £25 per week]
e-mail: enquiries@dalelodgehotel.co.uk   website: www.dalelodgehotel.co.uk

LAKE VIEW COUNTRY HOUSE & SELF-CATERING APARTMENTS, GRASMERE LA22 9TD (015394 35384/35167). 4 rooms B&B or 3 Self-Catering apartments in unrivalled, secluded location in the village with wonderful views and lakeshore access. All B&B rooms en suite, some with whirlpool baths. Ground floor accommodation available. No smoking. Featured in Michelin Guide. ETC ★★★/★★★★★
website: www.lakeview-grasmere.com

Hawkshead

Quaint village in Lake District between Coniston Water and Windermere. The 16th century Church and Grammar School, which Wordsworth attended, are of interest. Ambleside 5 miles.

THE KINGS ARMS HOTEL, HAWKSHEAD, AMBLESIDE LA22 0NZ (015394 36372). Join us for a relaxing stay amidst the green hills and dales of Lakeland, and we will be delighted to offer you good food, homely comfort and warm hospitality in historic surroundings. We hope to see you soon! Self-catering cottages also available.[🐾]
website: www.kingsarmshawkshead.co.uk

LAKELAND HIDEAWAYS, THE SQUARE, HAWKSHEAD LA22 0NZ (015394 42435). Cottages in and around Hawkshead. Great walks and lakes for swimming, dog friendly pubs, open fires to lie in front of... owners will enjoy it too. [Pets £20 per week].
e-mail: bookings@lakeland-hideaways.co.uk   website: www.lakeland-hideaways.co.uk

Kendal

Market town and popular centre for touring the Lake District. Of historic interest is the Norman castle, birthplace of Catherine Parr. Penrith 25 miles, Lancaster 22, Ambleside 13.

MR WARREN PROBYN, THE GLEN GUESTHOUSE, OXENHOLME, KENDAL LA9 7RF (01539 726386). Family-run Kendal Bed and Breakfast, with an excellent reputation for warm and friendly service, excellent comfortable accommodation and large freshly cooked breakfasts. Set in a quiet location in its own grounds under the "The Helm". EnjoyEngland ★★★★. [Pets £3 per night]
e-mail: greenintheglen@btinternet.com   website: www.glen-kendal.co.uk

RIVERSIDE HOTEL, BEEZON ROAD, KENDAL LA9 6EL (015397 34861). Lovely riverside location. Best Lakes Breaks from £99 per person for 2 nights. [Pets £5 per night].
e-mail: info@riversidekendal.co.uk   website: www.bestlakesbreaks.co.uk

MRS HELEN JONES, PRIMROSE COTTAGE, ORTON ROAD, TEBAY CA10 3TL (015396 24791). Adjacent M6 J38 (10 miles north of Kendal). Excellent rural location for North Lakes and Yorkshire Dales. Superb facilities, jacuzzi bath, king and four-poster beds. One-acre garden. Self-contained ground floor flat and 3 purpose-built self-catering bungalows for disabled guests, with electric bed, jacuzzi and large, wheel-in bathroom. Pets welcome, very friendly. VisitBritain ★★★★ Guest Accommodation. [Pets £3 per night]
e-mail: info@primrosecottagecumbria.co.uk   website: www.primrosecottagecumbria.co.uk

STONECROSS MANOR HOTEL, MILNTHORPE ROAD, KENDAL LA9 5HP (01539 733559; Fax: 01539 736386). Stonecross Manor offers easy access to town, ample parking, local cuisine, conference and banquet facilities, indoor swimming pool, and four-poster bedrooms. [Pets £10 per stay]
e-mail: info@stonecrossmanor.co.uk   website: www.stonecrossmanor.co.uk

MRS L. HODGSON, PATTON HALL FARM, KENDAL LA8 9DT (01539 721590). 2 Modern caravans, fully double glazed, gas central heating. Double and twin bedrooms, kitchen, spacious lounge/dining area, toilet and shower. Traditional working farm set in 140 acres of beautiful countryside. [Pets £10/£15 per week].
e-mail: stay@pattonhallfarm.co.uk   website: www.pattonhallfarm.co.uk

Keswick

Famous Lake District resort at north end of Derwentwater with Pencil Museum. Carlisle 30 miles,

ROYAL OAK HOTEL, BORROWDALE, KESWICK CA12 5XB (017687 77214). Small, family-run hotel with friendly atmosphere. Home cooking, cosy bar, comfortable lounge and some riverside rooms. Winter and Summer discount rates. Brochure and tariff available. [🐾]
e-mail: info@royaloakhotel.co.uk   website: www.royaloakhotel.co.uk

OVERWATER HALL, OVERWATER, NEAR IREBY, KESWICK CA7 1HH (017687 76566). Elegant Country House Hotel in spacious grounds. Dogs very welcome in your room. 4 night mid-week breaks from £400 per person, inclusive of Dinner and Breakfast. Mini breaks also available all year. Award-winning restaurant. Northwest of England Tourism Award - Small Hotel of the Year 2010. AA ★★★ and Two Rosettes. See also advertisement on page 282 [pw! 🐾]
e-mail: welcome@overwaterhall.co.uk   website: www.overwaterhall.co.uk

WOODSIDE, PENRITH ROAD, KESWICK CA12 4LJ (017687 73522). Friendly family-run establishment. All our rooms are en suite. We have ample private parking and large gardens. Non-smoking. Dogs welcome. ETC ★★★★. [🐾]
website: www.woodsideguesthouse.co.uk

DERWENT WATER MARINA, PORTINSCALE, KESWICK CA12 5RF (017687 72912). Lakeside self-catering apartments. Three apartments sleep 2, one apartment sleeps 6. Superb views over the lake and fells. Includes TV/DVD, heating and bed linen. Free Wi-Fi. Non-smoking. Watersports and boat hire available on site. [🐾]
website: www.derwentwaterapartments.co.uk

THE COLEDALE INN, BRAITHWAITE, NEAR KESWICK CA12 5TN (017687 78272). Genuine Country Inn in peaceful situation. 20 warm and spacious en suite bedrooms with TV. Children and pets welcome. Open all year. EnjoyEngland ★★★ [🐾]
e-mail: info@coledale-inn.co.uk   website: www.coledale-inn.co.uk

MARK & HELEN SMITH, GREYSTOKE HOUSE, 9 LEONARD STREET, KESWICK CA12 4EL (017687 72603) Warm and comfortable accommodation in a quiet location within walking distance of Keswick town centre. Safe cycle storage; drying room. Non-smoking, dog-friendly. ETC ★★★★. [Pets £10 per stay]
e-mail: info@greystokeguesthouse.co.uk   website:www.greystokeguesthouse.co.uk

MARY MOUNT HOTEL, BORROWDALE, NEAR KESWICK CA12 5UU (017687 77223). Set in 4½ acres of gardens and woodlands on the shores of Derwentwater. 2½ miles from Keswick in picturesque Borrowdale. Superb walking and touring. All rooms en suite with colour TV and tea/coffee making facilities. Licensed. Brochure on request. [pw! 🐾]
e-mail: info@marymounthotel.co.uk   website: www.marymounthotel.co.uk

Warm, comfortable houses and cottages in Keswick and beautiful Borrowdale, welcoming your dog. Inspected and quality graded. LAKELAND COTTAGE HOLIDAYS, KESWICK CA12 4QX (017687 76065; Fax: 017687 76869). [Pets £2 per day, £14 per week]
e-mail: info@lakelandcottages.co.uk   website: www.lakelandcottages.co.uk

IRTON HOUSE FARM, ISEL, COCKERMOUTH, NEAR KESWICK CA13 9ST (017687 76380). Self-catering family accommodation (suitable for disabled guests - wheelchair accessible). Sleep 2/6. Children welcome. Ample parking. ETC ★★★★. [Pets £30 per week].
website: www.irtonhousefarm.com

ANDY & CHARLOTTE PETERS, ROOMS 36, 36 LAKE ROAD, KESWICK CA12 5DQ (01768 772764; Freephone: 0800 0566401; mobile: 07721 957899). Set in quiet cul-de-sac, 3 minutes' walk from town centre, Theatre by the Lake, and Derwentwater (Queen of the Lakes). 6 well appointed rooms, all en suite. Special diets catered for, as well as normal English breakfast. Open all year including Christmas. [Pets £9 per night]
e-mail: andy@rooms36.co.uk   website: www.rooms36.co.uk

HORSE AND FARRIER INN, THRELKELD, KESWICK CA12 4SQ (017687 79688; Fax: 017687 79823). Ideal location for walking or touring the Lake District. All 15 bedrooms en suite, with TV, tea/coffee making and hairdryer. Award-winning food and restaurant. Open all year. Pets welcome. ETC ★★★★ [Pets £7.50 per week]
e-mail: info@horseandfarrier.com   website: www.horseandfarrier.com

KESWICK COTTAGES, LAKELAND VIEW, HOW LANE, PORTINSCALE, KESWICK CA12 5RS (017687 80088). Cottages and apartments in and around Keswick. Properties are well maintained and clean. From traditional Lakeland cottages to luxurious apartments. Children and pets welcome. ETC ★★★★-★★★★★ [Pets £15 per week]
e-mail: info@keswickcottages.co.uk   website: www.keswickcottages.co.uk

---

🐾   Pets are welcome free of charge.

£   A charge is made for pets: nightly or weekly.

pw! Special provision for pets; exercise facility, feeding or accommodation arrangement.

⌂   Separate pets' accommodation.

Classified Symbols

Kirkby-in-Furness

Small coastal village (A595). 10 minutes to Ulverston, Lakes within easy reach. Ideal base for walking and touring.

SUNSET COTTAGE. Self-catering 17th century two/three bedroom character cottage with garden. Original features. Panoramic views over sea/mountains; Coniston/Windermere 30 minutes. Non-smoking. Open all year. VisitBritain ★★★★ Contact: JANET AND PETER, 1 FRIARS GROUND, KIRKBY-IN-FURNESS LA17 7YB (01229 889601). [Pets £20 per pet per week]
e-mail: enquiries@southlakes-cottages.com   website: www.southlakes-cottages.com

Kirkby Lonsdale

Georgian buildings and quaint cottages. Riverside walks from medieval Devil's Bridge.

MRS PAULINE BAINBRIDGE, ULLATHORNS FARM, MIDDLETON, KIRKBY LONSDALE LA6 2LZ (015242 76214; Mobile: 07800 990689). 17th Century farmhouse on a working farm situated in the Lune Valley. B&B from £28. Children and well-behaved pets welcome. Non-smoking. VisitBritain ★★★★ [🐕]
e-mail: pauline@ullathorns.co.uk   website: www.ullathorns.co.uk

Kirkby Stephen

Small town on River Eden, 9 miles South of Appleby.

COCKLAKE HOUSE, MALLERSTANG CA17 4JT (017683 72080). Charming, High Pennine Country House B&B in unique position above Pendragon Castle in Upper Mallerstang Dale offering good food and exceptional comfort to a small number of guests. Two double rooms with large private bathrooms. Three acres riverside grounds. Dogs welcome. [🐕]

Kirkoswald

Village in the Cumbrian hills, lying north west of the Lake District. Ideal for touring. Penrith 7 miles.

SECLUDED COTTAGES WITH PRIVATE FISHING, KIRKOSWALD CA10 1EU (24 hour brochure line 01768 898711, manned most Saturdays). Quality cottages, clean, well equipped and maintained. Centrally located for Lakes, Pennines, Hadrian's Wall, Borderland. Enjoy the Good Life in comfort. Pets' paradise. Guests' coarse fishing. Bookings/enquiries 01768 898711. ETC ★★★ [pw! £2 per pet per night, £14 per week].
e-mail: info@crossfieldcottages.co.uk   website: www.crossfieldcottages.co.uk

Lake District

North west corner of England between A6/M6 and the Cumbrian Coast. Fells, valleys and 16 lakes, the largest being Lake Windermere.

LAKE DISTRICT. Two luxury houses available to rent in the Lake District. Routen House, sleeps 12 plus cot. Fully modernised, outstanding position in 4 acres. Little Parrock, sleeps 10 plus cot, short walk from centre of Grasmere with real log fire and private garden. Both houses non-smoking. MRS J. GREEN (01604 505115).
e-mail: joanne@routenhouse.co.uk   www.routenhouse.co.uk/www.littleparrock.co.uk

LAKE DISTRICT HOTELS. Situated in picturesque town centres and stunning lakeside locations, our six family-run, dog-friendly hotels are warm, welcoming and full of atmosphere. Comfy beds, delicious food, real ales and cosy lounges. Dog beds and bowls provided. Freephone 0800 840 1240. [Pets £5/£10 per night]
website: www.lakedistricthotels.net

Lamplugh (near Loweswater)

Hamlet 7 miles south of Cockermouth.

ROSE COTTAGE. Three miles from Loweswater and four miles from Ennerdale, lovely throughout. Open plan kitchen and sitting room, cosy coal fire, two bedrooms and enclosed garden. Pets welcome. Contact SALLY FIELDING (017687 80571). [Pets £15 per week]
website: www.millgillhead.co.uk

FELLDYKE COTTAGE HOLIDAYS, LAMPLUGH. Visiting the Western Lakes? Then why not stay in this lovely 19th century cottage. Sleeps 4, short breaks can be arranged. Pets are welcome. Open all year. Contact MRS A. WILSON (01946 861151). VB ★★★★ [pw!🐾] .
e-mail: dockraynook@talk21.com   website: www.felldykecottageholidays.co.uk

Langdale

Dramatic valley area to the west of Ambleside, in the very heart of the National Park.

WHEELWRIGHTS HOLIDAY COTTAGES, ELTERWATER, NEAR AMBLESIDE LA22 9HS (015394 37635; Fax: 015394 37618). Some of the loveliest cottages in the Lake District with stunning scenery on their doorsteps are ready to welcome you and your pets. Prices vary. Please visit our website. ETC ★★★ - ★★★★★ [🐾]
e-mail: enquiries@wheelwrights.com   website: www.wheelwrights.com

Little Langdale

Hamlet 2 miles west of Skelwith Bridge. To west is Little Langdale Tarn, a small lake.

HIGHFOLD COTTAGE, LITTLE LANGDALE. Cosy Lakeland cottage, ideally situated for walking and touring. Superb mountain views. Sleeps 5. Pets welcome. Weekly £290–£550. VB ★★★. MRS C.E. BLAIR, 8 THE GLEBE, CHAPEL STILE, AMBLESIDE LA22 9JT (015394 37686). [🐾]
website: www.highfoldcottage.co.uk

Millom

Small coastal town in the South Western Lake District.

HOLIDAY COTTAGE - LAKE DISTRICT (01229 717174). 300-year- old two-bedroom cottage on the west coast of Cumbria within the National Park. Traditional cottage, oak beams etc. Secure garden and an attached 3-acre deer-fenced playground for dogs. Close to miles of dog-friendly beaches. [pw! 🐾]

Newby Bridge

Village 8 miles NE of Ulverston

MR A.S.G. SCOTT, OAK HEAD CARAVAN PARK, AYSIDE, GRANGE-OVER-SANDS LA11 6JA (015395 31475). A well tended, uncrowded and wooded site set amidst picturesque fells. Flush toilets, hot showers, laundry facilities, hair dryers, deep freeze, gas on sale. Tourers (30 pitches), Tents (30 pitches), Auto Homes. Open March 1st to October 31st. [🐾]
website: www.oakheadcaravanpark.co.uk

NEWBY BRIDGE HOTEL, NEWBY BRIDGE LA12 8NA (015395 31222). Overlooking the southern shores of Lake Windermere. Best Lakes Breaks from £99 per person for 2 nights. [Pets £5 per night].
e-mail: info@newbybridgehotel.co.uk   website: www.bestlakesbreaks.co.uk

Penrith

Market town and centre for touring Lake District. Of interest are 14th century castle, Gloucester Arms (1477) and Tudor House. Excellent sporting facilities. Windermere 27 miles, Keswick 18.

LYVENNET COTTAGES. Five different cottages in and around the small farming village of Kings Meaburn in beautiful unspoilt 'Lyvennet Valley'. Ideal touring centre for the Lakes and Dales. JANET ADDISON, KELD FARM, KINGS MEABURN, PENRITH CA10 3BS (01931 714661/714226; Fax: 01931 714598). ETC ★★★★/★★★★★
website: www.lyvennetcottages.co.uk

CARROCK COTTAGES. Four renovated, award-winning, stone-built cottages set on the fringe of the Lakeland Fells. Games room. Home cooked meals service. Ideal for fell walking. Excellent restaurants nearby. A warm welcome guaranteed. ETC ★★★★★ GOLD AWARD. Contact MALCOLM OR GILLIAN (01768 484111; Fax: 01768 488850). [Pets £25 per pet per stay].
e-mail: info@carrockcottages.co.uk   website: www.carrockcottages.co.uk

WESTMORLAND HOTEL, ORTON, PENRITH CA10 3SB (015396 24351). Family-owned hotel in Cumbrian Fells. 50 en suite bedrooms. Cosy lounge. All day lounge menu and bar. Pets welcome at small charge, maximum 2 pets per room. AA ★★★ /Rosette. [Pets £8 per night]
e-mail: reservations@westmorlandhotel.com   website: www.westmorlandhotel.com

CHURCH COURT COTTAGES, GAMBLESBY, PENRITH CA10 1HR. Four beautiful, well-equipped, sandstone cottages in picturesque village. Excellent traffic-free walks from doorstep. Wonderful views of the hills of the Lake District and North Pennines. Penrith 15 minutes. ETC ★★★/★★★★
Contact: MARK COWELL or PATRICIA CLOWES (01768 881682). [🐾]
e-mail: cottages@gogamblesby.co.uk   website: www.gogamblesby.co.uk

NORTH BANK, EAMONT BRIDGE, PENRITH (01768 862153; 07939 240214). Detached bungalow with private gardens. Two lounges, kitchen, utility room; two bathrooms, one with jacuzzi, the other a walk-in shower. Four bedrooms, sleeps 8/9. Parking. [Pets £20 per week]
website: www.northbankholidaycottage.com

Ravenstonedale

Conservation village in the Eden Valley, 5 miles from Kirkby Stephen.

MRS D. METCALFE, HIGH GREENSIDE, RAVENSTONEDALE, KIRKBY STEPHEN CA17 4LU (015396 23671). Superb B&B accommodation in 18th century farmhouse on 120-acre working hill farm. Double and single room with private shower; twin and double en suite. All have colour TV and tea/coffee making. Superb views across Eden Valley. [🐾]
website: www.farmhousebandbcumbria.com

Silloth-on-Solway

Solway Firth resort with harbour and fine sandy beach. Mountain views. Golf, fishing. Penrith 33 miles, Carlisle 23, Cockermouth 17.

TANGLEWOOD CARAVAN PARK, CAUSEWAY HEAD, SILLOTH CA7 4PE (016973 31253). Friendly country site, excellent toilet and laundry facilities. Tourers welcome or hire a luxury caravan. Open 1st March to January 31st. Telephone or e-mail for a brochure. ETC ★★★. [🐾]
e-mail: tanglewoodcaravanpark@hotmail.com   website: www.tanglewoodcaravanpark.co.uk

Skelwith Bridge

Small village in the southern area of the Lake District. 3 miles south of Grasmere.

MIDDLE BRIG HOW (015394 37635/31176). Tucked away up a private drive surrounded by a well kept garden. Good sized living room with open fire and French doors. Large kitchen/dining area. Bathroom and separate wc; double bedroom with king size bed. Sleeps 2. [🐾]
e-mail: enquiries@wheelwrights.com   website: www.wheelwrights.com

Ullswater

Lake stretching for 7 miles with attractive Lakeside walks.

LAND ENDS CABINS, WATERMILLOCK, NEAR ULLSWATER CA11 0NB (017684 86438). Only 1.5 miles from Ullswater, our four detached log cabins have a peaceful fellside location in 25-acre grounds with two pretty lakes. Doggy heaven! Sleep 2-5. ETC ★★★ [🐾]
e-mail: infolandends@btinternet.com   website: www.landends.co.uk

FARRIERS LOFT, FELL VIEW, GLENRIDDING, PENRITH CA11 0PJ (017684 82795). Sleep 2-5. Lovely, comfortable, well equipped accommodation in an idyllic location between Glenridding and Patterdale. Magnificent views of the surrounding fells. Short Breaks available out of season.
e-mail: enquiries@fellviewholidays.com   website: www.fellviewholidays.com

OLD COP SHOP, FELL VIEW, GLENRIDDING, PENRITH CA11 0PJ (017684 82795). Sleeps 4. Lovely, comfortable, well equipped accommodation in an idyllic location between Glenridding and Patterdale. Magnificent views of the surrounding fells. Shared use of garden.
e-mail: enquiries@fellviewholidays.com   website: www.fellviewholidays.com

COVE CARAVAN & CAMPING PARK, WATERMILLOCK, PENRITH CA11 0LS (017684 86549). Well-maintained and peaceful park overlooking Lake Ullswater surrounded by Fells. Ideally situated for walking, watersports and all Lake District attractions. Electric hook-ups with hardstandings, sheltered grass for campers. AA 3 PENNANTS. [Pets £1 per night]
website: www.cove-park.co.uk

LAKE DISTRICT COTTAGES, DOLPHIN HOUSE, ASKHAM CA10 2PF (01931 712067). Talbot House (sleeps 5) and Talbot Studio (sleeps 2) are ideally located in conservation village only 3 miles away from Ullswater. Children and well behaved pets welcome. Short breaks available all year. EnjoyEngland ★★★★. [🐾].
e-mail: enquiries@lakedistrict-cottages.com   website: www.lakedistrict-cottages.com

Wasdale

Hamlet 1 mile north east of Wast Water

THE BRIDGE INN, SANTON BRIDGE, HOLMROOK CA19 1UX (019467 26221; Fax: 019467 26026). Award-winning country inn providing good food and accommodation. 16 en suite bedrooms. Ideal for exploring the Western Lakes and fells. Well behaved dogs welcome. [Pets £6 per stay].
e-mail: info@santonbridgeinn.com   website: www.santonbridgeinn.com

Wigton

Market town 11 miles SW of Carlisle.

FOXGLOVES COTTAGE, WIGTON. Sleeps 2-8. Spacious, well-equipped comfortable cottage on working farm. Children and pets very welcome. Easy reach Lake District, Scottish Borders and Roman Wall. Available all year. Short breaks by arrangement. MR & MRS E. & J. KERR, GREENRIGG FARM, WESTWARD, WIGTON CA7 8AH (016973 42676). [pw! First pet free, second or more £10 per week]
e-mail: foxgloveswigton@hotmail.co.uk   website: www.foxgloves.moonfruit.com

Windermere

Famous resort on lake of same name, the largest in England. Magnificent scenery. Car ferry from Bowness, one mile distant. Kendal 9 miles.

A superb choice of over 400 self-catering holiday cottages, in the best locations, managed by our friendly, knowledgeable staff. Pets welcome. For brochure, contact: LAKELOVERS, BELMONT HOUSE, LAKE ROAD, BOWNESS-ON-WINDERMERE LA23 3BJ. (015394 88855; Fax: 015394 88857). ETC ★★★ - ★★★★★ [Pets £20 per week.]
e-mail: bookings@lakelovers.co.uk   website: www.lakelovers.co.uk

LANGDALE CHASE HOTEL, WINDERMERE LA23 1LW (015394 32201). Magnificent country house hotel with grounds sloping to the edge of Lake Windermere. Panoramic views, log fires, excellent food and friendly professional staff all ensure a memorable stay. ETC ★★★ [Pets £10 per night]
e-mail: sales@langdalechase.co.uk   website: www.langdalechase.co.uk

THE WILD BOAR INN, GRILL & SMOKEHOUSE, NEAR WINDERMERE LA23 3NF (08458 504 604). Nestled in the beautiful Gilpin Valley, former coaching Inn set within its own private 72 acres of woodland. Excellent restaurant with local produce and real ales. Windermere Golf Club and Leisure Club nearby. [Pets £10 per night, up to 2 dogs per stay - max. 4 nights.]
website: www.thewildboarinn.co.uk

WATERMILL INN & BREWERY, INGS, NEAR WINDERMERE LA8 9PY (01539 821309; Fax: 01539 822309). Ruby and friends (Dogs) welcome you to the award-winning Inn. 16 real ales. Cosy fires, en suite rooms, excellent bar meals. Doggie water and biscuits served in the bar. Good doorstep dog walking. ETC ★★★★ [Pets £4 per night (includes donation to Dogs' Trust).
e-mail: info@Lakelandpub.co.uk   website: www.Lakelandpub.co.uk

Carnforth

Town 6 miles North of Lancaster.

LOCKA OLD HALL COTTAGE, ARKHOLME, NEAR KIRKBY LONSDALE LA6 1BD (015242 21561). Small cottage with wood burning stove in easy reach of Lake District, Yorkshire Dales and Lancashire coast. Lawned garden with views over fells and Ingleborough. Quiet location. Sleeps 2 (+2 on sofa bed). [🐕]
e-mail: cottage@locka.co.uk   website: www.locka.co.uk

Clitheroe

Town in Ribble Valley, good base for exploring Forest of Bowland.

THE INN AT WHITEWELL, FOREST OF BOWLAND, NEAR CLITHEROE BB7 3AT (01200 448222). 14thC inn in the beautiful Forest of Bowland. 7 miles fishing from our doorstep - trout, sea trout and salmon. 23 glamorous bedrooms, award-winning kitchen. Voted by The Independent "One of the 50 Best UK Hotels". [🐕]
e-mail: reception@innatwhitewell.com   website: www.innatwhitewell.com

Thornley

Town 7 miles West of Clitheroe, 4 miles from Longridge.

LOUDVIEW BARN. Self-catering stone barn conversion in peaceful location in Forest of Bowland. Exceptional views across unspoilt countryside. Unit 1: one double, one twin and bunk beds; Unit 2: one double and one twin. ETC ★★★★ Contact: MR & MRS STARKEY, LOUDVIEW BARN, RAMS CLOUGH FARM, THORNLEY, PRESTON PR3 2TN (01995 61476). [🐕]
e-mail: loudview@ic24.net   website: www.loudview.co.uk

NORTH WALES HOLIDAY COTTAGES. Self-catering cottages and farmhouses in the beautiful regions of the Conwy Valley, coastal resorts, Vale of Clwyd, Northern and Southern Snowdonia, Lleyn Peninsula and Anglesey. Phone 01492 582 492. [🐾]
e-mail: info@nwhc.co.uk   website: www.pw.nwhc.co.uk

❖ Ty Gwyn ❖

Tel: 01678 521267 or 520234

• **TY GWYN** • Static six-berth luxury caravan with two bedrooms, shower, bathroom, colour TV, microwave, etc. on private grounds.

Situated two miles from Bala in beautiful country area. Ideal for walking, sailing, fishing and canoeing. 30 miles from nearest beach. Pets welcome

Contact: **MRS A. SKINNER, TY GWYN, RHYDUCHAF, BALA LL23 7SD**
E-mail: anntgwyn@hotmail.co.uk

Treborth Leisure • Gwynedd

In a beautiful part of Wales, we believe we have everything you need to make the most of your holiday. Our leisure complex encompasses beautifully appointed holiday cottages • 6 hole Par 3 golf course with artificial tees and greens • well-stocked fishing lake • superb camping and touring caravan facilities
Treborth Leisure Ltd, The Old Barn, Treborth Hall Farm, Bangor, Gwynedd LL57 2RX
Telephone: 01248 364399 • Fax: 01248 364333
e-mail: enquiries@treborthleisure.co.uk • www.treborthleisure.co.uk

---

Islawrffordd Caravan Park • Tal-y-Bont, Gwynedd LL43 2BQ

Situated on the Snowdonia coastline, just north of Barmouth, our park offers a limited number of caravans for hire. Our touring caravan field has been modernised to super pitch quality including hard standing with each plot being reservable. Camping field with new state-of-the-art toilet block.
AA Park facilities include:• shop • laundry • indoor heated pool • jacuzzi • sauna • bar
• amusements • food bars • **Tel: 01341 247269** • **Fax: 01341 242639** Cymru Wales
e-mail: info@islawrffordd.co.uk • www.islawrffordd.co.uk

Llwyndu Farmhouse

Llanaber, Barmouth, Gwynedd LL42 1RR

16th century farmhouse hotel. Stunning location with views over Cardigan Bay and its huge sandy beaches. All bedroom en suite and very individual, some in converted granary. Super food, local beers and good wine list. Cosy, informal atmosphere amidst oak beams, inglenooks and history.

Tel: 01341 280144
e-mail: intouch@llwyndu-farmhouse.co.uk
www.llwyndu-farmhouse.co.uk

Cymru Wales ★★★★

Croeso

• Comfortable three-bedroomed house
• Enclosed garden • Near beaches, common, forest
• Fully equipped; bedding and electricity inclusive
• Colour TV/DVD player, microwave • Dogs and children welcome. WTB ★★★

£240 to £450 per week

MRS J. GUNDRY, FARMYARD LODGE, BODORGAN, ANGLESEY LL62 5LW • Tel: 01407 840977

Dulas Bay, Dyffryn Ardudwy, Llanbedr, Pentraeth, Pwllheli, Trearddur Bay

Bala

Natural touring centre for Snowdonia. Narrow gauge railway runs along side of Bala lake, the largest natural lake in Wales. Golf, sailing, fishing, canoeing.

TY GWYN - two-bedroomed luxury caravan in private grounds. Situated just two miles from Bala in beautiful country area, ideal for walking, sailing, fishing and canoeing. Only 30 miles from seaside. Contact: MRS A. SKINNER, TY GWYN, RHYDUCHAF, BALA LL23 7SD (01678 521267). [🐾]
e-mail: anntygwyn@hotmail.co.uk

Bangor

Cathedral city and resort on Menai Strait. One of the smallest cities in Britain.

TREBORTH LEISURE LTD, THE OLD BARN, TREBORTH HALL FARM, BANGOR LL57 2RX (01248 364399; Fax: 01248 364333). In a beautiful part of Wales, our leisure complex encompasses beautifully appointed holiday cottages, 6-hole golf course, well-stocked fishing lake, superb camping and touring caravan facilities. [🐾]
e-mail: enquiries@treborthleisure.co.uk   website: www.treborthleisure.co.uk

Barmouth

Modern seaside resort with two miles of sandy beaches. Surrounding hills full of interesting archaeological remains.

ISLAWRFFORDD CARAVAN PARK, TAL-Y-BONT, GWYNEDD LL43 2BQ (01341 247269; Fax: 01341 242639). On the Snowdonia coastline, just north of Barmouth, our park offers a limited number of caravans for hire; touring caravan field and camping also available. Facilities include: shop, laundry, indoor heated pool, jacuzzi, sauna, bar, amusements, food bars. [Pets £2 per night].
e-mail: info@islawrffordd.co.uk   website: www.islawrffordd.co.uk

MRS PAULA THOMPSON, LLWYNDU FARMHOUSE, LLANABER, BARMOUTH LL42 1RR (01341 280144). Converted 16th century farmhouse retaining many original features. Cosy lounge and character dining room. Bedrooms are modern and well equipped, some with four-poster beds. WTB ★★★★ [🐾]
e-mail: intouch@llwyndu-farmhouse.co.uk   website: www.llwyndu-farmhouse.co.uk

Beaumaris

Elegant little town dominated by castle built by Edward I in 13th century. Museum of Childhood has Victorian toys and music boxes.

'QUALITY COTTAGES', CERBID, SOLVA, HAVERFORDWEST, PEMBROKESHIRE SA62 6YE (01348 837871). Cottages set in all coastal areas, enjoy unashamed luxury, highest residential standards. Log fires. Linen supplied. Pets welcome, free. [pw! 🐾]
website: www.qualitycottages.co.uk

Bodorgan

A rural area in South West Anglesey.

CROESO. Comfortable three-bedroomed house. Enclosed garden. Near beaches, common, forest. Fully equipped, bedding and electricity inclusive. Colour TV/DVD player, microwave. Dogs and children welcome. £240-£450 per week. WTB ★★★ [🐕] Contact: MRS J. GUNDRY, FARMYARD LODGE, BODORGAN, ANGLESEY LL62 5LW (01407 840977)

Caernarfon

Historic walled town and resort, ideal for touring Snowdonia. Museums, Segontium Roman Fort, magnificent 13th century castle. Old harbour, sailing trips.

PLAS-Y-BRYN CHALET PARK, BONTNEWYDD, NEAR CAERNARFON LL54 7YE (01286 672811). Two miles from Caernarfon. It offers safety, seclusion and beautiful views of Snowdonia. Ideally positioned for touring. Well behaved pets always welcome. WTB ★★★★ [Pets £20 per week].
e-mail: philplasybryn@aol.com   website: www.plasybryn.co.uk

TY'N RHOS 5★ COUNTRY HOUSE & RESTAURANT, SEION, LLANDDEINIOLEN, NEAR CAERNARFON LL55 3AE (01248 670489). A special place set in a beautiful location between Snowdonia and the Isle of Anglesey. Bedrooms are en suite, with flat screen TV, luxury bathrobes and toiletries. Menus feature fresh local ingredients prepared to the highest standards. Pets are welcome by arrangement. AA/VisitWales ★★★★★ [Pets £5-£10 per night, depending on room]
e-mail: enquiries@tynrhos.co.uk   website: www.tynrhos.co.uk

Criccieth

Popular family resort with safe beaches divided by ruins of 13th century castle. Salmon and sea trout fishing. Festival of Music and Arts in the summer.

'QUALITY COTTAGES', CERBID, SOLVA, HAVERFORDWEST, PEMBROKESHIRE SA62 6YE (01348 837871). Cottages set in all coastal areas, enjoy unashamed luxury, highest residential standards. Log fires. Linen supplied. Pets welcome, free. [pw! 🐕]
website: www.qualitycottages.co.uk

S A. M. JONES, RHOS COUNTRY COTTAGES, CRICCIETH, PORTHMADOG LL52 0PB (01758 720047 or 0776 986 4642). Superb collection of secluded country cottages with private gardens. Private fishing and rough shooting by arrangement. Open all year. VisitWales ★★★★★ [🐕]
e-mail: cottages@rhos.freeserve.co.uk   website: www.rhos-cottages.co.uk

PARC WERNOL PARK, CHWILOG, PWLLHELI LL53 6SW (01766 810506). Peaceful and quiet, ideal for touring. Self-catering holidays – 1,2 & 3 bedroom cottages, 2 and 3 bedroom caravans and chalets. Colour brochure. Wi-Fi available. [Pets £15 per dog per week.]
e-mail: catherine@wernol.co.uk   website: www.wernol.co.uk

A warm welcome awaits you in comfortable self-catering cottages. Easily accessible to numerous attractions, or enjoy tranquillity of countryside. Short breaks available. Pets welcome. MRS M. WILLIAMS, GAERWEN FARM, YNYS, CRICCIETH LL52 0NU (01766 810324).[🐕]
e-mail: gaerwen@btopenworld.com   website: www.gaerwenfarmcottages.co.uk

MIN Y GAER, PORTHMADOG ROAD, CRICCIETH LL52 0HP (01766 522151). Family-run guest house conveniently situated close to amenities and overlooking Esplanade. Warm friendly atmosphere. Good food and comfortable accommodation at a reasonable price. Walkers and Cyclists Welcome. WTB/AA ★★★★ [Pets £2.50 per night]
e-mail: enquiry@minygaer.co.uk   website: www.minygaer.co.uk

Dolgellau

Market town lying on the River Wyion, a tributary of the River Mawddach.

MRS HELEN ROWLANDS, LLWYN-YR-HELM FARM, BRITHDIR, DOLGELLAU LL40 2SA (01341 450254). Quiet, small working farm site, four miles from Dolgellau in beautiful countryside. Caravans, Dormobiles and tents; electric hook-ups. Facilities for the disabled. Toilet block. Laundry. Self-catering camping lodge available. Pets welcome. [🐕]
e-mail: info@llwynyrhelmcaravanpark.co.uk   website:www.llwynyrhelmcaravanpark.co.uk

Dulas Bay

On north-east coast of Anglesey, between Amlwch and Moelfre.

MRS G. McCREADIE, DERI ISAF, DULAS BAY, ANGLESEY LL70 9DX (01248 410536; Mobile: 07721 374471). Award winning Country House in 20 acres of woodland, gardens and fields. Family, twin and double rooms, all en suite. Pets welcome. Stabling/grazing available. WTB ★★★★ Country House [Dogs £3.00 per night, £20 per week]
e-mail: mccreadie@deriisaf.freeserve.co.uk   website: www.angleseyfarms.com/deri.htm

Dyffryn Ardudwy

Situated on the coastal road between Harlech and Barmouth.

BWTHYN BACH & BWTHYN CLYD. Refurbished cosy cottage in private grounds. One bedroom with king-size bed. Kitchen with oven, microwave, fridge/freezer, dishwasher. Bathroom with shower. Beach and village within walking distance, local pubs, fantastic walks. Two small dogs welcome. Contact BETHAN & GARRY NEWPORT (01341 242 628 or 07775 670 565/566.
website: www.buarthcottageswales.co.uk

Harlech

Small stone-built town dominated by remains of 13th century castle. Golf, theatre, swimming pool, fine stretch of sands

'QUALITY COTTAGES', CERBID, SOLVA, HAVERFORDWEST, PEMBROKESHIRE SA62 6YE (01348 837871). Cottages set in all coastal areas, enjoy unashamed luxury, highest residential standards. Log fires. Linen supplied. Pets welcome, free. [pw! 🐕]
website: www.qualitycottages.co.uk

Llanbedr

Ideal base for exploring mountains and coast of Snowdonia, just 3 miles from Harlech.

TAN-Y-RHIW HOLIDAY COTTAGE. A detatched secluded stone cottage set in its own grounds, offering a comfortable holiday whilst retaining its 18th century character. Sleeps up to eight people plus cot. Woodland walk at side of cottage. Contact: CAROL & PAUL RICHARDSON,15 CHESWARDINE LANE, NORTON, NEAR SHIFNAL TF11 9EQ (Tel/Fax 01952 730212). WTB ★★★★ [🐕]
e-mail: tan.y.rhiw@btinternet.com   website: www.tan-y-rhiw.co.uk

Llanddona

Village on Anglesey 3 miles north west of Beaumaris

'QUALITY COTTAGES', CERBID, SOLVA, HAVERFORDWEST, PEMBROKESHIRE SA62 6YE (01348 837871). Cottages set in all coastal areas, enjoy unashamed luxury, highest residential standards. Log fires. Linen supplied. Pets welcome, free. [pw! 🐕]
website: www.qualitycottages.co.uk

Morfa Nefyn

Picturesque village 2 miles west of Nefyn.

'QUALITY COTTAGES', CERBID, SOLVA, HAVERFORDWEST, PEMBROKESHIRE SA62 6YE (01348 837871). Cottages set in all coastal areas, enjoy unashamed luxury, highest residential standards. Log fires. Linen supplied. Pets welcome, free. [pw! 🐕]
website: www.qualitycottages.co.uk

Pentraeth

Village on Anglesey, near Red Wharf Bay.

PEN-Y-GARNEDD FARM COTTAGE, PENTRAETH (01248 450580). Cosy cottage on friendly working smallholding. Sleeps 5, log burner and heating. Wi-Fi, TV, DVD. Well behaved children and pets welcome. Close to Red Wharf Bay and coastal paths. Low Season Short Breaks. Caravan Club Approved Site. WTB ★★★ [🐕].
e-mail: sandypenygarnedd@yahoo.co.uk   website: www.penygarnedd.co.uk

Porthmadog

Harbour town with mile-long Cob embankment, along which runs Ffestiniog Narrow Gauge Steam Railway to Blaenau Ffestiniog. Pottery, maritime museum, car museum. Good beaches nearby.

'QUALITY COTTAGES', CERBID, SOLVA, HAVERFORDWEST, PEMBROKESHIRE SA62 6YE (01348 837871). Cottages set in all coastal areas, enjoy unashamed luxury, highest residential standards. Log fires. Linen supplied. Pets welcome, free. [pw! 🐕]
website: www.qualitycottages.co.uk

Pwllheli

Market town with harbour, 8 miles west of Criccieth

CEFN COED HOLIDAY COTTAGES, CEFN COED, CHWILOG, PWLLHELI LL53 6NX. (01766 810259) Three holiday cottages to let, sleep 4/6. On the south coast of the Lleyn Peninsula with sweeping panoramic views of Snowdonia, Cardigan Bay and the Meirionnydd Mountains. WTB ★★★★. [Pets £20 per week]
e-mail: enquiries@cefncoedholidays.co.uk   website: www.cefncoedholidays.co.uk

Red Wharf Bay

Deep curving bay with vast expanse of sand, very popular for sailing and swimming.

'QUALITY COTTAGES', CERBID, SOLVA, HAVERFORDWEST, PEMBROKESHIRE SA62 6YE (01348 837871). Cottages set in all coastal areas, enjoy unashamed luxury, highest residential standards. Log fires. Linen supplied. Pets welcome, free. [pw! 🐕]
website: www.qualitycottages.co.uk

Trearddur Bay

Attractive holiday spot set amongst low cliffs on Holy Island, near Holyhead. Golf, sailing, fishing and swimming.

TREARDDUR HOLIDAY BUNGALOWS, LON ISALLT, TREARDDUR BAY, ANGLESEY LL65 2UP (01407 860494). Comfortable self-catering holiday bungalows sleeping 2-7 near Trearddur's lovely beaches. Locally, beautiful headland walks, fishing, golf and horse riding. Ideal location to explore Anglesey and the North Wales coast. Terms from £100-£580 per week.
e-mail: trearholiday@btconnect.com   website: www.holiday-bungalows.co.uk

BLACKTHORN FARM, PENRHOS FEILW, TREARDDUR BAY LL65 2LT (01407 765262). Family-run Bed and Breakfast, Self-catering, Camping and Touring site in an idyllic spot on Holy Island in North Wales. Set in 18 acres of outstanding unspoilt beauty with panoramic views. VisitWales ★★★★. [Pets £5 per night B&B, £2 per night in caravan/campsite.]
e-mail: enquiries@blackthornfarm.co.uk   website: www.blackthornleisure.co.uk

Tywyn

Pleasant seaside resort, start of Talyllyn Narrow Gauge Railway. Sea and river fishing, golf.

'QUALITY COTTAGES', CERBID, SOLVA, HAVERFORDWEST, PEMBROKESHIRE SA62 6YE (01348 837871). Cottages set in all coastal areas, enjoy unashamed luxury, highest residential standards. Log fires. Linen supplied. Pets welcome, free. [pw! 🐕]
website: www.qualitycottages.co.uk

SNOWDONIA NATIONAL PARK SELF-CATERING CHALET. Delightful chalet in private holiday park. Swimming pool, games room and restaurant. Spectacular scenery, outdoor pursuits. A real family holiday – something for everyone! MERCEDES MORGAN (01568 780912) [🐕]
e-mail: vvmorgan100@aol.com   website: www.wiz.to/seventeen

Please mention PETS WELCOME!
when making enquiries about accommodation featured in this guide

Betws-y-Coed, Colwyn Bay, Conwy

FHG Guides publish a large range of well-known
accommodation guides. We will be happy to send you details or
you can use the order form at the back of this book.

Denbigh (Llandyrnog)

Llanrwst (Conwy Valley), Rhos-on-Sea (Conwy)

'QUALITY COTTAGES', CERBID, SOLVA, HAVERFORDWEST, PEMBROKESHIRE SA62 6YE (01348 837871). Cottages set in all coastal areas, enjoy unashamed luxury, highest residential standards. Log fires. Linen supplied. Pets welcome, free. [pw! 🐕]
website: www.qualitycottages.co.uk

Betws-y-Coed

Popular mountain resort in picturesque setting where three rivers meet. Trout fishing, craft shops, golf, railway and motor museums, Snowdonia National Park Visitor Centre. Nearby Swallow Falls are famous beauty spot.

MISS MORRIS, TY COCH FARM-TREKKING CENTRE, PENMACHNO, BETWS-Y-COED LL25 0HJ (01690 760248). Hill farm in Wales. TV, teamaking, en suite. Set in National Park/Snowdonia. Very quiet and well off the beaten track. A great welcome and good food. Many return visits. £27 B&B. [🐕]
e-mail: cindymorris@tiscali.co.uk

Colwyn Bay

Lively seaside resort with promenade amusements. Attractions include Mountain Zoo, Eirias Park; golf, tennis, riding and other sports. Good touring centre for Snowdonia. The quieter resort of Rhos-on-Sea lies at the western end of the bay.

NORTH WALES HOLIDAYS (01492 512903/512282). High quality cottages, cosy chalets and large coach house at Bron-y-Wendon and Nant-y-Glyn (16 units in total). Many leisure activities nearby. Short breaks all year. Pets welcome. VistWales 2-5 Stars. [🐕]
e-mail: stay@northwales-holidays.co.uk   website: www.northwales-holidays.co.uk

Classified Symbols

🐕 Pets are welcome free of charge.

£ A charge is made for pets: nightly or weekly.

pw! Special provision for pets; exercise facility, feeding or accommodation arrangement.

⌂ Separate pets' accommodation.

Conwy

One of the best preserved medieval fortified towns in Britain on dramatic estuary setting. Telford Suspension Bridge, many historic buildings, lively quayside (site of smallest house in Britain). Golf, pony trekking, pleasure cruises.

BRONGAIN, TYN-Y-GROES, CONWY. Homely Victorian stone cottage, picturesque Conwy Valley. Snowdonia Mountain views. Enjoy lakes, mountains, walking, bird watching, beaches, Bodnant, RSPB, Conwy Castle. £300-£375. Contact: MRS G. M. SIMPOLE, 105 HAYGREEN ROAD, TERRINGTON ST CLEMENT, KINGS LYNN, NORFOLK PE34 4PU (01553 828897; Mobile: 0798 9080 665) [pw! 🐕]
e-mail: gill@simpole.rlshost.net   website: www.simpole.rlshost.net

TAL-Y-FAN COTTAGE AND ALLTWEN COTTAGE. Two luxurious self-catering country cottages accommodating up to four people. Spectacular views. Ideal touring centre for Snowdonia. Pony trekking, golf and fishing locally. Pets and children welcome. Short Breaks available. Non-smoking. Contact: MR JOHN BAXTER, GLYN UCHAF, CONWY OLD ROAD, DWYGYFYLCHI, PENMAENMAWR, CONWY LL34 6SW (Tel & Fax: 01492 623737/622053) WTB ★★★★★. [🐕]
e-mail: bookings@glynuchaf.co.uk   website: www.glyn-uchaf.co.uk

Conwy Valley

Fertile valley with wood and moor rising on both sides. Many places of interest in the area.

Secluded cottages with log fire and beams. Dogs will love it. Plenty of walks around mountains and lakes. For 2 - 7 people plus their pet(s). MRS WILLIAMS (01724 733990 or 07711 217 448) week lets only. [🐕]

Denbigh (Llandyrnog)

Market town 13 miles from the seaside resort of Rhyl.

PENTRE MAWR COUNTRY HOUSE, LLANDYRNOG LL16 4LA (01824 790732) Ancestral home of 400 years with woodland, park and riverside meadows, within easy reach of Chester and coast. Heated swimming pool. All rooms en suite. Pets most welcome. AA ★★★★★ and Dinner Award [🐕]
e-mail: info@pentremawrcountryhouse.co.uk   www.pentremawrcountryhouse.co.uk

Llandudno

Coastal resort at base of peninsula running out to Great Ormes Head.

THE MOORINGS, 3 ABBEY ROAD, LLANDUDNO LL30 2EA (01492 876775). Offering you a range of accommodation to suit all, with great parking facilities and easy access to beautiful beaches, coastline and an assortment of attractions. Available all year round with a choice from 8 different Apartments to suit your needs. VisitWales ★★★ [🐕]
e-mail: stay@themooringsllandudno.co.uk   website: www.themooringsllandudno.co.uk

WARWICK HOUSE, 56 CHURCH WALKS, LLANDUDNO LL30 2HL (01492 876823; Fax: 01492 877908). Comfortable, relaxing and family friendly. 14 tastefully decorated en suite bedrooms with colour TV and tea and coffee making facilities. 5 minutes' walk to beach and town centre. WTB ★★★
e-mail info@thewarwickhotel.net   website: www.thewarwickhotel.net

Llangollen

Famous for International Music Eisteddfod held in July. Plas Newydd, Valle Crucis Abbey nearby. Standard gauge steam railway; canal cruises; ideal for golf and walking.

THE HAND AT LLANARMON, LLANARMON D.C., CEIRIOG VALLEY, NEAR LLANGOLLEN LL20 7LD (01691 600666). Standing in the glorious Ceiriog Valley, The Hand at Llanarmon radiates charm and character. 13 comfortable en suite bedrooms, log fires, and fabulous food, a wonderful base for most country pursuits. [🐾]
e-mail: reception@thehandhotel.co.uk   website: www.TheHandHotel.co.uk

GOLDEN PHEASANT COUNTRY HOTEL, GLYN CEIROG, NEAR LLANGOLLEN LL20 7BB (01691 718281; Fax: 01691 718479). Situated in the beautiful Ceiriog Valley. All 19 rooms en suite, colour TV and tea/coffee making facilities. Pets welcome in all rooms (except restaurant and lounge). WTB/AA ★★★ [pw! £5 per night per pet, £35 per week]
e-mail: info@goldenpheasanthotel.co.uk   website: www.goldenpheasanthotel.co.uk

Llanrwst (Conwy Valley)

Small town and community on the River Conwy. 11 miles south of Colwyn Bay.

MAENAN ABBEY HOTEL, MAENAN, LLANRWST LL26 0UL (01492 660247). All modern facilities. 14 bedrooms, all en suite, single, double, twin, family and four-poster bridal suite available. Spectacular views. Restaurant and bar. Small, well behaved dogs welcome.
e-mail: info@manab.co.uk   website: www.manab.co.uk

BODNANT CARAVAN PARK, NEBO ROAD, LLANRWST, CONWY VALLEY LL26 0SD (01492 640248). Picturesque location 10 minutes' walking distance from town. 35 caravan and motor-caravan pitches available, 14 tent pitches. Toilet blocks with free hot water and showers. Two well equipped caravans for hire also available. AA 4 Pennants, WTB ★★★★ [Pets 50p per night]
e-mail: ermin@bodnant-caravan-park.co.uk   website: www.bodnant-caravan-park.co.uk

Rhos-on-Sea (Conwy)

Popular resort at east end of Penrhyn Bay, adjoining Colwyn Bay to the north-west.

SUNNYDOWNS HOTEL, 66 ABBEY ROAD, RHOS-ON-SEA, CONWY LL28 4NU (01492 544256). A 3 star luxury family hotel just two minutes' walk to beach and shops. All rooms en suite with digital TV with approximately 40 channels, tea/coffee facilities and central heating. Hotel has bar, pool room and car park. A non-smoking hotel. [Pets £3 per night]
e-mail: sunnydowns@tiscali.co.uk   website: www.sunnydownshotel.co.uk

Bronwydd Arms, Ferryside, Gwernogle, Llandeilo, Llandovery

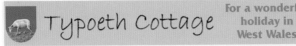

Bronwydd Arms

Village 2 miles north of Carmarthen.

CWMDWYFRAN FARM HOLIDAY COTTAGE, CWMDWYFRAN, BRONWYDD ARMS SA33 6JF (01267 281419) A beautiful holiday cottage in a secluded and peaceful location. Refurbished to a high standard. Sleeps 4. Ideal for exploring coast and countryside. WTB ★★★★. [Pets £15 per week]. e-mail: info@cwmdwyfran.co.uk   website: www.cwmdwyfran.co.uk

Ferryside

Seaside village 8 miles south of Carmarthen near to the mouth of the River Tywi.

THREE RIVERS HOTEL & SPA, FERRYSIDE, CARMARTHEN SA17 5TU (01267 267270). A quiet hotel nestling on the Three Rivers estuary. All bedrooms en suite, spacious and tastefully furnished. Health Suite with heated pool. Three self-catering cottages also available. WTB ★★★. e-mail: enquiries@threerivershotel.co.uk   website:www.threerivershotel.co.uk

Gwernogle

Hamlet on edge of Brechfa Forest.

THE BARN AT NANT LLWYD, NANT LLWYD, GWERNOGLE SA32 7RS (01267 220518). Self-catering accommodation sleeps 4. Open plan sitting room, with wood burner, and fully equipped kitchen. Two en suite bedrooms with views of surrounding countryside. Ideal for walkers and cyclists. Very dog-friendly. WTB ★★★★★. [🐾] e-mail: info@brechfaholiday.co.uk   website: www.brechfaholiday.co.uk

Llandeilo

Town on River Towy, 14 miles east of Carmarthen.

MAERDY COTTAGES, TALIARIS, LLANDEILO SA19 7DA (01550 777448). Six traditional cottages set within two acres of secure gardens. Each cottage is equipped to give maximum comfort, two cottages are fully wheelchair accessible, and all are ideal for families of all ages. Home cooked evening meals available. Open all year. WTB ★★★★. [First pet free, others £5 per night, £20 per week].
e-mail: enquiries@maerdyholidaycottages.co.uk   website: www.maerdyholidaycottages.co.uk

Llandovery

Small town 17 miles west of Brecon.

LLANERCHINDDA FARM GUEST HOUSE & SELF CATERING COTTAGES, CYNGHORDY, LLANDOVERY SA20 0NB (01550 750274). Family run guest house with 9 bedrooms; 2 self catering cottages sleeping up to 6 and 10 people. Situated near Llandovery. Pets welcome. B&B from £37 per night, self-catering charges on application. WTB ★★★ [Pets £5 per night]
e-mail: info@cambrianway.com   website: www.cambrianway.com

Llandysul

Small town in the valley of the River Teifi.

TYPOETH COTTAGE, LLANDYSUL SA44 4RS (01559 384483). 18th century Listed cottage in an ideal location. Kitchen, sunny living/dining room with multi-fuel stove, twin bedroom and shower room. Llandysul less than 10 minutes drive. Dogs welcome. For details please contact Suzanna.[🐾]
email: tourism@typoethcottage.co.uk   website: www.typoethcottage.co.uk

Llanelli

Village on the River Taf estuary, 10 mile north-west of Swansea.

THE DIPLOMAT HOTEL, FELINFOEL ROAD, AELYBRYN, LLANELLI SA15 3PJ (01554 756156; Fax: 01554 751649). Privately owned and operated with warmth and generous hospitality. The Diplomat Hotel offers a rare combination of charm and character with excellent well appointed facilities to ensure your comfort and convenience. WTB/AA ★★★ [Pets £5 per night]
e-mail: reservations@diplomat-hotel-wales.com   website: www.bw-diplomathotel.co.uk

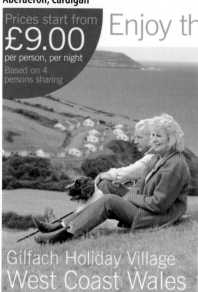

FREE or **REDUCED RATE** entry to Holiday Visits and Attractions –
see our **READERS' OFFER VOUCHERS** on pages 409-414

Aberaeron

Attractive little town on Cardigan Bay, good touring centre for coast and inland. The Aeron Express Aerial ferry offers an exciting trip across the harbour. Marine aquarium; Aberarth Leisure Park nearby.

GILFACH HOLIDAY VILLAGE, LLWYNCELYN, NEAR ABERAERON SA46 0HN (01545 580288). Choice of modern Bungalows (up to 6 persons) or luxury 2/3 person apartments. Fully equipped, linen available, colour TV. Horse and pony riding. Tennis. Write or phone for brochure pack to the Manager. [Pets £15 per week.]
e-mail: info@stratfordcaravans.co.uk   website: www.selfcateringinwales.com
                                              or www.stratfordcaravans.co.uk

Aberporth

Popular seaside village offering safe swimming and good sea fishing. Good base for exploring Cardigan Bay coastline.

'QUALITY COTTAGES', CERBID, SOLVA, HAVERFORDWEST, PEMBROKESHIRE SA62 6YE (01348 837871). Cottages set in all coastal areas, enjoy unashamed luxury, highest residential standards. Log fires. Linen supplied. Pets welcome, free. [pw! 🐕]
website: www.qualitycottages.co.uk

Cardigan

Historic town on the banks of the Teifi estuary, with excellent leisure facilities.

PENWERN FACH COTTAGES, PONTHIRWAUN, NEAR CENARTH, CARDIGAN SA43 2RL (01239 710694). Character stone cottages. Peaceful setting with lovely views. Beautiful coastline. Indoor swimming pool nearby. Log fires. WTB ★★★★.[Pets £20 per week]
e-mail: info@penwernfach.co.uk   website: www.penwernfach.co.uk

PENBONTBREN, GLYNARTHEN, LLANDYSUL, NEAR CARDIGAN SA44 6PE (01239 810248). Luxury Bed & Breakfast in West Wales in 32 acres of grounds, only two miles from wonderful National Trust beaches. 5 suites each with spacious sitting room, own garden, king-size bed and sumptuous décor and furnishings. Pets by prior arrangement. Visit Wales ★★★★★ Gold Award [🐕]
e-mail: contact@penbontbren.com   website: www.penbontbren.com

Ciliau Aeron

Village in undulating country just inland from the charming Cardigan Bay resorts of New Quay and Aberaeron. New Quay 12 miles, Aberaeron 6

'QUALITY COTTAGES', CERBID, SOLVA, HAVERFORDWEST, PEMBROKESHIRE SA62 6YE (01348 837871). Cottages set in all coastal areas, enjoy unashamed luxury, highest residential standards. Log fires. Linen supplied. Pets welcome, free. [pw! 🐕]
website: www.qualitycottages.co.uk

Llangrannog

Pretty little seaside village overlooking a sandy beach. Superb cliff walk to NT Ynys Lochtyn, a secluded promontory.

'QUALITY COTTAGES', CERBID, SOLVA, HAVERFORDWEST, PEMBROKESHIRE SA62 6YE (01348 837871). Cottages set in all coastal areas, enjoy unashamed luxury, highest residential standards. Log fires. Linen supplied. Pets welcome, free. [pw! 🐕]
website: www.qualitycottages.co.uk

🐕   Pets are welcome free of charge.

£   A charge is made for pets: nightly or weekly.

pw!   Special provision for pets; exercise facility, feeding or accommodation arrangement.

⌂   Separate pets' accommodation.

Classified Symbols

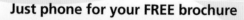

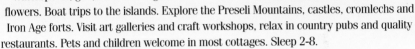
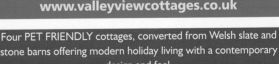

Broad Haven, Croft, Fishguard, Haverfordwest

Haverfordwest, Llanteg, Moylegrove, St Davids

Whitland

'QUALITY COTTAGES', CERBID, SOLVA, HAVERFORDWEST, PEMBROKESHIRE SA62 6YE (01348 837871). Cottages set in all coastal areas, enjoy unashamed luxury, highest residential standards. Log fires. Linen supplied. Pets welcome, free. [pw! 🐾]
website: www.qualitycottages.co.uk

Pembrokeshire Coast - Newport to St Davids. Charming, individual cottages situated near sandy beaches, rocky bays and spectacular cliff walks. All comfortably furnished and fully equipped. Pets and children welcome. Sleep 2-8. Details from CAROLE ROGERS, COTTAGE RETREATS IN PEMBROKESHIRE, 29 HEOL GLYNDWR, FISHGUARD SA65 9LN (01348 875318). [🐾]
e-mail: carole.rogers@talktalk.net   website: www.cottageretreats.net

Boncath

Small hamlet 5 miles south of Cardigan.

VALLEY VIEW COTTAGES, NEWCHAPEL, BONCATH SA37 0HH (01239 841850). Newly renovated luxury cottages with superb country views. Sleep 1-6. Fully equipped. Children and pets welcome. Prices from £245 per week. Heating, electricity, linen and towels included. WTB★★★★. [Pets £15 per week]
e-mail: info@valleyviewcottages.co.uk   website: www.valleyviewcottages.co.uk

CLYDEY COTTAGES PEMBROKESHIRE – COTTAGES AT FRON FAWR. Four pet-friendly cottages, 3/4 bedrooms. Enclosed gardens. 48 acres of fields and woodlands. Children's play area. Coast 5 miles. Tel: 01239 698619. [Pets £25 per week]
e-mail: info@clydeycottages.co.uk   website: www.clydeycottages.co.uk

Bosherton

Village 4 miles south of Pembroke, bordered by 3 man-made lakes, a haven for wildlife and covered in water lilies in early summer.

'QUALITY COTTAGES', CERBID, SOLVA, HAVERFORDWEST, PEMBROKESHIRE SA62 6YE (01348 837871). Cottages set in all coastal areas, enjoy unashamed luxury, highest residential standards. Log fires. Linen supplied. Pets welcome, free. [pw! 🐾]
website: www.qualitycottages.co.uk

Broad Haven

Village on St Bride's Bay, 6 miles west of Haverfordwest.

PEMBROKESHIRE NATIONAL PARK. Sleeps 6 + cot. Three-bedroom fully furnished Holiday Lodge. Walking distance sandy beaches and coastal footpath. £180 to £400 per week. MRS L.P. ASHTON, 10 ST LEONARDS ROAD, THAMES DITTON, SURREY KT7 0RJ (020-8398 6349). [🐾]
e-mail: lejash@aol.com   website: www.33timberhill.com

Croes Goch

Hamlet 6 miles north east of St Davids

'QUALITY COTTAGES', CERBID, SOLVA, HAVERFORDWEST, PEMBROKESHIRE SA62 6YE (01348 837871). Cottages set in all coastal areas, enjoy unashamed luxury, highest residential standards. Log fires. Linen supplied. Pets welcome, free. [pw! ⌐]
website: www.qualitycottages.co.uk

Croft

Located 2 miles SW of Cardigan.

CROFT FARM & CELTIC COTTAGES, CROFT, NEAR CARDIGAN SA43 3NT (01239 615179). Featured in Daily Mail. Stone barn conversions with luxury indoor heated pool, sauna, spa pool and gym. Colourful gardens, indoor and outdoor play areas. VisitWales ★★★★★/★★★★ *SELF CATERING*. Pets welcome. [Pets £5 per night, £35 per week, pw!]
e-mail: info@croft-holiday-cottages.co.uk   website: www.croft-holiday-cottages.co.uk

Fishguard

Small town at end of Fishguard Bay

IVYBRIDGE GUEST HOUSE, DRIM MILL, DYFFRYN, GOODWICK SA64 0JT (01348 875366). Stay at Ivybridge, all rooms en suite. Evening meals served. Small heated indoor pool. Private car park. Pets welcome! [Pets £7 per stay].
e-mail: info@ivybridgefishguard.co.uk   website: www.ivybridgefishguard.co.uk

CARTREF HOTEL, 15-19 HIGH STREET, FISHGUARD SA65 9AW (01348 872430; Fax: 01348 873664). A friendly, family-run hotel in the centre of Fishguard with licensed restaurant and residential bar. En suite rooms. Only 5 minutes' drive to the ferry port for Ireland. AA ★★. [Pets £5 per night; £10 per week]
e-mail: cartrefhotel@btconnect.com   website: www.cartrefhotel.co.uk

Haverfordwest

Administrative and shopping centre for the area; ideal base for exploring National Park. Historic town of narrow streets; museum in castle grounds; many fine buildings.

HAVEN COTTAGES. Quality beachfront cottages, sleep 2-8, adjacent sandy beach. Well equipped. Open all year. Winter breaks. Contact: SYCAMORE LODGE, NOLTON HAVEN SA62 3NH (01437 710200). [Pets £10 per week].
e-mail: info@havencottages.co.uk   website: www.havencottages.co.uk

GARN ISAF, ABERCASTLE, HAVERFORDWEST SA62 5HJ (Tel & Fax: 01348 831838; Mobile: 07969 529929). Within the Pembrokeshire National Park, surrounded by stunning scenery. 4★ B&B and 5★ self catering accommodation. Secluded campsite, picnic benches. [One pet free s/c, in B&B £5 per night].
website: www.garnisaf.com

NOLTON HAVEN QUALITY COTTAGES. Ideal for out of season breaks. Most with sea view. 30 yards from safe, sandy beach. Sleep 2-20. 8-bedroom farmhouse sleeps 20. WTB ★★★/★★★★/★★★★★ Self-Catering. Contact: JIM & JOYCE CANTON, NOLTON HAVEN FARMHOUSE, NOLTON HAVEN, HAVERFORDWEST SA62 6NH (01437 710263).
e-mail: PW8@noltonhaven.com   website: www.noltonhaven.com

KEESTON HILL COTTAGES, KEESTON, HAVERFORDWEST SA62 6EJ (01437 710440). Three well equipped holiday lets, sleep 4 and 6/7. Between Haverfordwest and St Davids. Garden and parking. Pets welcome. WTB ★★★★.[⌐]
e-mail: enquiries@keestonhillcottage.co.uk   website: www.keestonhillcottage.co.uk

---

⌐   Pets are welcome free of charge.   **Classified Symbols**

£   A charge is made for pets: nightly or weekly.

pw!   Special provision for pets; exercise facility, feeding or accommodation arrangement.

⌂   Separate pets' accommodation.

Llanteg

Hamlet 4 miles south of Whitland.

TONY & JANE BARON, LLANTEGLOS ESTATE, LLANTEG, NEAR AMROTH SA67 8PU (01834 831677 /831371). Self-contained Woodland Lodges. Sleep 6. Children's play area. Licensed bar. Visitor attractions. Open all year. Call for brochure. VisitWales ★★★/★★★★ Self Catering [Pets £6 per night, £40 per week.]
e-mail: llanteglosestate@supanet.com   website: www.llanteglos-estate.com

Moylegrove

Village 4 miles west of Cardigan.

NORTH PEMBROKESHIRE COAST. 2 WELSH COTTAGES with enclosed gardens. Paddock for exercise. Dog-friendly bay and beaches within walking distance, with spectacular views. Bed linen included. (01239 881 280). [🐕]

CWM CONNELL COASTAL COTTAGES, MOYLEGROVE SA43 3BX (01239 881691) Six luxury self-catering cottages within the Pembrokeshire Coastal National Park. Sleep 2/4/7. A rural retreat to relax and unwind. Dogs with responsible owners welcome. WTB ★★★★
e-mail: info@cwmconnell.co.uk   website: www.cwmconnell.co.uk

Newgale

On St Bride's Bay 3 miles east of Solva. Long beach where at exceptionally low tide the stumps of a submerged forest may be seen.

'QUALITY COTTAGES', CERBID, SOLVA, HAVERFORDWEST, PEMBROKESHIRE SA62 6YE (01348 837871). Cottages set in all coastal areas, enjoy unashamed luxury, highest residential standards. Log fires. Linen supplied. Pets welcome, free. [pw! 🐕]
website: www.qualitycottages.co.uk

Newport

Small town at mouth of the River Nyfer, 9 miles south west of Cardigan. Remains of 13th-century castle.

'QUALITY COTTAGES', CERBID, SOLVA, HAVERFORDWEST, PEMBROKESHIRE SA62 6YE (01348 837871). Cottages set in all coastal areas, enjoy unashamed luxury, highest residential standards. Log fires. Linen supplied. Pets welcome, free. [pw! 🐕]
website: www.qualitycottages.co.uk

St Davids

Smallest cathedral city in Britain, shrine of Wales' patron saint. Magnificent ruins of Bishop's Palace. Craft shops, farm parks and museums; boat trips to Ramsey Island.

'QUALITY COTTAGES', CERBID, SOLVA, HAVERFORDWEST, PEMBROKESHIRE SA62 6YE (01348 837871). Cottages set in all coastal areas, enjoy unashamed luxury, highest residential standards. Log fires. Linen supplied. Pets welcome, free. [pw! 🐕]
website: www.qualitycottages.co.uk

FFYNNON DDOFN, LLANON, LLANRHIAN, NEAR ST DAVIDS. Comfortable, well-equipped cottage with panoramic coastal views. Sleeps six in three bedrooms. Central heating. Large games room. Open all year. Pets welcome free of charge. Brochure on request from: MRS B. REES WHITE, BRICKHOUSE FARM, BURNHAM RD, WOODHAM MORTIMER, MALDON, ESSEX CM9 6SR (01245 224611). [🐕]
website: www.ffynnonddofn.co.uk

MRS MARGO EVANS, LOCHMEYLER FARM GUEST HOUSE, LLANDELOY, NEAR SOLVA, ST DAVIDS SA62 6LL (01348 837724; Fax: 01348 837622). Welcome Host Gold Award. 7 en suite luxury bedrooms. B&B from £35pppn. Children welcome. WTB ★★★★★, AA ★★★★★ [pw! 🐕]
e-mail: stay@lochmeyler.co.uk   website: www.lochmeyler.co.uk

ST DAVIDS HOLIDAY COTTAGES. Superbly appointed self-catering cottages (sleep 2-10) situated on the spectacular North Pembrokeshire coast. Available all year round. Dogs welcome in most. For details contact: PETER DAVIES, 6 HAMILTON STREET, FISHGUARD SA65 9HL (01348 872266/07811 111568). [🐾]
e-mail: peter@stdavidsholidays.co.uk   website: www.stdavidsholidays.co.uk

PEMBROKESHIRE SHEEPDOGS, TREMYNYDD FACH, ST DAVIDS SA62 6DB (01437 721677). B&B (in cosy cottages) and Self-catering (in farmhouse and chalet) on working sheep farm. Spectacular and unspoilt stretch of coastal path with plants and wildlife. [🐾 ⌂]
e-mail: info@sheepdogtraining.co.uk   website: www.sheepdogtraining.co.uk

FELINDRE COTTAGES, PORTHGAIN, ST DAVIDS SA62 5BH (01348 831220). Self-catering cottages with panoramic sea and country views. Five minutes' walk from Coastal Path, picturesque fishing village of Porthgain and a great pub! Peaceful location. Short breaks available. One well-behaved dog welcome, except school holidays. WTB graded. [pw! £10 per week]
e-mail: sheilacraft@supanet.com   website: www.felindrecottages.co.uk

Saundersfoot

Popular resort and sailing centre with picturesque harbour and sandy beach. Tenby 3 miles

VINE COTTAGE GUEST HOUSE, THE RIDGEWAY, SAUNDERSFOOT SA69 9LA (01834 814422). Coastal village outskirts. Sandy beaches and coast path nearby. Award-winning garden for guests' and dogs' relaxation and exercise. Non-smoking throughout. AA ★★★★ [pw! Pets £5 per stay.]
e-mail: enquiries@vinecottageguesthouse.co.uk   website: www.vinecottageguesthouse.co.uk

Solva

Picturesque coastal village with sheltered harbour and excellent craft shops. Sailing and watersports; sea fishing, long sandy beach.

'QUALITY COTTAGES', CERBID, SOLVA, HAVERFORDWEST, PEMBROKESHIRE SA62 6YE (01348 837871). Cottages set in all coastal areas, enjoy unashamed luxury, highest residential standards. Log fires. Linen supplied. Pets welcome, free. [pw! 🐾]
website: www.qualitycottages.co.uk

Tenby

Popular resort with two wide beaches. Fishing trips, craft shops, museum. Medieval castle ruins, 13th-century church. Golf, fishing and watersports; boat trips to nearby Caldy Island with monastery and medieval church.

'QUALITY COTTAGES', CERBID, SOLVA, HAVERFORDWEST, PEMBROKESHIRE SA62 6YE (01348 837871). Cottages set in all coastal areas, enjoy unashamed luxury, highest residential standards. Log fires. Linen supplied. Pets welcome, free. [pw! 🐾]
website: www.qualitycottages.co.uk

Whitland

Village 6 miles east of Narberth. Whitland Abbey 2 km.

MRS ANGELA COLLEDGE, GWARMACWYDD FARM, LLANFALLTEG, WHITLAND SA34 0XH (0800 321 3699). Country estate with six character stone cottages, fully furnished and equipped. All linen and electricity included; heated for year-round use. WTB ★★★★ [pw! Pets £10 per pet per week]
website: www.davidsfarm.com

Hay-on-Wye, Kington, Llandrindod Wells, Llangurig

Self-Catering & B&B Accommodation near Offa's Dyke Path

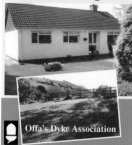

Ingleside · Self-catering Bungalow with large conservatory on working farm. 3 bedrooms – sleeps 5. Living room with colour TV. Kitchen/dining room. Fully equipped. Well behaved dog allowed. 4 miles from Offa's Dyke Path. Lovely countryside, lovely walks, great views.
5 Star B&B also available.

Cymru Wales ★★★★

Glenice Jones, Lloran Ganol Farm,
Llansilin, Oswestry, Shropshire SY10 7QX
Tel: 01691 791296/791287 · Fax: 791296
Mob: 07779 935009

Offa's Dyke Association

PETS WELCOME at
The Wynnstay Hotel
Maengwyn Street, Machynlleth, Powys SY20 8AE
Tel: 01654 702941
Award-winning food, wine and beer.
Glorious countryside and miles of sandy beaches.
Masses to do and see.
Good Food Guide & Good Beer Guide Recommended,
Les Routiers "Best Wine List in Britain".
Pets free in kennels, £5 one-off charge in rooms.

Cymru Wales ★★★

e-mail: info@wynnstay-hotel.com • **www.wynnstay-hotel.com**

Whitehall Cottage

Cosy cottage in lovely Border countryside, two miles from Offa's Dyke • Central heating, washing machine, dishwasher, microwave, colour TV, inglenook, woodburner, linen included • Power shower over bath • Sleeps 4 plus cot • Ample parking • Sun-trap garden • On working farm in peaceful hamlet • Children and pets welcome

MRS R. L. JONES, UPPER HOUSE, KINNERTON, NEAR PRESTEIGNE LD8 2PE
Tel: 01547 560207

Looking for pet-friendly accommodation around Britain?

Visit the FHG website
www.holidayguides.com

Carreg-Ddu in the spectacular Elan Valley,
just a 10 minute drive from Oak Wood Lodges

Llwynbaedd, Rhayader, Powys LD6 5NT
Luxurious Self Catering Log Cabins

situated at approximately 1000 ft above sea level with spectacular views of the
Elan Valley and Cambrian Mountains. Enjoy pursuits such as walking,
pony trekking, mountain biking, fishing and bird watching in the most
idyllic of surroundings. Excellent touring centre.
Dogs welcome. Short Breaks as well as full weeks. Open all year round.

www.oakwoodlodges.co.uk

Builth Wells

Old country town in lovely setting on River Wye amid beautiful hills. Lively markets; host to Royal Welsh Agricultural Show

MRS LINDA WILLIAMS, OLD VICARAGE, ERWOOD, BUILTH WELLS LD2 3SZ (01982 560680).
Superior views from elevated position in Wye Valley. Comfortable ornate beds, one en suite room,
two sharing guests' own bathroom. Drinks tray, TV, washbasin. Bacon and sausage from local pigs,
farm eggs, home baked bread and preserves. VisitWales ★★★ Farm, FHG Diploma Winner 2004.[🐾]
e-mail: linda@oldvicwyevalley.co.uk   website: www.oldvicwyevalley.co.uk

MRS KATHARINE SMITH, CAER BERIS MANOR, BUILTH WELLS LD2 3NP (01982 552601; Fax: 01982
552586). Family-owned country house hotel set in 27 acres of parkland. Free salmon and trout fishing; golf
nearby, superb walking and touring. All rooms en suite. AA ★★★ [Pets £5 per night, £30 per week].
e-mail: caerberis@btconnect.com   website: www.caerberis.com

Cilmery

Village 2½ miles west of Builth Wells.

PWLLGWILYM HOLIDAY COTTAGES, PWLLGWILYM, LLANAFAN ROAD, CILMERY, BUILTH WELLS
LD2 3NY (01982-552140/ 07909-681881). A large barn tastefully converted into 3 spacious 4-star
cottages with hardwood stairs, flagstone floors. Surrounded by a 60 acre farm with lovely views,
two miles from Builth Wells. Sleep 4-8. WTB ★★★★ [Pets £12 per week].
e-mail: bookings@pwllgwilym-cottages.co.uk   website: www.pwllgwilym-cottages.co.uk

Hay-on-Wye

Small market town at north end of Black Mountains, 15 miles north-east of Brecon.

MRS E. BALLY, LANE FARM, PAINSCASTLE, BUILTH WELLS LD2 3JS (Tel & Fax: 01497 851605). 17th century farm in rural Radnorshire, five miles Hay-on-Wye. Wonderful walking country. Self-catering apartments sleeping 2-14. A warm welcome for you and your pet(s). WTB ★★★ [🐾]
e-mail: lanefarm@onetel.com   website: www.lane-farm.co.uk

BASKERVILLE ARMS HOTEL, CLYRO, NEAR HAY-ON-WYE HR3 5RZ (01497 820670). Delightfully placed comfortable retreat with well appointed en suite bedrooms. Tasty, home-cooked food in bar and restaurant, using the best local produce. Special break rates. WTB ★★★.
e-mail: info@baskervillearms.co.uk   website: www.baskervillearms.co.uk

Kington

Market town near the English Welsh border. Hereford 21 miles.

THE ROCK COTTAGE, HUNTINGTON, KINGTON. Secluded, stone-built cottage near Offa's Dyke footpath. Ideal for touring, birdwatching, golf and pony trekking. Sleeps 4/7. Fully equipped kitchen, lounge with wood-burner. Central Heating. Spacious garden. Children and pets welcome. Details from MRS C. WILLIAMS, RADNOR'S END, HUNTINGTON, KINGTON HR5 3NZ (01544 370289). [🐾]
website: www.the-rock-cottage.co.uk

Llandrindod Wells

Popular inland resort, Victorian spa town, excellent touring centre. Golf, fishing, bowling, boating and tennis. Visitors can still take the waters at Rock Park Gardens.

THE PARK HOUSE, CROSSGATES, LLANDRINDOD WELLS LD1 6RF (01597 851201; 07918 660647). In three acres, amidst beautiful countryside near Elan Valley. Static caravans, touring pitches and fully equipped bungalows and cottages. Restaurant. Pets welcome. [Pets £3 per night, £20 per week. Guide dogs free.]
e-mail: ian_barr@btconnect.com   website: www.barrscountryparks.com

THE PINES CARAVAN PARK, DOLDOWLOD, LLANDRINDOD WELLS LD16NN. (Tel/Fax: 01597 810068). Small, peaceful, family-run caravan park in good position for exploring Elan and Wye Valleys. Luxury modern holiday homes for hire or sale. Shop and cafe close by. Weekly hire from £235. Pets welcome. [Pets £3 per night, £20 per week]
e-mail: info@pinescaravanpark.co.uk   website: www.pinescaravanpark.co.uk

Llangurig

Village on River Wye, 4 miles south-west of Llanidloes. Ideal walking countryside.

THE OLD VICARAGE, LLANGURIG SY18 6RN (Tel & Fax: 01686 440280). A late Victorian property tastefully converted to a cosy Guest House. All bedrooms are well furnished and have full en suite facilities, plus little extras for your comfort. WTB/AA ★★★★.
e-mail: info@theoldvicaragellangurig.co.uk   website:www.theoldvicaragellangurig.co.uk

Llansilin

Village 6 miles west of Oswestry.

Self catering bungalow on working farm. 3 bedrooms, sleeps 5. Living room with colour TV; kitchen/dining room. Fully equipped. 4 miles from Offa's Dyke Path. Well behaved dog allowed. 5 Star B&B also available. GLENICE JONES, LLORAN GANOL FARM, LLANSILIN, OSWESTRY, SHROPSHIRE SY10 7QX (01691 791296/791287; Mob: 07779 935009). Visit Wales ★★★★.

Machynlleth

Attractive old town with half-timbered houses. Ideal for hillside rambles.

THE WYNNSTAY HOTEL, MAENGWYN STREET, MACHYNLLETH SY20 8AE (01654 702941). Award-winning food, wine and beer. Glorious countryside and miles of sandy beaches. Masses to do and see. WTB ★★★. Good Food Guide & Good Beer Guide Recommended, Les Routiers "Best Wine List in Britain". [Pets free in kennels, £5 one-off charge in rooms]
e-mail: info@wynnstay-hotel.com   website: www.wynnstay-hotel.com

Presteigne

Attractive old town with half timbered houses. Ideal for hillside rambles and pony trekking.

WHITEHALL COTTAGE. Cosy cottage two miles from Offa's Dyke. Central heating, washing machine, dishwasher, microwave, colour TV, inglenook, woodburner, linen included. Power shower over bath. Sleeps 4 plus cot. Children and pets welcome. MRS R. L. JONES, UPPER HOUSE, KINNERTON, NEAR PRESTEIGNE LD8 2PE (01547 560207).[🐾].

Rhayader

Small market town on River Wye north of Builth Wells. Popular for angling and pony trekking

OAK WOOD LODGES, LLWYNBAEDD, RHAYADER LD6 5NT (01597 811422). Luxurious self-catering log cabins with spectacular views of the Elan Valley and Cambrian Mountains. Walking, pony trekking, mountain biking, fishing and bird watching in idyllic surroundings. Phone for brochure. [First dog £3 per night, additional dogs half price].
website: www.oakwoodlodges.co.uk

FREE or **REDUCED RATE** entry to Holiday Visits and Attractions – see our **READERS' OFFER VOUCHERS** on pages 409-414

Taking your pet on holiday?
for quality properties where pets will be warmly welcomed visit:
www.pets-welcome.co.uk

CASTLE NARROWBOATS CHURCH ROAD WHARF, GILWERN NP7 0EP (01873 830001). The Monmouthshire & Brecon Canal in South Wales. Discover the beauty of Wales onboard one of our excellent narrowboats. 2-8 berth boats, short breaks available. Pets welcome.For a free colour brochure call Castle Narrowboats:
website: www.castlenarrowboats.co.uk

Abergavenny

Historic market town at south-eastern gateway to Brecon Beacons National Park. Pony trekking, leisure centre; excellent touring base for Vale of Usk.

HALF MOON INN, LLANTHONY, NEAR ABERGAVENNY NP7 7NN (01873 890611). B&B, good food and real ale in 17thC inn. Wonderful scenery of Black Mountains. Good base for walking, pony trekking, birdwatching. Dogs welcome.[Pets £1.50 per night]
e-mail: halfmoon@llanthony.wanadoo.co.uk   website: www.halfmoon-llanthony.co.uk

Gower Peninsula

Britain's first designated Area of Outstanding Natural Beauty with numerous sandy beaches and lovely countryside to explore.

CULVER HOUSE HOTEL, PORT EYNON, GOWER SA3 1NN (01792 390755). One and two bedroom apartments offer modern fully equipped accommodation, stunning accessible Blue Flag beach location. Continental breakfast available. Prices from £90 per night.
website: www.culverhousehotel.co.uk

HOME FROM HOME offers a wide variety of pet friendly holiday accommodation in the seaside village of Mumbles and on the beautiful Gower Peninsula. Whether you prefer a countryside walk or a stroll on one of the many stunning beaches, the area offers something for everyone. Contact: 01792 360624. [Pets £20 per week]
e-mail: enquiries@homefromhome.com   website: www.homefromhome.com

Neath

Town on River Neath 8 miles NE of Swansea.

MRS C. JONES, GREEN LANTERNS GUEST HOUSE, HAWDREF GANOL FARM, CIMLA, NEATH SA12 9SL (01639 631884). 18th Century luxury Guest House with spacious en suite rooms, all with views over the Vale of Neath. Licensed bar and restaurant. Vegetarian & other diets catered for. Pets welcome by arrangement. WTB ★★★★.
e-mail: info@greenlanterns.co.uk   website: www.greenlanterns.co.uk

Swansea

Second largest city in Wales with a wide variety of leisure activities and excellent shopping.

BEST WESTERN ABERAVON BEACH HOTEL, NEATH PORT TALBOT, SWANSEA BAY SA12 6QP (01639 884949). Modern seafront hotel. A warm Welsh welcome awaits you and your pets. 2 miles of flat promenade and a pet friendly beach. Pets Paradise!! And for you... newly refurbished rooms, fine cuisine, leisure centre and many local attractions. AA ★★★ [🐾]
e-mail: sales@aberavonbeach.com   website: www.aberavonbeach.com

🐕   Pets are welcome free of charge.

£   A charge is made for pets: nightly or weekly.

pw! Special provision for pets; exercise facility, feeding or accommodation arrangement.

⌂   Separate pets' accommodation.

Classified Symbols

Ballater

Village and resort 14 miles east of Braemar.

CAMBUS O'MAY HOTEL, BALLATER AB35 5SE (Tel & Fax: 013397 55428). Family-run country house hotel 4 miles east of Ballater. Excellent food; 12 en suite bedrooms. Ideal area for hill walking, golf, fishing and visiting Balmoral Castle etc. STB ★★★. [🐕]
e-mail: mckechnie@cambusomay.freeserve.co.uk   website: www.cambusomayhotel.co.uk

Braemar

Village 16 miles south west of Ballater. Popular tourist centre with famous Highland Games.

BRAEMAR HOLIDAY LODGES, GLENSHEE ROAD, BRAEMAR AB35 5YO. SELF CATERING LOG CABINS (Tel/Fax: 013397 41627). One and three bedroom cabins set in hotel grounds. Spacious open-plan layout with French doors leading to verandah. Open all year round. STB ★★★
e-mail: mail@braemarlodge.co.uk   website: www.braemarlodge.co.uk

Glenlivet

Located 8 miles north of Tomintoul. Distilleries and State forest.

BEECHGROVE COTTAGES, GLENLIVET. Traditional stone cottages set amidst beautiful surroundings near rivers Avon and Livet. All modernised and very comfortable. Fishing available. Ideal for exploring Highlands, Castle and Whisky Trails, walking, skiing, golf. Contact: THE POST OFFICE, TOMNAVOULIN, BALLINDALLOCH AB37 9JA (01807 590220) [🐕]
website: www.beechgrovecottages.co.uk

🐕   Pets are welcome free of charge.

£   A charge is made for pets: nightly or weekly.

pw! Special provision for pets; exercise facility, feeding or accommodation arrangement.

⌂   Separate pets' accommodation.

Classified Symbols

Rattray Head

Headland on North East coast 7 miles north of Peterhead.

SAND DUNES & SECLUDED 11-MILE BEACH. Eco-hostel and holiday flat in doggy heaven. Homely, relaxing retreat on generally sunny, dry, midge-free coast. Suit nature lovers, cyclists, walkers, even giant dogs. Washroom for clothes, kit and pets. ROB & VAL, LIGHTHOUSE COTTAGES, RATTRAY HEAD, PETERHEAD AB42 3HA (01346 532236) STB ★★★ Hostel.[pw! 🐕]
e-mail: hostel@rattrayhead.net   website: www.rattrayhead.net/hostel

Stonehaven

Fishing port on East Coast, 13 miles south of Aberdeen.

MRS AILEEN PATON, 'WOODSIDE OF GLASSLAW', STONEHAVEN AB39 3XQ (01569 763799). Modern bungalow with six centrally heated en suite bedrooms with colour TV and hospitality trays. Stonehaven two miles. Accessible for disabled guests. STB/AA ★★★★ [🐕]
e-mail: aileen@woodsideofglasslaw.co.uk   website: www.woodsideofglasslaw.co.uk

Turriff

Small town in agricultural area, 9 miles south of Banff.

SIMON PEARSE, COUNTRY COTTAGES, FORGLEN ESTATE, TURRIFF AB53 4JP (01888 562918). Estate on the beautiful Deveron River. Sandy beaches only nine miles away, Turriff two miles. 5 cottages sleeping 4–9. From £209 weekly. Open all year. Ideal for top golf courses, free brown trout fishing. Well-behaved dogs welcome. [🐕]
e-mail: reservations@forglen.co.uk   website: www.forglen.co.uk

Cairndow, Craignure (Isle of Mull), Dalmally, Dunoon

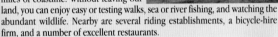

Appin

Mountainous area bounded by Loch Linnhe, Glen Creran and Glencoe.

MRS J PERY, ARDTUR, APPIN PA38 4DD (01631 730223 or 01626 834172). Two adjacent cottages in secluded surroundings. Ideal for hill walking, climbing, pony trekking, boating and fly fishing. Shop one mile; sea 200 yards; car essential; pets allowed.[🐕]
e-mail: pery@btinternet.com   website: www.ardturcottages.com

Ardfern

On west side of Loch Craignish, 4 miles west of Kilmartin.

THE GALLEY OF LORNE INN, ARDFERN PA31 8QN (01852 500284). 17thC drovers' inn in lochside location near Oban and Lochgilphead. Cosy en suite bedrooms, mouthwatering menu, friendly staff. Log fires, real ales and malts. Pets welcome, with miles of beach, forest and hill walks. [Pets £7.50 per night]
website: www.galleyoflorne.co.uk

Ardnamurchan

Peninsula on West Coast running from Salen to Ardnamurchan Point.

STEADING HOLIDAYS, ARDNAMURCHAN & MULL (01972 510262). Miles and miles of forestry, coastal and hill walks amidst spectacular scenery. Pets welcome in our cosy self-catering cottages, many of which have sea views and log fires.
website: www.steading.co.uk

Cairndow

Village at mouth of Kinglas Water on Loch Fyne in Argyll, near head of Loch.

Comfortable holiday cottage at the head of the longest sea loch in Scotland, in lovely walking country. Sleeps up to eight people. Linen and electricity included. STB ★★★ Self Catering. MRS DELAP, ACHADUNAN, CAIRNDOW, ARGYLL PA26 8BJ (Tel & Fax: 01499 600238).
website: www.argyllholidaycottages.com

Craignure (Isle of Mull)

Village and main ferry port on Isle of Mull located around the bay.

CRAIGNURE INN, ISLE OF MULL PA65 6AY (016808 12305). A small drovers' inn with three en suite rooms with colour TV and tea/coffee facilities. Home-cooked bar menu using local produce. Well behaved pets welcome. Ideal centre for walks, trips and tours.
e-mail: craignureinn@btconnect.com   website: www.craignure-inn.co.uk

Dalmally

Small town in Glen Orchy to the south-west of Loch Awe, with romantic Kilchurn Castle (14th century). Edinburgh 98 miles, Glasgow 69, Ardrishaig 42, Oban 25, Inveraray 16.

ARDBRECKNISH HOUSE, SOUTH LOCHAWESIDE, BY DALMALLY PA33 1BH (01866 833223). Self-catering properties and holiday cottage set in 10 acres of garden woodland on the south shore of Loch Awe. Breathtaking panoramic views over loch, mountain and glen. See our website to view properties. [Pets £15 per week]
e-mail: enquiries@loch-awe.co.uk   website: www.loch-awe.co.uk

ROCKHILL WATERSIDE SELF-CATERING COTTAGES, ARDBRECKNISH, BY DALMALLY PA33 1BH (01866 833218).Where comfort, peace and tranquillity reign supreme, on waterside with spectacular views over Loch Awe. Ideal for climbing, walking, bird and animal watching; great touring base.
website: www.rockhillfarmguesthouse.co.uk

Dunoon

Town and resort in Argyll, 4 miles west of Gourock across Firth of Clyde.

ABBOTS BRAE HOTEL, WEST BAY, DUNOON PA23 7QJ (01369 705021; Fax: 01369 701191). Small welcoming hotel at the gateway to the Western Highlands with breathtaking views. Comfortable, spacious, en suite bedrooms, quality home cooking and select wines. STB ★★★★ [🐾]
e-mail: info@abbotsbrae.co.uk   website: www.abbotsbrae.co.uk

Inveraray

18thC Royal burgh on the shores of Loch Fyne, 35 miles south of Oban.

HALFTOWN COTTAGES, ST CATHERINE'S (01369 860750). Heart of the West Highlands. 55 miles from Glasgow and across Loch Fyne from Inveraray. Two radically modernised 18thC farm cottages. Wholly secluded woodland site just above the loch. A real 'chill out' place for humans and animals. [Pets £10 per week.]
website: www.argyllcottages.com

Isle of Gigha

A tranquil island, one of the Inner Hebrides just of the west coast of Scotland. A haven for birds and wildlife.

GIGHA HOTEL, ISLE OF GIGHA PA41 7AA (01583 505254; Fax: 01583 505244). Beautiful, tranquil island. Explore the white sandy bays and lochs; famous Achamore Gardens. Easy walking, bike hire, birds, wildlife and wild flowers. Dog-friendly. Holiday cottages also available. [🐾]
website: www.gigha.org.uk

Loch Crinan

The village of Crinan is at the entrance to the canal at the eastern end of the Loch.

DUNTRUNE CASTLE HOLIDAY COTTAGES. Sleep 2-5. Five traditional self-catering cottages in spacious grounds of castle. Estate comprises 5000 acres and 5 miles of coastline. For further details please contact: ROBIN MALCOLM, DUNTRUNE CASTLE, KILMARTIN, ARGYLL PA31 8QQ (01546 510283). STB ★★★ Self Catering. [🐾]
website: www.duntrune.com

Loch Goil

Six mile long loch stretching from Lochgoilhead to Loch Long.

DARROCH MHOR, CARRICK CASTLE, LOCH GOIL PA24 8AF (01301 703249; Mobile: 07747 802792). Five self-catering Chalets on the shores of Loch Goil in the heart of Lomond & Trossachs National Park. Fully equipped except linen. Colour TV, fitted kitchen. Pets very welcome. Open all year. [🐾]
e-mail: mail@argyllchalets.com   website: www.argyllchalets.com

Oban

Popular Highland resort and port, yachting centre, ferry services to Inner and Outer Hebrides. Sandy bathing beach at Ganavan Bay. McCaig's Tower above town is Colosseum replica built in 1890s.

COLIN & JO MOSSMAN, LAGNAKEIL HIGHLAND LODGES, LERAGS, OBAN PA34 4SE (01631 562746). Our Timber Lodges and four cottages are set in a tranquil, scenic wooded glen overlooking Loch Feochan, only 3 miles from the picturesque harbour town of Oban: "Gateway to the Isles". Lodges equipped to a high standard, including linen and towels, country pub a short walk. OAP discount. Free loch fishing. Special Breaks from £65 per lodge per night, weekly from £290-£1450. Sleep 1-12 comfortably. VisitScotland ★★★/★★★★ Self-Catering. [Pets £3 per night].
e-mail: info@lagnakeil.co.uk   website: www.lagnakeil.co.uk

TRALEE BAY HOLIDAYS, BENDERLOCH, BY OBAN PA37 1QR (01631 720255/217). Overlooking Ardmucknish Bay. The wooded surroundings and sandy beaches make Tralee the ideal destination for a self-catering lodge or caravan holiday anytime of the year. STB ★★★★★ [Pets £21 per week]
e-mail: tralee@easynet.co.uk   website: www.tralee.com or www.traleecottages.com

MRS STEWART, GLENVIEW, SOROBA ROAD, OBAN PA34 4JF (01631 562267). Small family-run guest house, 10 minutes' walk from train, boat and bus terminal. A warm welcome awaits you all year round. [🐾]
e-mail: morven.stewart@hotmail.co.uk

LOCH MELFORT HOTEL & RESTAURANT, ARDUAINE, BY OBAN PA34 4XG (01852 200233; Fax: 01852 200214). Stunning views down the Sound of Jura to the Islands. Located between Inveraray and Oban, beside the famous Arduaine Gardens. Excellent award-winning cuisine, comfortable accommodation, and friendly and attentive service. [Pets £8.50 per night]
e-mail: reception@lochmelfort.co.uk   website: www.lochmelfort.co.uk

MELFORT PIER AND HARBOUR, KILMELFORD, BY OBAN PA34 4XD (01852 200333; Fax: 01852 200329). Superb Lochside houses each with Sauna, Spa bath, Digital TV, Telephone, Wifi, on the shores of Loch Melfort. Excellent base for touring Argyll and the Isles. From £90 to £240 per night. Sleeps 2-6. 2 pets very welcome. Service with a smile. [Pets £15 each per stay]
website: www.mellowmelfort.com

THE LANCASTER, ESPLANADE, OBAN PA34 5AD (01631 562587). A family-run, sea front hotel with 27 bedrooms. All public rooms enjoy sea views. Indoor swimming pool, steam room, sauna and spa. An ideal location from which to explore the Highlands and Islands.
e-mail: lancasteroban@btconnect.com   website: www.lancasteroban.co.uk

ARDMADDY CASTLE HOLIDAY COTTAGES (01852 300778). Five cottages in stunning locations. Wonderful environment for dogs (and people!) Fantastic walking by the sea, through the woods and over the moors – fresh air, peace and tranquillity. The perfect place to unwind with all the family. STB ★★★★.
e-mail: janwolfe@btinternet.com   website: www.ardmaddy.com

Rothesay

Principal town on the Isle of Bute. Reached by ferry from Wemyss Bay.

DAVID & ELAINE DANIELS, ARDENCRAIG HOUSE APARTMENTS, ARDENCRAIG ROAD, ROTHESAY PA20 9EP (Tel & Fax: 01700 505077; Mobile: 07881 825653 or 07990 838350). Five spacious and comfortable apartments in a beautifully converted Georgian mansion. Overlooking the Firth of Clyde. Pets are welcome by prior arrangement. STB ★★★★.[🐾]
e-mail: EBDan10@aol.com   website: www.ardencraig.org.uk

Strontian

Village lying on the north shore of Loch Sunart, close to the head of the Loch.

KILCAMB LODGE HOTEL & RESTAURANT, STRONTIAN PH36 4HY (01967 402257). If good food, fine wine and fine dining and a touch of luxury are on your list of priorities when looking for a small, pet-friendly hotel, look no further than this Country House on the edge of Loch Sunart. STB ★★★ Gold, AA ★★★ and 2 Rosettes.
e-mail: enquiries@kilcamblodge.co.uk   website: www.kilcamblodge.co.uk

Tarbert

Fishing port on isthmus connecting Kintyre to the mainland.

DUNMORE COURT, KILBERRY ROAD, NEAR TARBERT PA29 6XZ (01880 820654). Four cottages sleeping 2-7. Wonderful walks and scenery, peace and quiet. Winter breaks available. Easy access to island ferries. Terms from £250-£600. Open all year. ASSC member. STB ★★ SELF CATERING. [🐾]
e-mail: bookings@dunmorecourt.com   website: www.dunmorecourt.com

Peaceful, unspoilt West Highland estate. Traditional cottages, with open fires. Sleep 4–10. Pets welcome. Walks, pony trekking, golf nearby. APPLY SOPHIE JAMES, SKIPNESS ESTATE, BY TARBERT PA29 6XU (01880 760207; Fax: 01880 760208). STB ★★/★★★ [🐾]
e-mail: sophie@skipness.freeserve.co.uk

Taynuilt

Village in Argyll 1km south west of Bonawe.

INVERAWE COTTAGES, TAYNUILT PA35 1HU (01866 822777). Three self-catering cottages offer a wonderful haven to relax. Comfortable, cosy and welcoming. Sleep 2, 4 and 6. Inverawe is a paradise for dogs, children and adults alike.
e-mail: cottages@inverawe.co.uk   website: www.inverawe-cottages.co.uk

Esplanade, Ayr KA7 1DT
Ayr's only seafront hotel, just five minutes' walk from town centre.
Lunches, dinners and bar suppers served.

HORIZON HOTEL

A welcome guest. In all my years of experience of this business, I have never received a complaint about a dog slamming bedroom doors late at night, talking loudly in the corridors or driving away noisily from the car park when other guests are trying to sleep. Never has a dog made cigarette burns on the carpets, furniture or in the bath. No dog has ever stolen my towels, sheets or ashtrays. No cheque written by a dog has ever bounced and no dog has ever tried to pay with a stolen credit card. Never has a dog insulted my waitress or complained about food or wine. Neither have we ever had a dog who was drunk. In short you are welcome whenever you wish to come to this hotel and if you can vouch for your master, you are welcome to bring him along too!!

Phone now for free colour brochure. Under the personal supervision of Mr & Mrs A.H. Meikle.

Tel: 01292 264384 • Fax: 01292 264011
e-mail: reception@horizonhotel.com
www.horizonhotel.com

The Isle of Arran
AA "Inspectors' Choice" Hotel
VisitScotland "Gold Award"Hotel
& 5-Star Self-catering Cottages
www.kilmichael.com • 01770 302219

Dyemill Lodges · Isle of Arran
Six Scandinavian designed pinewood lodges and two holiday homes offer comfortable accommodation in surroundings full of natural beauty and interest, yet close to all the amenities of Lamlash village .
**Contact: Dyemill House, Monamhor Glen, Lamlash, Isle of Arran KA27 8NT
Tel: 01770 600419 • e-mail: enquiries@dyemill.co.uk • www.dyemill.co.uk**

Please note...
All the information in this book is given in good faith in the belief that it is correct. However, the publishers cannot guarantee the facts given in these pages, neither are they responsible for changes in policy, ownership or terms that may take place after the date of going to press. Readers should always satisfy themselves that the facilities they require are available and that the terms, if quoted, still apply.

Ayr

Popular family holiday resort with sandy beaches. Excellent shopping, theatre, racecourse.

HORIZON HOTEL, ESPLANADE, AYR KA7 1DT (01292 264384; Fax: 01292 264011). Highly recommended for golf breaks; special midweek rates. Coach parties welcome. Lunches, dinners and bar suppers served. Phone now for free colour brochure. [🐕]
e-mail: reception@horizonhotel.com   website: www.horizonhotel.com

Brodick

Resort on east coast of Isle of Arran, Ferry connection to mainland.

KILMICHAEL HOTEL (01770 302219). AA "Inspectors' Choice" Hotel. VisitScotland "Gold Award" Hotel and 5-Star Self-catering Cottages [🐕]
website: www.kilmichael.com

Lamlash

Village on east coast of Isle of Arran, 3 miles south of Brodick.

DYEMILL LODGES, ISLE OF ARRAN. Six Scandinavian designed pinewood lodges and two holiday homes offer comfortable accommodation in surroundings full of natural beauty and interest, yet close to all the amenities of Lamlash village. Contact: PAUL & SUE ARCHER, DYEMILL HOUSE, MONAMHOR GLEN, LAMLASH, ISLE OF ARRAN KA27 8NT (01770 600419). STB ★★★.
e-mail: enquiries@dyemill.co.uk   website: www.dyemill.co.uk

BORDER HOLIDAY HOMES, ROOTSVILLE, ALLANTON, DUNS TD11 3JY (01890 817186) Three self catering properties in Northumberland and Scottish Borders, each suitable for two people. Centrally heated, double glazed. Pets welcome at some properties. Short breaks available. ETC ★★★★ [🐾]
e-mail: info@borderholidayhomes.co.uk   website: www.borderholidayhomes.co.uk

Bonchester Bridge

Village on Rule Water, 6 miles east of Hawick. To east is Bonchester Hill surmounted by ancient earthworks.

WAUCHOPE COTTAGES, BONCHESTER BRIDGE, HAWICK TD9 9TG (01450 860630). Four single storey detached timber cottages sleeping 2-4, each with enclosed large garden. Quiet location with stunning scenery and forest walks direct from the door. Dogs most welcome. Self-catering. [🐾]
e-mail: wauchope@btinternet.com   website: www.wauchopecottages.co.uk

Cockburnspath

Village situated at the eastern extremity of the Southern Upland Way.

MARION LAUDER, CLOVERKNOWE COTTAGES, PATHHEAD FARM,COCKBURNSPATH TD13 5XB (01368 830318). Two detached sandstone cottages on the border of Berwickshire and East Lothian. Modernised and equipped to high standards. Large enclosed gardens. Ample parking. En suite and ground floor bedrooms available. [🐾]
e-mail: mlauder@supanet.com

Coldingham

Historic village near coast north of Eyemouth

EMMA EDMONDSON, PRESS MAINS COTTAGES, COLDINGHAM TD14 5TS (Tel/Fax: 01890 771310; Mobile: 07850 834953 / 07850 834940). Luxury self-catering in the beautiful Scottish Borders, offering peace, relaxation and the chance of a brush with nature. Four different cottages sleeping 2/6 with spa baths, four-poster beds and open fires. STB ★★★★.
e-mail: emma@watchbadgers.co.uk   website: www.watchbadgers.co.uk

Galashiels

Picturesque town on the A7 Carlisle to Edinburgh. with a good choice of shops and leisure activities.

KINGSKNOWES HOTEL, SELKIRK ROAD, GALASHIELS TD1 3HY (01896 758375; Fax: 01896 750377). A Baronial mansion set in attractive gardens and close to the River Tweed. Elegant public areas, spacious bedrooms. Ideal base for touring. AA ★★★
e-mail: enq@kingsknowes.co.uk   website: www.kingsknowes.co.uk

Jedburgh

Small town on Jed water, 10 miles north-east of Hawick. Ruins of abbey founded in 1138.

CHRISTINE SWANSTON, FERNIEHIRST MILL LODGE, JEDBURGH TD8 6PQ (01835 863279). A chalet style guest house set in grounds of 25 acres. All rooms en suite with tea/coffee making facilities. Well behaved pets (including horses) welcome by arrangement. AA ★★ [🐾]
e-mail: ferniehirstmill@aol.com   website: www.ferniehirstmill.co.uk

CRAILING OLD SCHOOL, CRAILING, BY JEDBURGH TD8 6TL (01835 850382). Peacefully situated B&B close to the River Teviot. Ideal area for walking, fishing, golf and horse riding. Self contained lodge with wheelchair/disabled friendly access. Self catering possible. Evening meals by arrangement. [pw! Pets £2 per night, £10 per week]
e-mail: info@crailingoldschool.co.uk   website: www.crailingoldschool.co.uk

---

🐾   Pets are welcome free of charge.

Classified Symbols

£   A charge is made for pets: nightly or weekly.

pw! Special provision for pets; exercise facility, feeding or accommodation arrangement.

⌂   Separate pets' accommodation.

Kelso

Market town 18 miles north-west of Hawick and 20 miles south-west of Berwick-upon-Tweed.

WESTWOOD HOUSE, OVERLOOKING SCOTLAND'S FAMOUS RIVER TWEED. Enclosed and secluded riverside cottage with walled gardens and own private island. Sleeps 2-8 persons plus child, from £385 per week. 2 person discounts. For brochure contact: DEBBIE CRAWFORD, PIPPIN HEATH FARM, HOLT, NORFOLK NR25 6SS (07788 134832). [🐎]

MRS KIRSTY B. SHAW, SMAILHOLM MAINS FARM COTTAGES, BY KELSO TD5 7RT (01573 460318). Two cosy farm cottages, each sleeping 5, in a peaceful setting 6 miles from Kelso. Both with open fires, central heating, Satellite TV. Close to golf, fishing, walking or a day at the races. Short breaks available. STB ★★★★[🐎]
e-mail: info@smailholm-mains.co.uk   website: www.kelsoaccommodation.co.uk

Melrose

Historic town in Borders with magnificent ruined abbey.

EILDON HOLIDAY COTTAGES, DINGLETON MAINS, MELROSE TD6 9HS. (01896 823258). Award-winning converted cottages, sleep 2/6. Very well equipped; most suitable for disabled guests. Free Wi-Fi. Dogs welcome by arrangement.
e-mail: info@eildon.co.uk   website: www.eildon.co.uk

Newcastleton

Small village in the valley of Liddesdale, ideal base for touring.

BAILEY MILL COURTYARD, BAILEY MILL, NEWCASTLETON TD9 0TR (016977 48617). Self-catering apartments nestling on the Roxburghshire / Cumbrian border. Also riding holidays, unaccompanied children welcome. B&B or Full Board. Licensed bar. Colour brochure available. [🐎]
e-mail: baileymillaccom@aol.com   website: www.baileycottages-riding-racing.com

Peebles

Royal Burgh 23 miles south of Edinburgh with a good choice of shops and outdoor activities.

TONTINE HOTEL, HIGH STREET, PEEBLES EH45 8AJ (01721 720892). Dog-friendly hotel in the heart of Peebles. 36 en suite bedrooms, some with views of the river and Tweed Green. Parking. Wonderful walks on the door step. STB ★★★ [🐎]
e-mail: stay@tontinehotel.com   website: www.tontinehotel.com

Selkirk

Town on hill above Ettrick Water, 9 miles north of Hawick

THE GARDEN HOUSE, WHITMUIR, SELKIRK TD7 4PZ (01750 721728; Mobile: 07768 707700). Comfortable, warm modern farm house B&B. Spacious bedrooms, private bathrooms. Good home cooking. Fishing, walking, cycling and horse riding nearby. Grazing available. Open all year. [🐎]
e-mail: whitmuir@btconnect.com   website: www.whitmuirfarm.co.uk

West Linton

Village on east side of Pentland hills, 7 miles south-west of Penicuik. Edinburgh 18 miles.

MRS C. M. KILPATRICK, SLIPPERFIELD HOUSE, WEST LINTON EH46 7AA (01968 660401). Two lovely cottages on hideaway country estate near Edinburgh. Sleep 4/6. Available all year. Perfect dog-friendly location. STB ★★★/★★★★★ [🐎]
e-mail: cottages@slipperfield.com   website: www.slipperfield.com

FREE or **REDUCED RATE** entry to Holiday Visits and Attractions – see our **READERS' OFFER VOUCHERS** on pages 409-414

Auldgirth, Castle Douglas, Crossmichael

Dalbeattie, Drummore, Dumfries, Gatehouse of Fleet

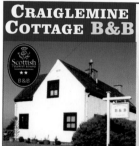

Auldgirth

Small village on A76, 7 miles from Dumfries.

FRIARS CARSE COUNTRY HOUSE HOTEL, AULDGIRTH DG2 0SA (01387 740388; Fax: 01387 740550). 21 en suite bedrooms. Restaurant serving excellent local cuisine. Private fishing. Snooker room. STB★★★. Pets welcome.
website: www.friarscarse.co.uk

Castle Douglas

Old market town at the northern end of Carlingwalk Loch, good touring centre for Galloway

MRS CELIA PICKUP, "CRAIGADAM", CASTLE DOUGLAS DG7 3HU (Tel & Fax: 01556 650233). Family-run 18th century famhouse. All bedrooms en suite. Billiard room/honesty bar. Lovely oak-panelled dining room offering Cordon Bleu cooking using local produce such as venison, pheasant and salmon. Trout fishing, walking and golfing available. STB ★★★★; AA ★★★★ and Breakfast & Dinner Awards. [🐾]
e-mail: inquiry@craigadam.com   website: www.craigadam.com

ROSE COTTAGE, GELSTON, CASTLE DOUGLAS DG7 1SH (01556 502513). Holiday cottage near secluded sandy beaches, water sports, birdwatching, walking, golf and fishing. Two double and two twin bedrooms; two bathrooms. Fully equipped kitchen. Sun room. Utility room. Enclosed courtyard. Ample parking. No smoking

LOCH KEN HOLIDAY PARK, PARTON, CASTLE DOUGLAS DG7 3NE (01644 470282). A natural, unspoilt place for a family holiday. Ideal for fishing, sailing, walking and golfing. Boats, bikes & canoes for hire, touring and camping, lochside caravans to let. STB ★★★★, David Bellamy Gold Award. [Pets £2 per night, £10 per week]
website: www.lochkenholidaypark.co.uk

CATHY AND RICHARD AGNEW, GLENLEE HOLIDAY HOUSES, NEW GALLOWAY, CASTLE DOUGLAS DG7 3SF (01644 430212). Five charming holiday cottages in quiet secluded woodland set around a central courtyard. Each cottage is well equipped and comfortably furnished. An excellent base for exploring Galloway. STB ★★★. [🐾]
e-mail: agnew@glenlee-holidays.co.uk   website: www.glenlee-holidays.co.uk

Crossmichael

Small village on east side of Loch Ken, 4 miles north of Castle Douglas.

DEESIDE BED & BREAKFAST 42 MAIN STREET, CROSSMICHAEL, CASTLE DOUGLAS DG7 3AU (01556 670239) Small, family-run accommodation, surrounded by the unspoiled beauty of the Galloway countryside. One double en suite, twin/double with private facilities. STB ★★★. [Pets £3 per night].
e-mail: info@deesidebandb.co.uk   website: www.deesidebandb.co.uk

Dalbeattie

Small town in wooded valley on Urr Water, 12 miles form Dumfries.

BAREND HOLIDAY VILLAGE, SANDYHILLS, DALBEATTIE DG5 4NU (01387 780663). Our log cabins are well equipped and centrally heated for all year comfort. On-site boules courts, bar, restaurant, sauna and indoor pool. Wi-Fi internet access available. [Pets £3 per night]. Quote PW1 for 5% discount on new bookings.
website: www.barendholidayvillage.co.uk

Drummore

Coastal location, 4 miles north of Mull of Galloway.

MULL OF GALLOWAY, DRUMMORE. A few short steps from the beach. STB 3/4-Star cottages; non-smoking cottages available. Tranquil and unspoiled village. Logan Botanical Gardens, golf, fishing, birdwatching nearby. Unrestricted beaches. ASSC. Contact SALLY COLMAN (01776 840631). [Pets £15 per pet per week]
website: www.harbourrow.co.uk

Dumfries

County town of Dumfries-shire and a former seaport. Dumfries contains many interesting buildings including an 18th century windmill containing a camera obscura. Robert Burns lived in the town before his death in 1796.

DAVID & GILL STEWART, AE FARM COTTAGES, GUBHILL FARM, DUMFRIES DG1 1RL (01387 860648). 2 & 3 Star accommodation in old stone buildings on a working farm in a peaceful valley. Beautiful views, plentiful wildlife and cycle tracks on the doorstep. Between Dumfries, Moffat and Thornhill. STB ★★★ SELF CATERING, CATEGORY ONE DISABILITY. [🐕]
e-mail: gill@gubhill.co.uk   website: www.aefarmcottages.co.uk

Gatehouse of Fleet

Small town near mouth of Water of Fleet, 6 miles north-west of Kirkcudbright

RUSKO HOLIDAYS, GATEHOUSE OF FLEET, CASTLE DOUGLAS DG7 2BS (01557 814215). Two charming, cosy cottages near beaches, hills, gardens, castles and golf course. Walking, fishing, tennis. Pets welcome. Sleep 2-4. STB ★★ to ★★★ Self-Catering. [Pets £20 per week.]
e-mail: info@ruskoholidays.co.uk   website: www.ruskoholidays.co.uk

CARRICK HOLIDAY COTTAGES. Range of self-catering cottages and chalets in beautiful Carrick Bay and Brighouse Bay. Safe sandy beaches, sailing, cycling, walking, birdwatching, golf. Pets welcome. Contact CATHIE TENNANT, C/O CARRICK COTTAGE, CARRICK SHORE, GATEHOUSE OF FLEET DG7 2DT (01556 505485; Mobile: 07719 263098). [🐕]
e-mail: cathie.tennant@googlemail.com   website: www.carrickcottagesscotland.com

Gretna Green

Scottish Border village, famous for runaway weddings. Shopping outlet is popular tourist attraction.

KIRKCROFT GUEST HOUSE, GLASGOW ROAD, GRETNA GREEN DG16 5DU (01461 337403). Bed and Breakfast accommodation ideally situated for touring the Lake District, Galloway coast, the Scottish Borders and Northumberland.   Short breaks available. STB ★★★. Pets welcome.
e-mail: info@kirkcroft.co.uk   website: www.kirkcroft.co.uk

Kirkcudbright

Town in a sheltered position on north Solway shore, 25 miles from Dumfries.

BAYTREE HOUSE, 110 HIGH STREET, KIRKCUDBRIGHT DG6 4JQ (01557 330824). Award-winning Georgian townhouse in a conservation area of the historic harbour town of Kirkcudbright. Four en suite bedrooms. Dogs welcome by arrangement; plenty of picturesque dog walks nearby. STB ★★★★. [Pets £10 per night (£5 per night for 3 nights or more) B&B; Free in s/c Garden Studio)
e-mail: info@baytreekirkcudbright.co.uk   website: www.baytreekirkcudbright.co.uk

Moffat

At head of lovely Annandale, grand mountain scenery. Good centre for rambling, climbing, angling and golf. The 'Devil's Beef Tub' is 5 miles, Edinburgh 52, Peebles 33, Dumfries 21.

BARNHILL SPRINGS COUNTRY GUEST HOUSE, MOFFAT DG10 9QS (01683 220580). Early Victorian country house overlooking some of the finest views of Upper Annandale. Comfortable accommodation, residents' lounge with open fire. Situated on the Southern Upland Way half-a-mile from A74/M74 Moffat Junction. Pets free of charge. Bed & Breakfast from £33; Evening Meal by arrangement. AA ★★ [🐕 pw!]
e-mail: barnhillsprings@yahoo.co.uk

ANNANDALE ARMS HOTEL, HIGH STREET, MOFFAT DG10 9HF (01683 220013; Fax: 01683 221395). A warm welcome is offered at the Annandale Arms to dogs with well-mannered and house-trained owners. Excellent restaurant and a relaxing panelled bar. AA ★★★ and Rosette [pw! 🐕]
e-mail: reception@annandalearmshotel.co.uk   website: www.annandalearmshotel.co.uk

---

Terms quoted in this publication may be subject to increase if rises in costs necessitate

Sanquhar

Small town on the Southern Upland Way.

NEWARK FARM, SANQUHAR DG4 6HN (01659 50263; Fax: 01659 50975). Three different types of quality accommodation and a wide range of facilities. Bed and Breakfast; Self-catering; Caravan Club Certified caravan location. Ideal location for fishing, walking, mountain biking. STB ★★★ B&B
e-mail: info@newarkfarm.com   website: www.newarkfarm.com

Stranraer

Scotland's gateway to Ireland, only 90 minutes away by fast ferry. Ideal base for outdoor activities.

CORSEWALL LIGHTHOUSE HOTEL, KIRKCOLM, STRANRAER DG9 0QG (01775 853220; Fax: 01776 854231). An unique hotel perched on the shores of North Rhinns of Galloway. Fine wines and modern Scottish cuisine. Accommodation offers views over Ailsa Craig, the Isle of Arran, Kintyre Peninsula and Northern Ireland. Pets welcome. STB/AA ★★★
e-mail: info@lighthousehotel.co.uk   website: www.lighthousehotel.co.uk

CROSS HAVEN GUEST HOUSE, LEWIS STREET, STRANRAER DG9 7AL (01776 700598). Family-run Guest House convenient for Cairnryan ferries, offering quality service and value for money. En suite bedrooms. Ideal for couples, ferry passengers and visitors to Ireland. Pets welcome. STB ★★★. [Pets £7 per booking]
e-mail: crosshavengh@yahoo.co.uk   website: www.crosshaven.co.uk

Thornhill

Small town on River Nith 13 miles north-west of Dumfries. Site of Roman signal station lies to the south.

TRIGONY HOUSE HOTEL, THORNHILL DG3 5EZ (01848 331211). Standing in over 4 acres of woodland and gardens, Trigony is a luxury Country House Hotel with a combination of relaxed style and excellent rustic cuisine. Should you have a dog they will be more than welcome at our pet-friendly hotel. [pw!]
e-mail: info@trigonyhotel.co.uk   website: www.countryhousehotelscotland.com

HOPE COTTAGE, THORNHILL DG3 5BJ (01848 331510; Fax: 01848 331810). Pretty stone cottage in the peaceful conservation village of Durisdeer. Well-equipped self-catering cottage with large secluded garden. Sleeps 5/6. Towels, linen, heating and electricity included. Phone MRS S. STANNETT for brochure. STB ★★★★ [🐾]
e-mail: a.stann@btinternet.com   website: www.hopecottage.co.uk

TEMPLAND COTTAGES, TEMPLAND MAINS, THORNHILL DG3 5AB (01848 330775). Set in the heart of the Nith Valley near Thornhill, with shops, hotels and restaurants. Tastefully converted cottages sleep from 2-6. Own patio with BBQ, heated indoor pool and sauna. [🐾]
e-mail: jacqui@templandcottages.co.uk   website: www.templandcottages.co.uk

Whithorn

Small town 9 miles south of Wigtown.

MIKE AND HELEN ALEXANDER, CRAIGLEMINE COTTAGE B&B, GLASSERTON, NEAR WHITHORN DG8 8NE (01988 500594). Our rural location makes this a wonderful place to unwind. Ideal for touring, your dog will love the nearby beaches. Evening meal available. STB ★★ [🐾]
e-mail: cottage@fireflyuk.net   website: www.startravel.fireflyinternet.co.uk

KATH & TIM ANNISON, CHAPEL OUTON FARMHOUSE B&B, WHITHORN DG8 8DH (01988 500136) Old-fashioned hospitality in comfortable and informal surroundings. Non-smoking, spacious yet cosy accommodation and wholesome home cooked food. Let us spoil you and your family and pamper your pet. [pw! 🐾]
e-mail: kath@chapelouton.co.uk   website: www.chapelouton.co.uk

Wigtown

Small town on hill above River Cree, known as "Scotland's Book Town".

HILLCREST HOUSE, MAIDLAND PLACE, WIGTOWN DG8 9EU (01988 402018). Beautiful character Victorian villa set on edge of national book town. Fabulous views over nature reserve. Six bedrooms, residents' lounge. Award winning evening meals using fresh local produce. STB ★★★★. [Pets free in kennels, £3 per night indoors]
e-mail: info@hillcrest-wigtown.co.uk   website: www.hillcrest-wigtown.co.uk

WEST FENTON Court

Luxury self-catering holiday cottages near North Berwick

www.westfenton.co.uk

perfect for families, golf, walking, beaches and relaxation

Kitchen & dining areas for enjoying long, relaxed meals.
Lounge rooms with hardwood floors and sumptuous sofas for relaxing after a day's golf or sightseeing.
Bathrooms - beautifully tiled and equipped.
Bedrooms - tastefully furnished for a comfortable sleep in the quiet of the country.
Patio gardens - lawned and fenced, ideal for barbecues, alfresco dining or an evening drink.

West Fenton Court is located in a conservation area, adjacent to a nature reserve, just one mile south of Gullane and close to North Berwick, ideal for golf, beaches and coastal walks. Edinburgh is just 35 minutes by car or train.

West Fenton, North Berwick, East Lothian EH39 5AL • 01620 842154 • e-mail: info@westfenton.co.uk

---

Hunter Holiday Cottages

Thornton Farm, Rosewell, Edinburgh EH24 9EF

Hunter Holiday Cottages have 2 x two-bedroom and 1 x 3-bedroom cottages situated on our working farm just 20 minutes' drive south of Edinburgh city centre. Pets welcome, great walks on tracks and through woods. For more information visit our website. Contact Margot Crichton. Telephone for availability for Short Breaks

Tel: 0131-448 0888 • Fax: 0131-440 2082 • e-mail: info@edinburghcottages.com • www.edinburghcottages.com

---

CROSSWOODHILL FARM
HOLIDAY COTTAGES near Edinburgh

Please quote PW

Award-winning? Well-equipped? Spacious? Family, pet and disabled friendly?
Yes to all these questions. And so much more.... explore our livestock farm, relax in front of a blazing fire with a book, let the kids loose on the toy and games cupboards once home from a wealth of exciting days out. Or play outside. Spoilt for choice with both the area and with 3 very different properties. Each sleeps up to 6.
Winner of 2008 VisitScotland Thistle Award for Accommodation: Customer Care.

Explore: **www.crosswoodhill.co.uk** or **www.fivestarholidaycottage.co.uk**
Contact: Geraldine Hamilton, Crosswoodhill,
West Calder, West Lothian, EH55 8LP
Tel. 01501 785205 • e-mail: cottages@crosswoodhill.co.uk

North Berwick

Town and resort 19 miles east of Edinburgh.

WEST FENTON COURT, WEST FENTON, NORTH BERWICK EH39 5AL(01620 842154). Luxury self-catering holiday cottages near North Berwick, perfect for families, golf, walking, beaches and relaxation. Just 35 minutes from Edinburgh. Superbly equipped. STB ★★★★ [Pets £10 per week].
e-mail: info@westfenton.co.uk   website: www.westfenton.co.uk

Rosewell

Village 4 miles south west of Dalkeith.

HUNTER HOLIDAY COTTAGES, THORNTON FARM, ROSEWELL, EDINBURGH EH24 9EF (0131 448 0888; Fax: 0131 440 2082). 2 x two-bedroom cottages and 1 x 3-bedroom cottage on working farm 20 minutes' drive Edinburgh. Great walks on tracks and through woods. Contact MARGOT CRICHTON. [Pets £10 per night/week].
e-mail: info@edinburghcottages.com   website: www.edinburghcottages.com

West Calder

Village in West Lothian 4 miles west of Livingston.

CROSSWOODHILL FARM HOLIDAY COTTAGES, NEAR EDINBURGH. Well equipped and spacious properties, family, pet and disabled friendly. Ideal base for exploring this scenic area and for visiting Edinburgh. STB 3/5 Stars. Contact: GERALDINE HAMILTON, CROSSWOODHILL, WEST CALDER, WEST LOTHIAN EH55 8LP (01501 785205).[Pets £20 per week]
e-mail: cottages@crosswoodhill.co.uk   website: www.crosswoodhill.co.uk
                                                   www.fivestarholidaycottage.co.uk

Lower Largo

Village on the bay, 2 miles NE of Leven. Birth place of Alexander Selkirk of Robinson Crusoe fame.

THE CRUSOE HOTEL, MAIN STREET, LOWER LARGO, NEAR ST ANDREWS KY8 6BT (01333 320759; Fax: 01333 320865). Old-world ambience with fine harbour views. En suite accommodation, outstanding cuisine, free house. Excellent centre for sailing, golf, birdwatching, wind surfing, coastal walks. STB ★★★ Hotel. [🐾]
email: relax@crusoehotel.co.uk   website: www.crusoehotel.co.uk

St Andrews

Home of golf - British Golf Museum has memorabilia dating back to the origins of the game. Remains of castle and cathedral. Sealife Centre and beach Leisure Centre. Excellent sands. Ideal base for exploring the picturesque East Neuk.

MR & MRS PATRICK WEDDERBURN, ST ANDREWS COUNTRY COTTAGES, MOUNTQUHANIE ESTATE, FREEPOST, CUPAR KY15 4BR (01382 330318; Fax: 01382 330480). Quality self-catering houses and cottages in St Andrews and on a tranquil Country Estate. Central heating, TV. Enclosed gardens. STB ★★★ to ★★★★ Self Catering. [pw! Dogs £15 per week, Cats F.O.C.].
e-mail: enquiries@standrews-cottages.com   website: www.standrews-cottages.com

---

🐾 Pets are welcome free of charge.

£ A charge is made for pets: nightly or weekly.

pw! Special provision for pets; exercise facility, feeding or accommodation arrangement.

⌂ Separate pets' accommodation.

Classified Symbols

Fort William, Gairloch, Glen Shiel, Inverness, Kingussie

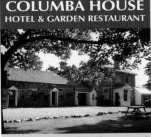

Kincraig, Loch Ness, Muir of Ord, Nethybridge

Nethy Bridge, Newtonmore, Poolewe

Whitebridge

HIGHLAND HOTEL COLLECTION. A warm welcome awaits you in the Highlands of Scotland. BALLACHULISH HOTEL (0844 855 9133). ISLES OF GLENCOE HOTEL, BALLACHULISH (0844 855 9134). OBAN CALEDONIAN HOTEL, OBAN (0844 855 9135). STB ★★★
e-mail: reservations@akkeronhotels.com   website: www.akkeronhotels.com

HIGHLAND TRAVEL INNS. A warm welcome at quality accommodation in Caithness and Morayshire. THE WEIGH INN, THURSO (01847 893722). www.weighinn.co.uk. THE FERRY INN, SCRABSTER (01847 892814) www.ferryinnscrabster.co.uk. THE RED LION TAVERN, FOCHABERS (01343 820455). www.redlionfochabers.co.uk. GORDON ARMS HOTEL, FOCHABERS (01343 820508) www.gordonarms.co.uk

Aviemore (Inverness-shire)

Scotland's leading ski resort in Spey valley with superb sport and entertainment facilities. All-weather holiday centre.

CAIRNGORM HIGHLAND BUNGALOWS, GLEN EINICH, 29 GRAMPIAN VIEW, AVIEMORE PH22 1TF (01479 810653, Fax: 01479 810262). Well equipped bungalows ranging from one to four bedrooms. Open all year. Leisure facilities nearby. Children and pets welcome. Phone for brochure. STB ★★★-★★★★ [🐕]
e-mail: linda.murray@virgin.net   website: www.cairngorm-bungalows.co.uk

PINE BANK CHALETS, AVIEMORE (01479 810000). Self-catering log cabins, chalets and apartments by the River Spey. STB ★★★/★★★★ accommodation with easy access to the mountains and the stunning scenery of the Cairngorms National Park, yet also within walking distance of the village. Pine Bank Chalets is your ideal base for a stay in Aviemore. Pets welcome.
e-mail: info@pinebankchalets.co.uk   website: www.pinebankchalets.co.uk

FIONA GRANT, AVIELOCHAN FARM HOLIDAY COTTAGES, AVIELOCHAN FARM, AVIEMORE PH22 1QD (01479 810846). Situated beside a small loch within the Cairngorms National Park, Avielochan Holiday cottages enjoy spectacular views of the mountains. Sleep 5/7; caravan also available. Pets welcome. STB ★★★, Green Tourism Silver Award. [🐕]
e-mail: info@avielochancottages.co.uk   website:www.avielochancottages.co.uk

Beauly (Inverness-shire)

Town at head of Beauly Firth, 11 miles west of Inverness.

FRANK & JULIET SPENCER-NAIRN, CULLIGRAN COTTAGES, GLEN STRATHFARRAR, STRUY, NEAR BEAULY IV4 7JX (Tel & Fax: 01463 761285). Pure magic! Come for a spell in a chalet or cottage and this glen will cast one over you! Conservation Area with native woodlands and wildlife. Open March - November. Brochure. Terms from £209-£539. [🐕]
e-mail: info@culligrancottages.co.uk   website: www.culligrancottages.co.uk

KERROW HOUSE, GLEN AFFRIC, CANNICH, BY BEAULY IV4 7NA (01456 415243; Mobile: 07944 726489). A selection of self-catering accommodation situated in 12 acres of wooded grounds, from Scandinavian-style chalets to a traditional riverside lodge. Sleep 2-7. Free fishing; rod hire available.   B&B also available (no pets). [Pets £30 per week - SC only].
email: info@kerrow-house.co.uk   website: www.kerrow-house.co.uk

Contin (Ross-shire)

Village 2 miles south west of Strathpeffer.

COUL HOUSE HOTEL, CONTIN, BY STRATHPEFFER IV14 9ES (01997 421487; Fax: 01997 421945). Privately owned and operated 20-bedroom Country House Hotel with miles of forest walks, many log fires, and great food. Both you and your dog are made to feel most welcome.
e-mail: stay@coulhousehotel.com   website: www.coulhousehotel.com

Drumnadrochit (Inverness-shire)

Village on the shores of Loch Ness with "Monster" visitor centre. Sonar scanning cruises.

GLENURQUHART LODGES, BY DRUMNADROCHIT IV63 6TJ (01456 476234; Fax: 01456 476286). Situated between Loch Ness and Glen Affric in a spectacular setting ideal for walking, touring or just relaxing in this tranquil location. Four spacious chalets all fully equipped for six people, set in wooded grounds. Owner's hotel adjacent where guests are most welcome in the restaurant and bar. [Pets £10 per week.]
e-mail: carol@glenurquhartlodges.co.uk   website: www.glenurquhart-lodges.co.uk

Fort William (Inverness-shire)

Small town at foot of Ben Nevis, ideal base for climbers and hillwalkers.

THE CLAN MACDUFF HOTEL, FORT WILLIAM PH33 6RW (01397 702341; Fax: 01397 706174). This family-run hotel overlooks Loch Linnhe, two miles south of Fort William, excellent for touring the West Highlands. All rooms have TV, hairdryer, hospitality tray and private facilities. B&B from £32.50pppn. Three nights DB&B from £144pp (Spring/Autumn). STB ★★★ Hotel. Phone or write for colour brochure and tariff. [🐕]
e-mail: reception@clanmacduff.co.uk   website: www.clanmacduff.co.uk

LOCH LEVEN HOTEL, OLD FERRY ROAD, NORTH BALLACHULISH, NEAR FORT WILLIAM PH33 6SA (01855 821236). Twelve en suite rooms, many with loch views. Meals using freshly prepared Scottish produce. Secluded garden down to shore. Safe, private parking. Extensive grounds. Great walks. [pw! 🐕]
e-mail: reception@lochlevenhotel.co.uk   website: www.lochlevenhotel.co.uk

GREAT GLEN HOLIDAYS, TORLUNDY, FORT WILLIAM PH33 6SW (Tel/Fax: 01397 703015). Sleep 4-6. Eight spacious, two-bedroom timber chalets on working Highland farm. Riding, fishing and walking on farm. Ideal for family holidays, excellent touring base. [Pets £15 per week]
e-mail: chris.carver@btconnect.com   website: www.fortwilliam-chalets.co.uk

LINNHE LOCHSIDE HOLIDAYS, CORPACH, FORT WILLIAM PH33 7NL (01397 772376; Fax: 01397 772007). Linnhe is unique and one of the most beautiful lochside parks in Britain. Close to Ben Nevis and Fort William. Excellent facilities. Pets welcome. Open mid December-end October. Colour brochure. (Pets £5 per night, £25 per week).
e-mail: relax@linnhe-lochside-holidays.co.uk   website: www.linnhe-lochside-holidays.co.uk

Gairloch (Ross-shire)

Small village on shore of Loch Gairloch.

THE OLD INN, FLOWERDALE GLEN, GAIRLOCH IV21 2BD (01445 712006; Fax: 01445 712933). A Traditional Highland Coaching Inn overlooking Gairloch harbour on the west coast of Scotland. Well known for its friendly welcome and relaxed atmosphere. Excellent accommodation, outstanding seafood, "Pub of the Year" awards. Own microbrewery. VisitScotland ★★★.[Pets £5 per night].
e-mail: enquiries@theoldinn.net   website: www.theoldinn.net

Glen Shiel (Inverness-shire)

Valley on River Shiel in Skye & Lochalsh District.

KINTAIL LODGE HOTEL, SHIEL BRIDGE, GLENSHIEL IV40 8HL (01599 511275). Beautifully situated on the shores of Loch Duich 6 miles south of Eilean Donan Castle. We guarantee your comfort and we promise you the best of Highland food and hospitality. Dogs welcome. [🐕]
e-mail: kintaillodgehotel@btinternet.com   website: www.kintaillodgehotel.co.uk

Inverness (Inverness-shire)

Known as "The Capital of the Highlands". Airport, excellent shopping. Ideal touring base.

LOCH NESS HIDEAWAYS. Charming timber cottage and chalet (quarter-mile apart). Fully equipped. Lovely views. Ideal for dog lovers. Contact: MRS JANET SUTHERLAND, LOCH NESS HIDEAWAYS, AULTNAGOIRE, ERROGIE, BY INVERNESS IV2 6UH (01456 486711). [First 2 dogs free, £10 per week for additional dogs]
e-mail: janet@lochnesshideaways.co.uk   website: www.lochnesshideaways.co.uk

Kincraig (Inverness-shire)

Attractive Highland village close to Loch Insh and Glenfeshie, midway between Aviemore and Kingussie.

"FRASER" and "TELFORD" cottages, close to Loch Insh and Glenfeshie, are an ideal holiday base from which to explore the Cairngorms National Park. In the Highland village of Kincraig, equidistant from Aviemore and Kingussie. Well behaved dogs and children welcome. STB ★★★ Silver GTBS Award. Contact: NICK & PATSY THOMPSON, GLEBE HOUSE, KINCRAIG PH21 1NU (01540 651377). [🐾] e-mail: glebecottages@gmail.com   website: www.glebecottages.co.uk

Kingussie (Inverness-shire)

Small town on River Spey 28 miles south of Inverness.

COLUMBA HOUSE HOTEL AND GARDEN RESTAURANT, MANSE ROAD, KINGUSSIE PH21 1JF (07748 361718/01540 661402). Quiet Highland retreat offering highest standards of hospitality, care and accommodation. Candlelit Garden Restaurant. Wi-Fi. [pw! Pets £5 per night, £15 per week] e-mail: myra@columbahousehotel.com   website: www.columbahousehotel.com

Loch Ness (Inverness-shire)

Home of 'Nessie', extending for 23 miles from Fort Augustus to south of Inverness.

WILDERNESS COTTAGES. Quality self-catering properties throughout Scotland, including small cottages, large houses and luxury apartments on banks of Loch Ness. Pets welcome. Please see website for details or for a brochure contact: WILDERNESS COTTAGES, ROEBUCK COTTAGE, ERROGIE IV2 6UH (01456 486358). STB★★★/★★★★/★★★★★ SELF CATERING e-mail: server@wildernesscottages.co.uk   website: www.wildernesscottages.co.uk

Muir of Ord (Inverness-shire)

Village 20km west of Inverness.

ORD HOUSE HOTEL, MUIR OF ORD IV6 7UH (01463 870492). 17th Century country house. Extensive gardens and woodlands for dogs to run around in. Large, airy bedrooms. Log fires. Restaurant. STB/AA ★★ and Rosette. [pw! 🐾] e-mail: admin@ord-house.co.uk   website: www.ord-house.co.uk

Nethy Bridge (Inverness-shire)

Popular resort on River Nethy with extensive Abernethy Forest to the south. Impressive mountain scenery. Grantown-on-Spey 5 miles.

MONDHUIE CHALETS & B&B, NETHY BRIDGE PH25 3DF (01479 821062). Situated in the country between Aviemore and Grantown-on-Spey, two comfortable, self-catering chalets, or you can have Dinner, B&B in the house. A warm welcome awaits you. Pets welcome. Red squirrels seen daily. Free internet access. [🐾] e-mail: david@mondhuie.com   website: www.mondhuie.com

SPEYSIDE COTTAGES, NETHY BRIDGE. Relax in 3 comfortable cottages (sleep 2-6) with fenced gardens, on riverbank with wonderful forest walks. Pets welcome. Includes full linen and towels. Contact BRIAN AND MOIRA PATRICK, 1 CHAPELTON PLACE, FORRES, MORAY IV36 2NL (01309 672505). [First dog FREE, extra dogs £25 per week] e-mail: brian@speysidecottages.co.uk   website: www.speysidecottages.co.uk

BALNAGOWAN MILL AND WOODLARK, NETHY BRIDGE. Comfortable, modern 3 bedroom cottages in secluded locations in the Cairngorms National Park. Woodland and riverside walks on the doorstep. Ideal for pets. Furnished to a high standard with full central heating. £290-£570 per week incl. of electricity, bed linen and towels. VisitScotland ★★★★. ASSC MEMBER. Contact PAULA FRASER, 33 ARGYLE GROVE, DUNBLANE FK15 9DT (01786 824957) [🐾] e-mail: paulajfraser@aol.com

🐾   Pets are welcome free of charge.

£   A charge is made for pets: nightly or weekly.

pw!   Special provision for pets; exercise facility, feeding or accommodation arrangement.

⌂   Separate pets' accommodation.

Classified Symbols

Newtonmore (Inverness-shire)

Small village at the heart of the Scottish Highlands. Officially the geographic centre of Scotland.

CRUBENBEG HOUSE, FALLS OF TRUIM, BY NEWTONMORE PH20 1BE (01540 673300) Relaxing country haven, in stunning surroundings, perfect for dog-walking. Delightful, spacious bedrooms, a splendid lounge, crackling fire, home-cooked evening meals, great wines, beer, malts and a warm welcome all ensure you'll enjoy your stay to the full. Dogs welcome! VisitScotland ★★★★ GOLD AWARD, AA ★★★★ Highly Commended. [🐾]
e-mail: enquiries@crubenbeghouse.com   website: www.crubenbeghouse.com

Poolewe (Ross-shire)

Village lying between Lochs Ewe and Maree with the River Ewe flowing through.

POOLEWE, WESTER ROSS. (01445 781765) Dogs welcome in non-smoking Bed & Breakfast. Convenient for local beaches and Torridon Mountains. Please phone or e-mail for further information. STB ★★★ B&B [🐾]
e-mail: dgeorge@globalnet.co.uk   website: www.davidgeorge.co.uk

MR A. URQUHART, CROFTERS COTTAGES, 15 CROFT, POOLEWE IV22 2JY (01445 781 268). Two traditional cottages situated in a scenic and tranquil area, ideal for a "get away from it all" holiday. Comfortably furnished with all mod cons. [🐾]
e-mail: croftcottages@btopenworld.com   website: www.crofterscottages.co.uk

INNES-MAREE BUNGALOWS, POOLEWE, BY GAIRLOCH IV2 2JU (Tel & Fax 01445 781454). Six superb modern bungalows, all equipped to the highest standards of luxury and comfort. Each sleeps 6, with main bedrooms en suite. Children and pets welcome. ASSC. STB ★★★ Self Catering. [Pets £15 per week]
e-mail: info@poolewebungalows.com   website: www.poolewebungalows.com

Rhiconich (Sutherland)

Locality at the head of Loch Inchard on west coast of Sutherland District.

RHICONICH HOTEL, SUTHERLAND, N. W. HIGHLANDS IV27 4RN (01971 521224; Fax: 01971 521732). She's your best friend so why leave her at home, bring her to Rhiconich Hotel, she'll be made equally as welcome as you will. A place where we put service, hospitality and really fresh food as a priority, but why don't you come and see for yourself? STB ★★★ [🐾]
e-mail: info@rhiconichhotel.co.uk   website: www.rhiconichhotel.co.uk

Spean Bridge (Inverness-shire)

Village on River Spean at foot of Loch Lochy. Site of WWII Commando Memorial.

RIVERSIDE LODGES, INVERGLOY, SPEAN BRIDGE PH34 4DY (01397 712684). The ultimate Highland location. Three lodges, each sleep 6, in 12 acres of woodland garden on Loch Lochy. Free fishing. Open all year. Pets welcome. Brochure on request. STB ★★★★ [🐾]
e-mail: enquiries@riversidelodge.org.uk   website: www.riversidelodge.org.uk

NEIL & ELIZABETH OCKENDEN, ACHNABOBANE FARMHOUSE, ACHNABOBANE, SPEAN BRIDGE PH34 4EX (01397 712919). Excellent accommodation and comfort. An ideal central base for exploring the Highlands. Local area has wide variety of outdoor pursuits, wildlife and attractions. STB ★★★. [£5 per dog per stay]
e-mail: enquiries@achnabobane.co.uk   website: www.achnabobane.co.uk

Whitebridge (Inverness-shire)

Hamlet in the heart of the Scottish Highlands, 4 miles from Loch Ness and 9 miles from Fort Augustus.

WHITEBRIDGE HOTEL, WHITEBRIDGE, SOUTH LOCH NESS IV2 6UN (01456 486226; Fax: 01456 486413). Peaceful location with magnificent mountain views and excellent walks. Friendly locals' bar with home-cooked food. 12 en suite rooms. B&B from £40pppn. AA ★★[🐾]
e-mail: info@whitebridgehotel.co.uk   website: www.whitebridgehotel.co.uk

Terms quoted in this publication may be subject to increase if rises in costs necessitate

Biggar, Harthill

Biggar

Small town set round broad main street. Gasworks museum, puppet theatre seating 100, street museum displaying old shop fronts and interiors. Peebles 13 miles.

CARMICHAEL COUNTRY COTTAGES, CARMICHAEL ESTATE, BY BIGGAR ML12 6PG (01899 308336;
Fax: 01899 308481). Our stone cottages nestle in the woods and fields of our historic family-run
estate. Ideal homes for families, pets and dogs. 15 cottages, 32 bedrooms. STB ★★/★★★★ Self
catering. Open all year. £225 to £595 per week. [pw! 🐾]
e-mail: information@carmichael.co.uk   website: www.carmichael.co.uk

WALSTON MANSION FARMHOUSE, WALSTON, CARNWATH, BY BIGGAR ML11 8NF (01899
810338; Fax: 01899 810334). Well known for its real home-from-home atmosphere, hearty breakfast
menu and delicious evening meals. Pets by arrangement. Ideal touring base.
e-mail: margaret.kirby@walstonmansion.co.uk   website: www.walstonmansion.co.uk

Harthill

Village 5 miles south-west of Bathgate.

MRS STEPHENS, BLAIRMAINS FARM, HARTHILL ML7 5TJ (01501 751278; Fax: 01501 753383).
Attractive farmhouse on small farm. Ideal for touring. Children welcome. Bed and Breakfast from
£20; weekly rates available. Reduced rates for children. Open all year. [🐾]
e-mail: heather@blairmains.freeserve.co.uk   website: www.blairmains.co.uk

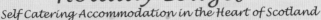
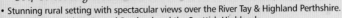

Aberfeldy

Small town standing on both sides of Uriar Burn near its confluence with the River Tay. Pitlochry 8 miles.

DRUMCROY LODGES, MAINS OF MURTHLY, ABERFELDY PH15 2EA (01887 820978) Self-catering holiday accommodation in a stunning rural setting. Deluxe en suite chalets, sleeping 4-6. Ideal base to explore Central Scotland. Nature walks, fishing, mountain bike trails. £225-£450 per week. STB ★★★★ [Pets £10 per week]
e-mail: info@highland-lodges.com   website: www.highland-lodges.com

LOCH TAY LODGES, ACHARN, ABERFELDY PH15 2HS (01887 830209). Enjoy hill walking, golf, sailing or touring. Salmon and trout fishing available. Log fires. Pets welcome. Walks along loch shore from house. STB ★★★ SELF CATERING in village close to Loch. For brochure, contact MR J DUNCAN MILLAR at above address. [🐕]
e-mail: remony@btinternet.com   website: www.lochtaylodges.co.uk

SHEILA AND PETER CAMPBELL, DULL FARM HOLIDAY LODGES, ABERFELDY PH15 2JQ (01887 820270). Luxury accommodation in 2 pine lodges on small farm. Fully equipped, well maintained; completely fenced. Panoramic views. Touring, walking, fishing, golf. Short Breaks available. [Pets £10 per week].
e-mail: info@dullfarm.freeserve.co.uk   website: www.self-cateringperthshire.com

Blairgowrie

Town in picturesque location near Ericht Gorge. Fine touring centre. Several castles in the vicinity. Pitlochry 23 miles, Dundee 20, Forfar 20, Perth 15.

MRS ROSALIND YOUNG, HOLMRIGG B&B, WESTER ESSENDY, BLAIRGOWRIE PH10 6RD, (Tel & Fax: 01250 884309). Double, double four-poster and double/twin en suite bedrooms. Full cooked breakfast, home cooking. Golf, fishing and walking nearby. B&B from £28.50–£32pp. Pets by arrangement. STB ★★★. Self-catering available. [🐕]
e-mail: info@holmrigg.co.uk   website: www.holmrigg-bnb.co.uk

Crieff

Town and resort 16 miles west of Perth.

ABERTURRET COTTAGE, CRIEFF. Beautiful traditional cottage with enormous private garden by the river. Three bedrooms (sleeps 4 or 5). Excellent base for walking, cycling and exploring Perthshire. Heating, bedlinen and towels incl. in price. Contact JUDY WATT (01764 650064). [Pets £15 per week]
e-mail: judywatt@aberturret.com   website: www.aberturret.com

STRONACHLACHAR COTTAGE, MILNAB TERRACE, CRIEFF PH7 4ED (01764 655595; 07887 984240). Situated in the 'Gateway to the Highlands', the cottage is set within landscaped gardens. Lounge/dining room, kitchen, bathroom and two bedrooms. Sleeps 4. Pets welcome.
website: www.cottageguide.co.uk/stronachlachar

Killiecrankie

Village on River Garry 3 miles south east of Blair Atholl.

ATHOLL COTTAGE, KILLIECRANKIE, PERTHSHIRE. Delightful stone cottage offers high quality accommodation for 5 people. Log fire. Private grounds. Good walking, golf, fishing locally. Contact: JOAN TROUP, DALNASGADH, KILLIECRANKIE, PITLOCHRY PH16 5LN (01796 470017; Fax: 01796 472183). [🐾]
e-mail: info@athollcottage.co.uk   website: www.athollcottage.co.uk

Killin

Village at confluence of Rivers Dochart and Lochay at head of Loch Tay.

GILL & DAVE HUNT, THE STEADING, WESTER LIX, KILLIN FK21 8RD (01567 820990 & 07747 862641). Two fully equipped self contained properties with Sky TV, wood-burning stove/open fire. One with sauna and private decking. Well behaved pet, or pets by arrangement. [Pets £15 per week for first pet, then £5 per pet]
e-mail: gill@westerlix.co.uk   website: www.westerlix.com

Kinloch Rannoch

Village at foot of Loch Rannoch.

KILVRECHT CARAVAN & CAMP SITE, KINLOCH RANNOCH PH16 5QA (01350 727284; Fax: 01350 727811). Secluded campsite on a level open area in quiet, secluded woodland setting. Fishing available for brown trout on Loch Rannoch. Several trails begin from campsite. Please write, fax or telephone for further information. [🐾]
e-mail: tay.fd@forestry.gsi.gov.uk

Lochearnhead

Village at head of Loch Earn 6 miles South of Killin.

CLACHAN COTTAGE HOTEL, LOCHEARNHEAD FK19 8PU (01567 830247; Fax: 01567 830300). Well placed in central Scotland for touring. Excellent walking, mountain biking and fishing. Water-sports available from the hotel. Award-winning "Taste of Scotland" restaurant. [🐾]
website: www.clachancottagehotel.com

🐾   Pets are welcome free of charge.

£   A charge is made for pets: nightly or weekly.

pw!   Special provision for pets; exercise facility, feeding or accommodation arrangement.

⌂   Separate pets' accommodation.

Classified Symbols

Pitlochry

Popular resort on River Tummel in beautiful Perthshire Highlands. Excellent golf, loch and river fishing. Famous for summer Festival Theatre; distillery, Highland Games.

DALSHIAN CHALETS, OLD PERTH ROAD, PITLOCHRY PH16 5TD (01796 472173). Four lovely pine lodges and two caravan holiday homes set in woodland garden. Five minutes from Pitlochry. Well behaved pets welcome in all units. ASSC. STB ★★★★ [Pets £15 per week]
e-mail: dalshian@btconnect.com   website: www.dalshian-chalets.co.uk

THE WHITE HOUSE, MOULIN, PITLOCHRY PH16 5EL. A mid 17th Century cottage on quiet village side street. Sleeps 6. Fully equipped. Many historical attractions and golf courses nearby. STB ★★.
Contact: GUY JAMES, THE YELLOW HOUSE, SPRINGHILL, EASTINGTON, STONEHOUSE, GLOUCESTERSHIRE GL10 3AT (01453 755552; Mob:07767 330986). [Pets £15 per week]
e-mail: whitehouse@jamesth9.co.uk   website: www.thewhitehousemoulin.co.uk

ROSEMOUNT HOTEL, PITLOCHRY PH16 5HT (01796 472302). We're just mad about dogs, and we have been known to welcome the occasional human companion, subject to behavioural considerations, naturally! Friendly, attentive service. Great food. Beautiful views. Fabulous walks. [🐕]
e-mail: rosemounthotel@tiscali.co.uk   website: www.scottishhotels.co.uk

St Fillans

Village at foot of Loch Earn, 5 miles west of Comrie.

THE FOUR SEASONS HOTEL, ST FILLANS PH6 2NF (01764 685333). Ideal holiday venue for pets and their owners. Spectacular Highland scenery, walking, fishing, watersports. Wonderful food. Full details on request. STB ★★★ Hotel, AA ★★★ and 2 Red Rosettes, Signpost, Best Loved Hotels. [pw! 🐕]
e-mail: sham@thefourseasonshotel.co.uk   website: www.thefourseasonshotel.co.uk

FORTRENN, ST FILLANS (01887 822819). Walkers and their dogs have forestry and open hillside at the door, with the Trossachs just across the loch. Sailors, waterskiers and fishermen need look no further than Loch Earn. Log fires, four poster master suite. Secure area for dogs. Sleeps 7. STB ★★★★ [Pets £25 per week]
e-mail: enquiries@heartofperthshire.co.uk   website: www.heartofperthshire.co.uk

Strathyre

Village set in the centre of Strathyre State Forest.

THE MUNRO INN, STRATHYRE FK18 8NA (01877 384333). Chilled out Robbie warmly welcomes doggy friends to the Munro Inn in beautiful Highland Perthshire. Perfect base for walking, cycling, climbing, water sports, fishing or relaxing! Great home cooking, lively bar, luxurious en suite bedrooms, drying room, broadband internet.
website: www.munro-inn.com

YVONNE & JOHN HOWES, ARDOCH LODGE, STRATHYRE FK18 8NF (01877 384666). Two log cabins and cottage in wonderful mountain scenery, excellent touring base. Comfortably furnished and well equipped. Pets most welcome. STB ★★★/★★★★ SELF CATERING. [pw! 🐕]
e-mail: ardoch@btinternet.com   website: www.ardochlodge.co.uk

Aberfoyle

Aberfoyle

Small town at heart of Loch Lomond and Trossachs National Park.

TROSSACHS HOLIDAY PARK, BY ABERFOYLE FK8 3SA (01877 382 614; Fax: 01877 382 732; Freephone: 0800 1971192). 40 acre landscaped park with 45 exclusive touring pitches - mostly fully serviced. The perfect base to explore the Trossachs National Park. Enclosed dog walk. STB ★★★★★. David Bellamy Gold Award.
e-mail: info@trossachsholidays.co.uk   website: www.trossachsholidays.co.uk

Isle of Harris

SCARISTA HOUSE, SGARASTA BHEAG, ISLE OF HARRIS HS3 3HX (01859 550238: Fax: 01859 550277). In one of the most beautiful and remote places to stay in Britain, traditional comfort in well-furnished guest rooms; skilled cooking and good wines, stunning views. STB ★★★★. Self catering cottage also available. [🐾]
e-mail: timandpatricia@scaristahouse.com   website: www.scaristahouse.com

Isle of Islay
Portnahaven

Portnahaven

Picturesque village built round small sheltered harbour where seals can often be spotted.

AN SABHAL COTTAGES, PORTNAHAVEN, ISLE OF ISLAY. Two cottages (each sleeps 6) with separate access. Bedrooms on the ground floor; large lounge on the upper floor. Views across to Rhinns Lighthouse and the Donegal coast. For details contact: MRS MONA MACARTHUR, 7 SHORE STREET, PORTNAHAVEN PA47 7SH (01496 860293). [Pets £10 per week]
e-mail: mona@ansabhalcottages.co.uk   website: www.ansabhalcottages.co.uk

Isle of Lewis
Stornoway

Stornoway

Chief town of Lewis, with large natural harbour.

JANNEL BED & BREAKFAST, 5 STEWART DRIVE, STORNOWAY, ISLE OF LEWIS HS1 2TU (0800 634 3270). Excellent Stornoway-based Bed & Breakfast in light, modern and spacious 7-bedroomed family home. Enclosed garden. Off-street parking. Children and pets welcome. STB ★★★★.[🐾]
e-mail: stay@jannel-stornoway.co.uk   website: www.jannel-stornoway.co.uk

Dounby, Orphir, South Ronaldsay, Stenness

ORKNEY ISLANDS COUNCIL (01856 873535). Point of Ness Campsite, Stromness: 3-star campsite in quiet shoreline location. Birsay Caravan & Camping Site, Birsay: stunning location near Orkney's Neolithic heartland, suitable for touring caravans, motorhomes and tents. [🐾]
e-mail: leisure.culture@orkney.gov.uk   www.orkney.gov.uk or www.hostelsorkney.co.uk

Dounby

North of the Loch or Harray, 14 miles north west of Kirkwall. Nearby at Sandwick is the Neolithic village of Skara Brae.

HANNABRECK, DOUNBY. Charming old-style cottage, two bedrooms. Bathroom with bath and level access shower, living room with open fire, kitchen. TV/internet access. Pets welcome. 15 miles Kirkwall, 10 miles ferry. Contact: MRS P. NORQUOY, BIGGING, DOUNBY KW17 2HR (01856 771340). STB ★★★★ [🐾]
e-mail: enquiries@lochlandchalets.co.uk   website: www.hannabreck.co.uk

Orphir

Located midway between Stromness and Kirkwall.

LITTLE BU, ORPHIR, ORKNEY. Little Bu is a self-catering chalet-bungalow maintained to a very high standard and sleeping six. Open-plan livingroom/dining area and newly fitted kitchen, verandah, patio/decking area, large garden and garden furniture. Close to the sea. STB ★★★ Self Catering. Contact: MRS SHEPHARD, WINDBRECK, BUTCHERS LANE, BOUGHTON, NORTHAMPTON NN2 8SL (01604 843275) [🐾]
e-mail: jshephard@northamptonshire.gov.uk   website: www.littlebu.co.uk

South Ronaldsay

Most southerly of the main islands of Orkney .

BANKS OF ORKNEY SELF-CATERING AND B&B. Two cottages (STB ★★★) and converted barn (STB ★★★★). Located close to ferries, with stunning views over the Pentland Firth. Each cottage sleeps up to 2, and the barn sleeps 5. Licensed restaurant on site. For details contact: CAROLE MOWATT, BANKS OF ORKNEY, SOUTH RONALDSAY KW17 2RW (01856 831605). [Pets £15 per week]
website: www.banksoforkney.co.uk

Stenness

Situated at the south east end of Loch of Stenness, south west of Finstown on mainland Orkney.

ADRIAN AND LESLEY FRANCIS, OUTBRECKS, STENNESS KW16 3EY (01856 851 223) Exceptional self-catering cottages in fabulous sea and loch locations in outstanding National Scenic Area. Sleep 2-8. Open all year. Non-smoking. Dogs welcome. STB ★★★★.
e-mail: accommodation@outbreckscottages-orkney.co.uk
website: www.outbreckscottages-orkney.co.uk

Locheport

Location on shore of sea loch, 5 miles south west of Lochmaddy.

TIGH ALASDAIR, NORTH UIST. Set on the family croft at Sidinish, Locheport, this beautiful self catering cottage enjoys unhindered views of Locheport, the hills of Bureaval, Eaval and Lees, not to mention spectacular sunsets. It offers all modern comforts in a traditional island setting. Sleeps 4. For details contact: JANET MACDONALD, TWO ISLAND COTTAGES, 285 HILLPARK DRIVE, GLASGOW G43 2SD (0141 585 3155 / 0778 0937 278). [pw! 🐕]
website: www.tighalasdair.co.uk

Co Kerry
Lauragh

Creveen Lodge *Immaculately run small hill farm overlooking Kenmare Bay in a striking area of County Kerry. Reception is found at the Lodge, which also offers guests a comfortable sitting room, while a separate block has well-equipped and immaculately maintained toilets and showers, plus a communal room with a large fridge, freezer and ironing facilities. The park is carefully tended, with bins and picnic tables informally placed, plus a children's play area with slides and swings.*

There are 20 pitches in total, 16 for tents and 4 for caravans, with an area of hardstanding for motor caravans. Electrical connections are available. Fishing, bicycle hire, water sports and horse riding available nearby. SAE please, for replies.

Mrs M. Moriarty, Creveen Lodge, Healy Pass Road, Lauragh
Tel: 00 353 64 66 83131
e-mail: info@creveenlodge.com • www.creveenlodge.com

Lauragh

Rural location on Ring of Beara.

MRS M. MORIARTY, CREVEEN LODGE, HEALY PASS ROAD, LAURAGH (00 353 64 66 83131). Small, carefully tended, well equipped park, 16 pitches for tents, 4 for caravans, with hardstanding for motor caravans. Fishing, bicycle hire, water sports and horse riding available nearby. [🐕]
e-mail: info@creveenlodge.com   website: www.creveenlodge.com

Co Mayo
Ballina

Bru Chiann Lir

Tirrane, Clogher, Belmullet, Ballina, Co. Mayo • Tel: 00 353 9785741
Unspoilt peninsula location. Surrounded by sea, boat trips and angling arranged.
Quiet Blue Flag beaches. Walks, golf, birdlife – we have it all. Pets welcome.

Ballina

Largest town in County Mayo, noted for salmon fishing.

JOSEPHINE GERAGHTY, BRU CHIANN LIR, TIRRANE, CLOGHER, BELMULLET, BALLINA (00 353 9785741). Visit the unspoilt peninsula location. Surrounded by sea, boat trips and angling arranged. Quiet Blue Flag beaches. Walks, golf, birdlife - we have it all. Pets welcome. [🐕]

Visit the FHG website
www.holidayguides.com
for all kinds of holiday
acccommodation in Britain

Pet-Friendly Pubs

A selection of Pubs and Inns where pets are especially welcome!

The Coledale Inn
Braithwaite, Near Keswick, Cumbria CA12 5TN
Tel: 017687 78272
e-mail: info@coledale-inn.co.uk • www.coledale-inn.co.uk

Genuine Country Inn in peaceful location. Ideally situated for touring and walking direct from the hotel grounds. Fine selection of wines and local real ales. Families and pets welcome.

PORT LIGHT Hotel, Restaurant & Inn
Bolberry Down, Malborough, Near Salcombe, Devon TQ7 3DY
Tel: (01548) 561384 or (07970) 859992 • Sean & Hazel Hassall
e-mail: info@portlight.co.uk • www.portlight.co.uk

Luxury en suite rooms, easy access onto the gardens. Close to secluded sandy cove (dogs permitted). No charge for pets which are most welcome throughout the hotel. Outstanding food and service. Winner 2004 "Dogs Trust" Best Pet Hotel in England. Self-catering cottages also available.
Pets may dine in bar area • Pet food fridge available

The Maltsters Arms
Tuckenhay, Devon TQ9 7EQ • 01803 732350
e-mail: maltsters@tuckenhay.com • www.tuckenhay.com

Bar food served daily at lunchtimes and evenings. Separate restaurant. Accommodation available. Charcoal barbecue on quay during summer
Pets Facilities: pets welcome in public rooms and bedrooms. Dog biscuits available in bars. Hudsons dog bowl.
Pets Regulars: Harvey, Gypsey, Garlic, Ollie, Reg, Barney, Frank, Wellington

Horse and Jockey
9 Chorlton Green, Manchester M21 9HS • 0161 860 7794
info@horseandjockeychorlton.com • www.horseandjockeychorlton.com

Traditional pub in village green setting. 6 cask ales, 50 bin wine cellar. Disabled access. Traditional pub menu served all day, every day. Sunday lunch. Separate restaurant and function room.
Pets Facilities: all dogs get a biscuit, water bowl and lots of attention. Pet Regulars: resident dog Eddie, Golden Labrador.

FHG
KUPERARD

Bestselling holiday accommodation guides for 65 years

The White Horse Inn, Clun

The Square, Clun, Shropshire SY7 8JA
Tel: 01588 640305 • e-mail: room@whi-clun.co.uk
www.whi-clun.co.uk

A characterful, friendly and comfortable inn. Ideal for walkers,
cyclists and those just wanting a relaxing break.
All rooms en suite; dogs welcome.

The Bat and Ball

15 Bat and Ball Lane, Boundstone, Farnham GU10 4SA
Tel: 01252 792108
info@thebatandball.co.uk • www.thebatandball.co.uk
Traditional village pub. • Selection of 6 ales. • Extensive home made
menu. • Garden and patio area. • Situated on five converging
footpaths - ideal drop-in place for walkers. • Children's play area. • Pets on leads allowed in the pub.
Pet Regulars: Mac (Assistant Landlord)

The Oak, Baginton

Coventry Road, Baginton, Coventry CV8 3AU
Tel: 02476 518855 • Fax: 02476 518866
e-mail: thebagintonoak@aol.com • www.thebagintonoak.co.uk
Bed & Breakfast accommodation. 13 en suite bedrooms. Quality
home-cooked food - 2 meals for £12 available all day. Pets welcome.
Extensive exercise area. Water bowls and waste bags available.
Dog treats for sale. Pet Residents: Beau and Jasper (Border Collies)

The Lamb Inn

High Street, Hindon, Wiltshire SP3 6DP
Tel: 01747 820573 • Fax: 01747 820605
www.lambathindon.co.uk

12th Century historic inn with bedrooms full of character.
Outstanding food and great wine selection.
Pets welcome in the bar and bedrooms. ETC/AA ★★★★

The Castle Inn

7 Wistowgate, Cawood
Selby, North Yorkshire YO8 3SH
Tel: 01757 268324
info@castleinncawood.co.uk • www.castleinncawood.co.uk

18thC village pub with a 60-seat restaurant and an
18-pitch caravan site. All food is local and fresh.

Pets Welcome • Water bowls outside.

The Bradford Arms

Llanymynech, Shropshire SY22 6EJ • Tel: 01691 830582
e-mail: catelou@tesco.net • www.bradfordarmshotel.com
Former coaching inn in historic village of Llanymynech. Restored and
upgraded, with five superb en suite bedrooms. High quality home-cooked
cuisine. CAMRA 2012 Guide, AA ★★★★

Pets Facilities: beds and chews available
Pet Resident: Charlie, 3-legged cat

Holidays with Horses

A selection of accommodation where horse and owner/rider can be put up at the same address – if not actually under the same roof!

We would be grateful if readers making enquiries and/or bookings from this supplement would mention **Pets Welcome!**

TODDY AND CLIVE HAMILTON-GOULD
TOWER FIELDS, TUSMORE ROAD, NEAR SOULDERN, BICESTER OX27 7HY
(01869 346554)
e-mail: toddyclive@towerfields.com   website: www.towerfields.com

Ground floor en suite rooms, all with own entrance and ample parking. Breakfast using local produce. Easy reach of Oxford, Stratford-upon-Avon, many National Trust houses. Silverstone, Towcester. Dogs and horses welcome by arrangement. VisitBritain ★★★★

JUNE AND GEORGE COLLIER
COLLIERS B&B, 55 NETHERCOTE ROAD, TACKLEY, KIDLINGTON,
OXFORD OX5 3AT
(01869 331255)
e-mail: junecollier@btinternet.com   website: www.colliersbnb.co.uk

Bed and Breakfast in Tackley for you and your horse. Riding or carriage driving fully detailed routes. Leave your horse with us while you visit Blenheim Palace, Oxford and Cotswolds. Parking for lorries and camping. Train and bus service from the village.

PAWS-A-WHILE,
KILNWICK PERCY, POCKLINGTON, EAST YORKSHIRE YO42 1UF
(01759 301168; Mobile: 07711 866869)
e-mail: paws.a.while@lineone.net • website: www.pawsawhile.net
www.dickyphotos.com

Small family B & B set in forty acres of parkland twixt York and Beverley. Golf, walking, riding. Pets and horses most welcome. Brochure available. ETC ★★★★

WINALOT® Puppy
With Vitamin D and minerals

Winalot® Puppy food is full of the vitamins and minerals your puppy needs for strong bones and healthy teeth. Optimal nutrition during a dog's first years of growth helps set him up for many years to come. It also gives him the energy and strength he needs to grow into an active member of the family!

For more information about how to feed your puppy, go to
www.winalot-dog.co.uk

SINCE 1927

Winalot
iron for vitality & protein for muscles

WINALOT® Senior
With key nutrients to help maintain mobility

Dogs over approximately 7 years of age (depending on breed and body size), have different nutrional requirements from growing and adult dogs. To help keep him enjoying life, we use a different formula with quality protein and carefully adjusted proportions of vitamin D and minerals to help maintain strong muscles and bones and help support mobility.

For more information about how to feed your senior dog, go to
www.winalot-dog.co.uk

iron for vitality & protein for muscles

TOGETHER, WE CAN

To help boost recycling in the UK, **FELIX**® and **WINALOT**® have joined force to create the **Together We Can** campaign.

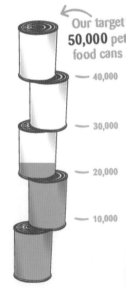

Using **Winalot** and **FELIX** multipacks, the campaign invited consumers to visit **www.purina.co.uk/wecan** to pledge to recycle their pet food cans in return for Purina donating £30,000 to charity partners.

Our target
50,000 pet food cans

The 50,000 pet food cans target was achieved and the donations will be used by the charities for individual projects.

Cats Protection plan to build a maternity block in their Eastbourne Adoption Centre, Canine Partners will train one puppy, while Dublin Society for the Prevention of Cruelty to Animals will vaccinate cats and dogs.

Together We Can will be back in 2012 with a new challenge.
For details visit **www.purina.co.uk/wecan**
You'll be barking mad not to take part!

LEIGHTON BUZZARD RAILWAY

Page's Park Station, Billington Road,
Leighton Buzzard, Bedfordshire LU7 4TN
Tel: 01525 373888
e-mail: station@lbngrs.org.uk
www.buzzrail.co.uk

One FREE adult/child with full-fare adult ticket
Valid 18/3/2012 - 28/10/2012

FHG
·K·U·P·E·R·A·R·D·
READERS' OFFER 2012

NOT TO BE USED IN CONJUNCTION WITH ANY OTHER OFFER

BUCKINGHAMSHIRE RAILWAY CENTRE

Quainton Road Station, Quainton,
Aylesbury HP22 4BY
Tel: 01296 655720
e-mail: office@bucksrailcentre.org
www.bucksrailcentre.org

One child FREE with each full-paying adult
Not valid for Special Events or Day Out with Thomas

FHG
·K·U·P·E·R·A·R·D·
READERS' OFFER 2012

NOT TO BE USED IN CONJUNCTION WITH ANY OTHER OFFER

CRICH TRAMWAY VILLAGE

Crich, Matlock
Derbyshire DE4 5DP
Tel: 01773 854321 • Fax: 01773 854320
e-mail: enquiry@tramway.co.uk
www.tramway.co.uk

One child FREE with every full-paying adult
Valid during 2012

FHG
·K·U·P·E·R·A·R·D·
READERS' OFFER 2012

NOT TO BE USED IN CONJUNCTION WITH ANY OTHER OFFER

THE BIG SHEEP

Abbotsham, Bideford,
North Devon EX39 5AP
Tel: 01237 472366 • Fax: 01237 477916
e-mail: info@thebigsheep.co.uk
www.thebigsheep.co.uk

£1 OFF per person up to £5.

FHG
·K·U·P·E·R·A·R·D·
READERS' OFFER 2012

NOT TO BE USED IN CONJUNCTION WITH ANY OTHER OFFER

A 70-minute journey into the lost world of the English narrow gauge light railway. Features historic steam locomotives from many countries.

WELL BEHAVED PETS WELCOME

Open: Sundays and Bank Holiday weekends 18 March to 28 October. Additional days in summer, and school holidays.

Directions: on south side of Leighton Buzzard. Follow brown signs from town centre or A505/A4146 bypass.

FHG GUIDES, ABBEY MILL BUSINESS CENTRE, PAISLEY PA1 1TJ • www.holidayguides.com

---

A working steam railway centre. Steam train rides, miniature railway rides, large collection of historic preserved steam locomotives, carriages and wagons.

Open: daily April to October 10.30am to 4.30pm. Variable programme - check website or call.

Directions: off A41 Aylesbury to Bicester Road, 6 miles north west of Aylesbury.

FHG GUIDES, ABBEY MILL BUSINESS CENTRE, PAISLEY PA1 1TJ • www.holidayguides.com

---

A superb family day out in the atmosphere of a bygone era. Explore the recreated period street and fascinating exhibitions. Unlimited tram rides are free with entry. Play areas, woodland walk and sculpture trail, shops, tea rooms, pub, restaurant and lots more.

Open: daily April to end October 10am to 5.30pm.

Directions: eight miles from M1 Junction 28, follow brown and white signs for "Tramway Museum".

FHG GUIDES, ABBEY MILL BUSINESS CENTRE, PAISLEY PA1 1TJ • www.holidayguides.com

---

The best day of your holiday baa none! Sheep racing, dog and duck trialling, huge indoor playground, animal barn with pets' corner and lamb bottle feeding, train and tractor rides, and much more.

Open: 10am-6pm daily April to October. From Nov-March weekends and school holidays only. Please check opening times before visiting.

Directions: two miles west of Bideford, on the A39 Atlantic Highway. Look for the big flag.

FHG GUIDES, ABBEY MILL BUSINESS CENTRE, PAISLEY PA1 1TJ • www.holidayguides.com

THE MILKY WAY ADVENTURE PARK
The Milky Way, Clovelly,
Bideford, Devon EX39 5RY
Tel: 01237 431255
e-mail: info@themilkyway.co.uk
www.themilkyway.co.uk

READERS'
OFFER
2012

10% discount on entrance charge.
Valid Easter to end October (not August).

NOT TO BE USED IN CONJUNCTION WITH ANY OTHER OFFER

DORSET HEAVY HORSE FARM PARK
Edmondsham Road,
Near Verwood,
Dorset BH21 5RJ
Tel: 01202 824040
www.dorset-heavy-horse-centre.co.uk

**DORSET
HEAVY HORSE
FARM PARK**

READERS'
OFFER
2012

£1 off adult ticket. One voucher per person.
Not valid with any other offer or family ticket/concessions

NOT TO BE USED IN CONJUNCTION WITH ANY OTHER OFFER

KILLHOPE - THE NORTH OF ENGLAND LEAD MINING MUSEUM
Near Cowshill, Upper Weardale,
Co Durham DL13 1AR
Tel: 01388 537505 • Fax: 01388 537617
e-mail: info@killhope.org.uk
www.killhope.org.uk

READERS'
OFFER
2012

2-4-1 (cheapest free) or Like-4-Like
Valid April - October 2012

NOT TO BE USED IN CONJUNCTION WITH ANY OTHER OFFER

MUSEUM OF RAIL TRAVEL
Ingrow Railway Centre, Near Keighley,
West Yorkshire BD21 5AX
Tel: 01535 680425
e-mail: admin@vintagecarriagestrust.org
www.vintagecarriagestrust.org

READERS'
OFFER
2012

"ONE for ONE" free admission
Valid during 2012 except during special events (ring to check)

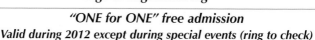

NOT TO BE USED IN CONJUNCTION WITH ANY OTHER OFFER

The day in the country that's out of this world! With 5 major rides and loads of great live shows.
See Merlin from 'Britain's Got Talent' 5 days a week. All rides and shows included in entrance fee.

Open: daily Easter to October. Please call or check online for full details.

Directions: on the main A39 one mile from Clovelly.

Entertainment for all ages: fascinating daily shows, FREE wagon and tractor rides, straw fun barn, go-kart arena, gypsy wagons and Romany talks, blacksmith's workshop. Drive a real tractor, pony rides, 'hands-on' activities with the farm animals, over 20 rescued heavy horses. Lots undercover; cafe and gift shop.

Open: 10am to 5pm Easter to end October.

Directions: On the Edmondsham Road, approx. 1½ miles from Verwood. Within easy reach of Bournemouth, Poole, Southampton, Ringwood and surrounding areas.

Killhope is a multi-award winning Victorian Lead Mining Museum, offering a grand day out. Accompany a guide on a mine tour. Our enthusiastic team ensure you have a day to remember, finding minerals, and working as a washerboy. Woodland trails, exhibitions, Killhope shop and cafe complete a great day out.

Open: April-October 10.30am-5pm

Directions: midway between Alston and Stanhope on A689

A fascinating display of railway carriages and a wide range of railway items telling the story of rail travel over the years.

ALL PETS MUST BE KEPT ON LEADS

Open: daily 11am to 4pm

Directions: approximately one mile from Keighley on A629 Halifax road. Follow brown tourist signs

Steam and heritage diesel passenger trains from Bo'ness to Manuel. Explore the history of Scotland's railways in the Scottish Railway Exhibition. Coffee shop and souvenir shop.

Open: weekends April to October, most days in July and August. See website for dates and timetables.

Directions: in the town of Bo'ness. Leave M9 at Junction 3 or 5, then follow brown tourist signs.

FHG GUIDES, ABBEY MILL BUSINESS CENTRE, PAISLEY PA1 1TJ • www.holidayguides.com

---

A unique, thriving, fully operational slateworks. Enter the workshops for a fascinating and inspiring insight into an ongoing era of techniques and expertise. Self-guided tours including Lettercutting and Calligraphy Exhibitions.

Open: seven days a week 9am-5pm. Closed Christmas/Boxing/New Year's days

Directions: main A487 6 miles south of Caernarfon going towards Porthmadog.

FHG GUIDES, ABBEY MILL BUSINESS CENTRE, PAISLEY PA1 1TJ • www.holidayguides.com

---

The Talyllyn Railway is a historic narrow-gauge steam railway running through the beautiful mid-Wales countryside, from Tywyn on the coast to the delightful Dolgoch Falls and wooded Nant Gwernol.

Open: daily from Easter to October and at other times of the year. See website for details of timetables.

Directions: on the A493 on the Aberdyfi side of Tywyn, 300 yards from Tywyn mainline rail station and bus stops.

FHG GUIDES, ABBEY MILL BUSINESS CENTRE, PAISLEY PA1 1TJ • www.holidayguides.com

---

During operating days we provide a trip back in time with a round trip on a steam-hauled locomotive in the scenic Gwili valley. Pay once and ride all day. Check website or phone for timetables.

Open: check website or phone for information.

Directions: just off the A484, three miles north of Carmarthen.

FHG GUIDES, ABBEY MILL BUSINESS CENTRE, PAISLEY PA1 1TJ • www.holidayguides.com

Index of Towns and Counties

Broadstairs, Kent	SOUTH EAST
Broadwoodwidger, Devon	SOUTH WEST
Brodick, Ayrshire & Arran	SCOTLAND
Bromyard, Herefordshire	HEART OF ENGLAND
Bronwydd Arms, Carmarthenshire	WALES
Broughton-in-Furness, Cumbria	NORTH WEST
Bude, Cornwall	SOUTH WEST
Budleigh Salterton, Devon	SOUTH WEST
Builth Wells, Powys	WALES
Bungay, Suffolk	EAST
Burford, Oxfordshire	SOUTH EAST
Burford, Shropshire	HEART OF ENGLAND
Burnham Market, Norfolk	EAST
Burton Bradstock, Dorset	SOUTH WEST
Burton Joyce, Nottinghamshire	EAST MIDLANDS
Burwell, Cambridgeshire	EAST
Bury St Edmunds, Suffolk	EAST
Buxton, Derbyshire	EAST MIDLANDS
Caernarfon, Anglesey & Gwynedd	WALES
Cairndow, Argyll & Bute	SCOTLAND
Caister-on-Sea, Norfolk	EAST
Canterbury, Kent	SOUTH EAST
Cardigan, Ceredigion	WALES
Carlisle, Cumbria	NORTH WEST
Carnforth, Lancashire	NORTH WEST
Carperby, North Yorkshire	YORKSHIRE
Castle Douglas, Dumfries & Galloway	SCOTLAND
Chard, Somerset	SOUTH WEST
Charmouth, Dorset	SOUTH WEST
Chathill, Northumberland	NORTH EAST
Cheddar, Somerset	SOUTH WEST
Cheltenham, Gloucestershire	SOUTH WEST
Chesham, Buckinghamshire	SOUTH EAST
Chester, Cheshire	NORTH WEST
Chichester, West Sussex	SOUTH EAST
Chiddingly, East Sussex	SOUTH EAST
Chittlehamholt, Devon	SOUTH WEST
Christchurch, Dorset	SOUTH WEST
Chulmleigh, Devon	SOUTH WEST
Church Stretton, Shropshire	HEART OF ENGLAND
Ciliau Aeron, Ceredigion	WALES
Cilmery, Powys	WALES
Cirencester, Gloucestershire	SOUTH WEST
Clapham, North Yorkshire	YORKSHIRE
Clevedon, Somerset	SOUTH WEST
Clitheroe, Lancashire	NORTH WEST
Clun, Shropshire	HEART OF ENGLAND
Clun, Shropshire	PET-FRIENDLY PUBS
Cockburnspath, Borders	SCOTLAND
Cockermouth, Cumbria	NORTH WEST
Colchester, Essex	EAST
Coldingham, Borders	SCOTLAND
Colwyn Bay, North Wales	WALES
Combe Martin, Devon	SOUTH WEST
Coniston, Cumbria	NORTH WEST
Contin, Highlands	SCOTLAND
Conwy Valley, North Wales	WALES
Conwy, North Wales	WALES
Corbridge, Northumberland	NORTH EAST
Coventry, Warwickshire	PET-FRIENDLY PUBS
Coverdale, North Yorkshire	YORKSHIRE
Cowes, Isle of Wight	SOUTH EAST
Crackington Haven, Cornwall	SOUTH WEST
Crafthole, Cornwall	SOUTH WEST
Craignure (Isle of Mull), Argyll & Bute	SCOTLAND
Crantock, Cornwall	SOUTH WEST
Craven Arms, Shropshire	HEART OF ENGLAND
Criccieth, Anglesey & Gwynedd	WALES
Cricklade, Wiltshire	SOUTH WEST
Crieff, Perth & Kinross	SCOTLAND
Croes Goch, Pemebrokeshire	WALES
Croft, Pembrokeshire	WALES
Cromer, Norfolk	EAST
Crossmichael, Dumfries & Galloway	SCOTLAND
Crosthwaite, Cumbria	NORTH WEST
Cullompton, Devon	SOUTH WEST
Dalbeattie, Dumfries & Galloway	SCOTLAND
Dalmally, Argyll & Bute	SCOTLAND
Danby,North Yorkshire	YORKSHIRE
Darlington, Durham	NORTH EAST
Dartmoor, Devon	SOUTH WEST
Dartmouth, Devon	SOUTH WEST
Daventry, Northamptonshire	EAST MIDLANDS
Denbigh (Llandyrnog), North Wales	WALES
Dereham, Norfolk	EAST
Diss, Norfolk	EAST
Dolgellau, Anglesey & Gwynedd	WALES
Dorchester, Dorset	SOUTH WEST
Dounby, Isle of Orkney	SCOTLAND
Driffield, East Yorkshire	YORKSHIRE
Droitwich, Worcestershire	HEART OF ENGLAND
Dronfield, Derbyshire	EAST MIDLANDS

Mortehoe, Devon	SOUTH WEST
Moss Mayo, Devon	SOUTH WEST
Mousehole, Cornwall	SOUTH WEST
Moylegrove, Pembrokeshire	WALES
Muir of Ord, Highlands	SCOTLAND
Mundesley-on-Sea, Norfolk	EAST
Nailsworth, Gloucestershire	SOUTH WEST
Neath, South Wales	WALES
Nethy Bridge, Highlands	SCOTLAND
New Forest, Hampshire	SOUTH EAST
Newby Bridge, Cumbria	NORTH WEST
Newcastleton, Borders	SCOTLAND
Newgale, Pembrokeshire	WALES
Newport, Pembrokeshire	WALES
Newquay, Cornwall	SOUTH WEST
Newtonmore, Highlands	SCOTLAND
North Berwick, Edinburgh & Lothians	
	SCOTLAND
North Perrott, Dorset	SOUTH WEST
North Somercotes, Lincolnshire	
	EAST MIDLANDS
Northallerton, North Yorkshire	YORKSHIRE
Norwich, Norfolk	EAST
Nunthorpe, North Yorkshire	YORKSHIRE
Oban, Argyll & Bute	SCOTLAND
Old Hunstanton, Norfolk	EAST
Orford, Suffolk	EAST
Orphir, Isle of Orkney	SCOTLAND
Ossett, West Yorkshire	YORKSHIRE
Oswestry, Shropshire	HEART OF ENGLAND
Otterburn, Northumberland	NORTH EAST
Ottery St Mary, Devon	SOUTH WEST
Oxford, Oxfordshire	SOUTH EAST
Padstow, Cornwall	SOUTH WEST
Paignton, Devon	SOUTH WEST
Painswick, Gloucestershire	SOUTH WEST
Peak District National Park, Derbyshire	
	EAST MIDLANDS
Peebles, Borders	SCOTLAND
Penrith, Cumbria	NORTH WEST
Pentraeth, Anglesey & Gwynedd	WALES
Penzance, Cornwall	SOUTH WEST
Perranporth, Cornwall	SOUTH WEST
Pickering, North Yorkshire	YORKSHIRE
Pirton, Worcestershire	HEART OF ENGLAND
Pitlochry, Perth & Kinross	SCOTLAND
Plymouth, Devon	SOUTH WEST
Polegate, East Sussex	SOUTH EAST
Polruan, Cornwall	SOUTH WEST
Poole, Dorset	SOUTH WEST
Poolewe, Highlands	SCOTLAND
Porlock, Somerset	SOUTH WEST
Port Gaverne, Cornwall	SOUTH WEST
Port Isaac, Cornwall	SOUTH WEST
Port Mulgrave, North Yorkshire	YORKSHIRE
Porthleven, Cornwall	SOUTH WEST
Porthmadog, Anglesey & Gwynedd	WALES
Portland, Dorset	SOUTH WEST
Portnahaven, Isle of Islay	SCOTLAND
Portreath, Cornwall	SOUTH WEST
Portwrinkle, Cornwall	SOUTH WEST
Presteigne, Powys	WALES
Pulborough, West Sussex	SOUTH EAST
Pwllheli, Anglesey & Gwynedd	WALES
Quantock Hills, Somerset	SOUTH WEST
Rattray Head, Aberdeen, Banff & Moray	
	SCOTLAND
Ravenstonedale, Cumbria	NORTH WEST
Reading, Berkshire	SOUTH EAST
Red Wharf Bay, Anglesey & Gwynedd	WALES
Redruth, Cornwall	SOUTH WEST
Rhayader, Powys	WALES
Rhiconich, Highlands	SCOTLAND
Rhos-on-Sea (Conwy), North Wales	WALES
Ringwood, Hampshire	SOUTH EAST
Rosewell, Edinburgh & Lothians	SCOTLAND
Ross-on-Wye, Herefordshire	
	HEART OF ENGLAND
Rothesay, Argyll & Bute	SCOTLAND
Rutland, Leics & Rutland	EAST MIDLANDS
Ryde, Isle of Wight	SOUTH EAST
Rye, East Sussex	SOUTH EAST
St Agnes, Cornwall	SOUTH WEST
St Andrews, Fife	SCOTLAND
St Austell, Cornwall	SOUTH WEST
St Davids, Pembrokeshire	WALES
St Fillans, Perth & Kinross	SCOTLAND
St Ives, Cornwall	SOUTH WEST
St Margaret's Bay, Kent	SOUTH EAST
St Mawgan, Cornwall	SOUTH WEST
St Tudy, Cornwall	SOUTH WEST
Salcombe, Devon	PET-FRIENDLY PUBS
Salcombe, Devon	SOUTH WEST
Salisbury, Wiltshire	SOUTH WEST

© FHG Guides Ltd, 2012
ISBN 978-1-85055-449-3

Typeset by FHG Guides Ltd, Paisley.
Printed and bound in China by Imago.

Distribution. Book Trade: ORCA Book Services, Stanley House,
3 Fleets Lane, Poole, Dorset BH15 3AJ
(Tel: 01202 665432; Fax: 01202 666219)
e-mail: mail@orcabookservices.co.uk
Published by FHG Guides Ltd., Abbey Mill Business Centre,
Seedhill, Paisley PA1 ITJ (Tel: 0141-887 0428 Fax: 0141-889 7204).
e-mail: admin@fhguides.co.uk

PETS WELCOME! is published by FHG Guides Ltd,
part of Kuperard Group.

Cover design: FHG Guides
Cover Picture: YETI, courtesy of Ms Rachel McCann, Poole

All the advertisers in **PETS WELCOME!** have an entry in the appropriate classified section and each classified entry may carry one or more of the following symbols:

🐾   This symbol indicates that pets are welcome free of charge.

£   The £ indicates that a charge is made for pets. We quote the amount where possible, either per night or per week.

pw!   This symbol shows that the establishment has some special provision for pets; perhaps an exercise facility or some special feeding or accommodation arrangements.

⌂   Indicates separate pets' accommodation.

PLEASE NOTE that all the advertisers in **PETS WELCOME!** extend a welcome to pets and their owners but they may attach conditions. The interests of other guests have to be considered and it is usually assumed that pets will be well trained, obedient and under the control of their owner.

Other FHG Titles

FHG Guides Ltd have been publishing an attractive range of holiday accommodation guides for over 50 years. For all kinds of holiday opportunities, they make useful gifts at any time of year.

e Golf Guide Where to Play, Where to Stay
etails of 3000 Clubs and Courses in Britain and Ireland
ocation, facilities, statistics • Plus accommodation
2.99

0 Bed & Breakfasts
Britain
or holidaymakers
nd business travellers
overnight stops and Short Breaks
9.99

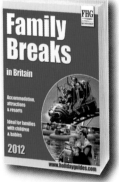

Family Breaks
in Britain
• Accommodation, attractions and resorts
• Ideal for holidays with young children
£7.99

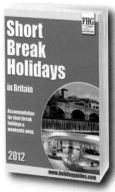

Short Break Holidays
in Britain
• Accommodation for holidays
and weekends away
£8.99

00 Great Places to Stay
Britain
he Best of British Holidays
ull range of family accommodation
7.99

Self Catering Holidays
in Britain
• Cottages, farms, apartments and chalets
• Pet-Friendly accommodation
£8.99

Caravan & Camping Holidays
in Britain
• Campsites and Caravan parks
£7.99

Our guides are available in most bookshops and larger newsagents but we will be happy to post you a copy direct if you have any difficulty.

POST FREE for addresses in the UK.

We will also post abroad but have to charge separately for post or freight.

☐ **The Original Pets Welcome!**

☐ **750 Bed & Breakfasts** in Britain

☐ **Family Breaks** in Britain

☐ **Short Break Holidays** in Britain

☐ **800 Great Places to Stay** in Britain

☐ **Self Catering Holidays** in Britain

☐ **Caravan & Camping Holidays** in Britain

☐ **The Golf Guide** Where to Play • Where to Stay in Britain & Ireland

Tick your choice above and send your order and payment to

FHG Guides Ltd. Abbey Mill Business Centre
Seedhill, Paisley, Scotland PA1 1TJ
TEL: 0141- 887 0428 • FAX: 0141- 889 7204
e-mail: admin@fhguides.co.uk

Deduct 10% for 2/3 titles or copies; 20% for 4 or more.

Send to: NAME ....

ADDRESS ....

....

....

POST CODE ....

I enclose Cheque/Postal Order for £ ....

SIGNATURE ....DATE ....

Please complete the following to help us improve the service we provide.

How did you find out about our guides?:

☐ Press   ☐ Magazines   ☐ TV/Radio   ☐ Family/Friend   ☐ Other